MW00528111

THE DARK HORSE

NUCLEAR POWER AND CLIMATE CHANGE

Rauli Partanen
Janne M. Korhonen

ISBN: 978-952-69474-0-2 (paperback)
ISBN: 978-952-69474-1-9 (ebook)

CONTENTS

For the Reader

This book was born out of both worry and frustration. Our worry has been fuelled by the state of the environment and, especially, climate change, and humanity's almost complete lack of progress in mitigating it regardless of decades of knowledge about its potential dangers and negotiations on what to do about it. The frustration has been caused by the astounding ease, and even eagerness, that those presenting themselves as most worried about climate change have shown in brushing aside our historically most effective tool in mitigating climate change: nuclear energy.

In this book, which is an updated and expanded translation of a book originally published in Finnish in 2016, we hope to convey our worry about the environment, climate, and human well-being. We also hope to convey our willingness to find solutions to these and other problems. While venting one's frustration can often feel good initially, we have noticed that it rarely leads to any actual progress. Instead, it often leads to even steeper animosity, personal grudges and estrangement of people and groups who might otherwise desire the same things. In short, venting frustration tends to lead to tribalism. We therefore apologize in advance for any and all inflammatory comments we might make in this book.

Janne wants to thank, first and foremost, dear Tanja for her support and feedback that enabled him to write the book and greatly improved the results. Thanks are also due to his PhD thesis supervisor, professor Liisa Välikangas, for understanding the various side projects with little bearing to the main thesis project. The PhD thesis funding from Jenny and Antti Wihuri Foundation, Foundation for Economic Education, and the Helsinki School of Economics Foundation has been flexible enough to permit the writing of this book, and it can be said that the support from the aforementioned foundations has been crucial for this book as well.

Rauli wants to thank his family for acting as a key motivator to write this book. Päivi, Niilo, Eino and Leila, thank you all so much for being there and allowing me to study, research and write, and then repeat. I also owe thanks for several grants that allowed me to write the Finnish edition of this book: The Finnish Association of Non-Fiction Writers, WSOY literary trust fund and the Committee for Public Information in Finland. A special thanks for the grant that permitted this translation goes to the People's Cultural Foundation.

Numerous people have given valuable feedback for the various drafts of this book; special thanks are due to Esko, Aila, Kaj, Jani-Petri, Ari, Aki and Tuomas. Countless others have offered us opportunities to learn more, and we extend our most sincere thanks for them. Thanks to Tea for going through the manuscript one more time, and Gary for doing it yet one more time after that. Whatever errors remain are of course solely our responsibility.

Finally, we'd like to thank professor Esko Valtaoja for his foreword in the Finnish edition, and our Finnish publisher Kosmos for their flexibility, and of course Mark Lynas for his foreword in this English edition. Thanks Mark, and keep up the great work you do!

Foreword by Mark Lynas

It is an enduring mystery to me why it is that most of those who insist that climate change is an existential crisis nevertheless continue to oppose what is perhaps the most obvious and scalable solution to the climate emergency: nuclear power. To quote one of these activists, Naomi Klein, 'climate changes everything' – except their long-standing opposition to this much demonized but incredibly promising form of zero-carbon energy.

Second only perhaps to GMOs, nuclear power is surely the world's most poorly understood technology. Most people think nuclear reactors can blow up like bombs, that waste is a deal-breaking unsolved problem, that radiation is uniquely dangerous and toxic, and that fuel for nuclear reactors can easily be repurposed into nuclear weapons. None of these things are true, but the truth is complicated – and that is why the anti-nuclear movement has been so enduringly successful. Simplistic fearmongering will always win out over sophisticated science.

To reverse this decadal tide of disinformation will take a herculean effort, but it is an effort which is much needed, and to which this very useful book by Rauli Partanen and Janne Korhonen will make a helpful contribution. The authors have reviewed the very latest insights and research on nuclear power, and organized them in a comprehensive format that should be accessible to a general audience. I doubt that anyone who reads this book with a genuinely open mind will come away with their misconceptions unchallenged.

And Naomi Klein is right – climate should change everything. My own book, Our Final Warning, outlines degree by degree what humanity faces if we do not get the climate crisis under some kind of control. Already at one degree we are seeing the loss of most coral reefs, dramatic increases in the melt rate of the polar ice caps and increased droughts and wildfires around the world. At two degrees, which looms very close, all the coral reefs will die, the North Pole will be ice-free, Arctic permafrost over two million square kilometres will collapse, and Greenland will cross a tipping point. At three and four degrees, humanity will not be able to feed itself, and large areas of the world will be too hot for humans to even inhabit at all.

At what stage in this unravelling catastrophe does the crisis become sufficiently severe that even environmentalists will reconsider nuclear power? Compared to coal, this energy source has already avoided millions of deaths, and billions of tonnes of carbon emissions, and is at least as benign to the living biosphere as renewables. I crossed the line back in 2004, when I abandoned my previous anti-nuclear sentiments and began to support the technology. This was directly related to my ongoing research and writing about climate change – which has only got worse since then.

Perhaps reading this book will help you cross the line. Or maybe you already have and need to be armed with the latest facts and figures to help others understand the reality rather than the myths about nuclear power. I wish you every success on the journey.

Mark Lynas, 13th May, 2020

Introduction

Today, humans are more reliant on the constant flow of energy than they have ever been. Accessible, high-quality energy is the crucial ingredient in the many services and products the modern world has to offer. Energy is the single most important factor behind humanity's prosperity and well-being. Affordable and plentiful energy has enabled technological advances and increased productivity, which in turn has increased our energy consumption, leading to a self-reinforcing cycle. Historically, living standards have increased, technology has advanced, and societies have democratized. Vastly increased use of external energy has played an important part in many of these positive changes.

The easy accessibility and growing demand for energy is also behind one of our generation's biggest challenges: the rapid change in our planet's climate system. Roughly 80 percent of the energy used by humans comes from fossil fuels. When burned, they release carbon dioxide, which acts as a greenhouse gas, trapping heat and changing our climate.

In the popular press, the solutions to climate change that get the most attention are various renewable energy sources, energy conservation and increased energy efficiency. But the scale of the challenge often eludes us, and all the potential solutions include hidden, surprising and often unwanted side effects, bottlenecks and constraints.

Perhaps the most significant constraint concerns our ability to reduce global consumption of materials and energy. There is ample evidence that the current global consumption patterns are unsustainable. For many westerners, the word "consumption" summons images of Black Friday shopping mania and ever-growing piles of broken, disposable plastic gadgets floating in the ocean. The problem with that perspective is that this "consumption" also includes and underpins all the other things in our modern society: education, culture, art, health care, relatively safe and civilized society, healthy and delicious food, a warm house with electric lighting, the ability to move people and things and ideas around the world with unforeseen speed and flexibility, and so forth. This results in unwillingness to downgrade the level of comfort which reducing consumption entails because of an abstract climate threat looming somewhere in the future.

There is no guarantee that people even in the abundantly rich countries will want to reduce their consumption significantly. There is even less evidence for people in the poor countries wanting to remain poor. In theory, consumption could remain stable or even increase at the same time as environmental effects decrease, if only the energy and materials efficiency of consumption increases sufficiently. Unfortunately, increases in efficiency tend to result in a rebound effect: more efficient and hence cheaper goods are used more often, and as a result, total resource use does not diminish nearly as much as calculations that ignore the rebound effect would assume.

The growth of renewables, including mainly wind power, solar power and bioenergy, has been staggeringly fast during the recent years. However, all of these have significant limitations. Wind and solar power are weather-dependent energy sources. This means that no matter how cheap individual generators become, wind and solar power by themselves will never be able to provide the constant, on-demand energy flows that a modern society needs. Providing such a level of service requires major technological breakthroughs in other technologies, and/or significantly increases infrastructure costs. Further, per energy unit produced, a renewable energy system may demand significant, perhaps even prohibitive amounts of rare natural resources to build.

Biomass, on the other hand, demands huge amounts of land, and is dependent on fossil fuel inputs and chemicals derived from fossil fuels. Biomass production also tends to harm biodiversity, and as a whole, bioenergy is unlikely to be as carbon neutral as many believe. Even though advances in renewable energy technologies mean that using them to decarbonize a small part of our energy system will become cheaper, their fundamental physical limitations will likely mean that using only renewables to decarbonize the entire energy system will remain prohibitively expensive.

When these risks and constraints, which we explain in detail in the first part of this book, are combined with the realities of anthropogenic climate change and the growing thirst for energy in relation to the growth of population, the picture looks bleak indeed. This is one of the reasons why an increasing number of people and organizations have asked the crucial question asked in this book: when faced with the realities of climate change, can we afford to ignore the potential of nuclear energy?

Nuclear energy, which we present in detail in the second part of this book, is a topic known to arouse powerful feelings. The people and traditional environmental organizations that tend to be most vocal about climate change are also those who have protested against nuclear energy, due to its military use in nuclear bombs, and later in civilian uses as well. It is understandable that such persons and organizations find it particularly hard to even seriously consider whether nuclear energy, their long-time favourite enemy, could or should be used to combat climate change and various other environmental problems as well.

However, the uncomfortable truth we explore in more detail in the second part of this book is that despite all the rhetoric and genuinely promising progress of renewable energy, no other actually tested alternative strategy has ever come even close to the speed and comprehensiveness of decarbonisation achieved entirely by accident in countries that built nuclear power in the 1980s. Another truth is that despite its genuine problems and the coverage any nuclear accident receives in the press, statistically speaking, nuclear power remains one of the safest and least environmentally damaging large-scale energy production methods humanity has ever deployed.

Accelerating climate change will almost certainly cause immense damage to the environment and human well-being. Unless we can dramatically curb energy generation by combustion, dangerous climate change will become a fact, not a risk. Furthermore, we only have a couple of decades at best to make significant changes to the world's energy supply. In this situation, is it ethical to continue to say no to nuclear, if by doing so we make it much harder to stop climate change? On top of this, our response to climate change will be far slower than it should. Or will the current global consumer culture and capitalistic system destroy itself anyway? The third part of this book looks deeper at energy and its role in modern society and the environment, and how nuclear energy might fit in it. What are the ethical, economic and social implications, problems and possibilities whether we choose to use or abandon nuclear power?

This book aims to present an evidence-based discussion of our energy production and environmental predicament. To us, it is eminently clear that not using all available tools can significantly increase the risks of losing the climate fight, with possibly catastrophic consequences to human civilization. It is understandable that many will find our conclusions very difficult to accept. Currently, mainstream media and even much of the academic discussion tends to present nuclear power in an extremely unfavourable light, while glossing over the issues facing large-scale renewable energy systems. Controversies over nuclear energy have been magnified by social media, and mainstream environmental organizations have both ideological and financial motives to sow fear and uncertainty and even resort to outright statistical manipulation (some examples are detailed later in the book) about nuclear power, even in issues where actual scientists are in general agreement.

We sincerely hope the evidence presented in this book will help people to consider one more time whether we ought to utilize nuclear energy as one of the valuable tools we have to halt climate change, and to ensure that future generations can also enjoy a habitable, biologically diverse planet.

PART 1

The Realities of Climate Change and Humanity's Energy Thirst

Climate Change Today

Climate change and humanity's role in it has been scientifically studied and verified in thousands of studies over several decades. Climate scientists have a high level of consensus that our actions are changing the climate, and that it is changing very rapidly when compared to past changes. The fundamentals have not been in doubt for decades: increases in the atmospheric content of heat-trapping greenhouse gases (GHG's) mean that more heat energy stays on the planet than leaves to outer space. Carbon dioxide (CO_2) is the most impactful of the manmade GHS's with roughly a 75 % share of the warming effect. Methane comes second with roughly a 16 % share, nitrous oxides have a ~6% share with the remainder being from minor gases like HFC's and PFC's.[1] The questions that remain are how that heat will be distributed and what the exact effects around the planet will be.

If we continue on our current trajectory, the average surface temperature of the planet will increase by 3.7 - 4.8 °C, compared to temperatures prior to industrialization.[2] In some areas the warming will be much more severe. From 1847 to 2013 Finland, for example, has seen an increase of over two degrees in surface temperature, which is more than double the global average. The warming has been fastest during the last 40 years[3], and in addition, the warming tends to be stronger during winter and in the northern parts of the globe.[4]

Many ecosystems have proven to be less resilient to increased extreme weather events than previously thought, even with just the 0.8 degrees of warming we have so far experienced. Extreme weather events are widely thought to increase in number and especially in severity as our planet's energy balance changes and more heat is trapped.

Rainfall patterns could fluctuate more than previously, which would make agriculture and forestry more vulnerable. Food production will become either less productive or even impossible in many current food-producing regions, leading not only to food shortages but to so-cietal unrest as well. While some areas could also see benefits, the net effect globally would be, without doubt, negative.[5]

Higher CO_2 content in the atmosphere leads to more carbon being dissolved into our oceans, acidifying the water. If unchecked, this acidifying will eventually kill off most of the plankton in the world's oceans and wreck the oceanic food chains, leading to a crash of fisher-ies already pressured by overfishing and a severe protein deficiency in fish-dependent regions.

Melting glaciers endangers local species and biodiversity as well as the human communities and ecosystems that are dependent on the melting waters from those glaciers. If the glaciers in Greenland and western Antarctic melt, the oceans might rise by up to 10 meters.[6] The majority of humanity that currently lives on coastal areas could see massive destruction of cities and infrastructure, which would lead to hundreds of millions of people migrating away from those areas. Many island nations and low-lying areas of poor countries – where dikes and seawalls may be difficult to build – will sink or become semi-permanently waterlogged long before that happens.

Rapidly changing climate will also speed up biodiversity loss, which is now primarily driven by human activities such as deforestation and agriculture, as species cannot adapt to rapid changes fast enough. Many species are already migrating from their current habitats due to a changing climate. The rhythm of species behaviour can change, which will disrupt their interaction with other species that coexist in the same ecosystem.

Human species will most likely survive unless something truly dras-tic happens. However, the survival of the civilization is by no means certain, and even if catastrophic global outcomes are averted, climate change will hit the world's poor nations the hardest, as they have less resources to adapt for the changing situation and problems they are facing. In absolute terms, the rich could suffer the biggest losses, but they also have the best resources to adapt and protect themselves.

Emission sources

There are other important emission sources besides energy, but at the moment, energy generation is by far the largest single source of greenhouse gas emissions. Globally, it is responsible for roughly two thirds of humanity's greenhouse gas emissions. Unless we can clean up our energy production – decarbonize it – we will be simply unable to seriously limit climate change. Our energy use can be roughly divided into three categories by the type of energy used:

- Electricity
- Transportation
- Heat (both for space heating and industrial processes) and other minor uses

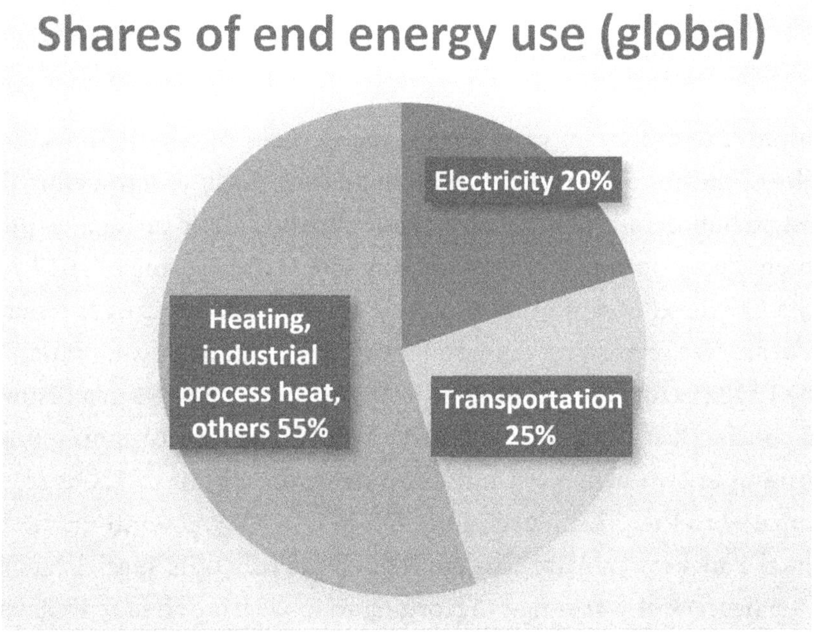

Shares of end energy use (global)

Electricity 20%

Heating, industrial process heat, others 55%

Transportation 25%

Figure 1: Approximate end-uses of global energy by type.

The rest of the emissions outside energy are mainly from:
- Agriculture
- Land-use change
- Chemical processes, cement etc

In 2010, humanity's total emissions were roughly 48 billion metric tons of CO_2-equivalent, of which around 31 billion tons resulted from burning fossil fuels such as coal, oil and natural gas. In 2018, fossil fuels emissions had grown to over 33 billion tons, growing at roughly 1 % per year for the last decade.[7] The stated goal for many rich countries is to reduce their emissions by 80 percent by 2050. In practice this means that the energy sector needs to be carbon neutral by that time, as emission reductions in other sectors, such as agriculture, are even more difficult.

The Reality and the Politics of Climate Change

Despite the mountain of evidence and decades of negotiations and policies, the annual emissions keep increasing. Each year we emit almost 50 billion tons of greenhouse gases. Atmospheric carbon dioxide content keeps on rising at an increasing rate.[8] In the spring of 2019 we saw a CO_2 level of 414 ppm, and the rate of increase was over 3 ppm per year.[9] We're heading the wrong way, and at an increasing rate.

The COP21 climate negotiations in Paris (2015) resulted in a historical contract between the world's nations. We agreed to limit global warming to two degrees at most and strive for a limit of 1.5 degrees compared to the pre-industrial period. In late 2018, the Intergovernmental Panel on Climate Change (IPCC) published its special report on 1.5 degrees of warming.[10] According to it, we have already warmed by roughly 1 °C, and at current rates will likely hit 1.5 °C between 2030 and 2052. The difference of 1.5 °C and 2 °C warming is significant, with the risks and damages likely increasing markedly when we approach the latter.

Looking at the current goals and promises made by various nations, even 2°C is a tall order. Even if the current emission pledges are fully realized, we are still headed for a 2.7 degrees of warming by 2100.[11] That said, the situation has improved markedly, as the goals set just a few years ago would have meant a warming of at least 3.7 degrees by 2100.[12] The 2019 COP25 was held in Madrid and hosted by Chile, and the results from that meeting were generally seen as disappointing.[13]

The 2°C limit is the result of decades of negotiations between the world's countries. This rather arbitrary target is an outcome of many different interactions, and probably has less basis in climate science or ethics than many think.[14] Limiting the change to two degrees or less means that the climate has a better chance of staying within the boundaries of what our civilization has both enjoyed and thrived in for the last 12,000 years.[15] 2°C warming is nevertheless likely to be enough to drown low-lying island nations and large swaths of poor countries, and cause significant disruption in agricultural output. Nevertheless, the 2°C limit has been chosen because of its simplicity: it is a simple goal to describe. The 2°C limit might avoid the most catastrophic risks of self-reinforcing climate change, while its lack of ambition means that costs of climate action are modest. The most important thing about the 2°C limit is arguably that it is the target many of us have agreed on.

Given the complexities of our climate system, targeting any single number as a "limit" remains an arbitrary choice. No climate scientist thinks that we will surely be safe if we limit the warming to 1.9 degrees and certainly doomed if the outcome is 2.1 degrees. If we want to prevent small island nations from disappearing, we would need to limit the warming to 1.5 degrees at most. There is a host of studies that indicate that the risks of climate change will increase rapidly after two degrees of warming. The faster and the more the climate warms, the greater and more likely these risks become.

The risks could be nothing short of catastrophic. Anatomically and most likely intellectually modern humans have been around for about

100,000 years. But agriculture, the prerequisite for a complex civilization, arose only some 12,000 years ago. It is almost certainly not a co-incidence that the birth of agriculture coincided with an exceptionally stable climate. If we lose that stable climate, the long-term survival of complex civilization is at serious risk. Even the World Bank has stated clearly that there are no certainties that modern society even could, much less that it would, adapt for a world four degrees warmer than the pre-industrial period.[16]

The human species is unlikely to go extinct as a result, but if agriculture fails, complex societies will fail. What is more, the impacts would not be distributed equally. The mass of the world's poor living near the equator would suffer the most, while also being the least able to afford adequate mitigation measures. The rich north will not be safe, however, even if the dikes and seawalls can be built higher. History tells us that when drought strikes and fisheries disappear, the poor are unlikely to stay home and die quietly. For the last couple of years the refugee problem has developed into a recurring issue in European politics and news, even though the world has "only" about 50 million refugees in total. If warming accelerates and conditions deteriorate, we might be facing a refugee problem on the scale of one or two billion people.

Another number that humanity has agreed upon is 450 parts per million (ppm). If we want to keep the warming under two degrees, the share of carbon dioxide in the atmosphere should not exceed 450 ppm, at least not in the long term. Many climatologists and researchers, such as James Hansen, the former chief climatologist at NASA, have said that we should strive to keep the atmospheric carbon dioxide content at 350 ppm, or at most 400 ppm. It is practically a certainty that we will push past 450 ppm at least temporarily, and we will need negative emissions, meaning the net removal of greenhouse gases from the atmosphere. Currently we have higher emissions than even the most pessimistic IPCC scenarios suggested just a few years ago[17].

Globally, annual emissions need to drop by 40-70 percent by 2050 and nearly 100 percent by 2100.[18] In the rich, industrialized coun-tries, the reduction rates need to be much faster: Several percentage points per year, every year, for the next 40 or so years, and even this is just the beginning. Many countries need to attain negative emis-sions sometime during the second half of this century, meaning that we need to sequester more CO_2 from the atmosphere than we emit. A lot more. The energy sector absolutely needs to be zero carbon by then, and deforestation needs to be turned into robust reforestation. It is also likely that we need to find other ways to remove the CO_2 from the atmosphere, such as direct air capture (DAC), and then store hun-dreds of billions of tons of it somewhere, somehow. Besides reducing our domestic emissions, we also need to cut emissions embedded in international trade. Currently, most rich countries outsource a sig-nificant chunk of their emissions to China and other manufacturing centres of the world. We in the rich world consume the goods while avoiding pollution on paper – but the atmosphere knows no national boundaries.

If we had aimed to minimize the risks and stabilize the carbon dioxide level at the relatively safe 350 ppm by around 2100, we would have needed to cut emissions from fossil fuels by six percent a year since 2013. Instead we have added more and more emissions every year. Besides, we would also need a significant amount of net reforestation to stay on target.[19]

The required rate of emission reductions keeps rising as long as we continue in the wrong direction or fail to meet the annual target. At the same time, the hope of stabilizing the climate at 350 ppm escapes into the far future. A heroic effort leading to a reduction of 1 ppm per year (while we currently add some 3.5 ppm per year) would take a full century for each 100 ppm we overshoot the 350 ppm target. Price-waterhouseCoopers' *Low Carbon Economy Index 2018*[20] pointed out that the global decarbonization rate of the economy is 6.4% for the rest of the century – while in 2017 we achieved a rate of 2.6%. No single country, let alone the world as a whole, achieved the needed constant rate even for a single year in 2017. Decoupling economic growth from emissions growth has failed miserably compared to the level that we would have needed to stay on the maximum 2 °C target. According to the report, global carbon budget for 2 °C will run out in 2036.

It should be noted that these numbers include assumptions on the level of economic growth the world may experience, so they depict the relative decoupling rate of economy and emissions (called *carbon intensity*). Only absolute numbers matter, however. If economic growth is faster than presumed, the rate of decarbonization needs to be faster as well. If we somehow get stuck in our current level of economic activity, a lower decarbonization rate of roughly three percent would be enough. In light of historical evidence, even this is an ambitious goal; for instance, since 2000, Germany has managed less than one percent reductions per year on average.

The realities of climate change can also be viewed from another perspective. How much known fossil fuel reserves do we have? And how much will we emit if we burn them?

To date, we have emitted over 500 gigatons (billion tons) of carbon dioxide, and its concentration in the atmosphere has risen from 280 to 414 ppm. The total "carbon budget" that would likely suffice to keep us under two degrees (with 63 to 92 percent confidence, given the current models) is 886 gigatons by 2050. In 2009, we had 565 gigatons left in our budget.[21] Since then, ten years have passed, and we have burned enough fossil fuels to emit around 300 gigatons more emissions by 2020. From the 2009 analysis:

- We will emit around 550 gigatons if we burn our known oil reserves.
- We will emit around 350 gigatons if we burn our known natural gas reserves.
- We will emit around 2,000 gigatons if we burn our known coal reserves.

The numbers above do not include unconventional reserves and resources like oil sands, oil shale (kerogen), shale (tight) oil, shale (tight) gas and methane clathrates. We also have not found all the conventional fossil fuel reserves yet. Indeed, even while burning fossil fuels at record rates, the known oil reserves have been replenished at higher rates than we have consumed them. No climate negotiation as far as we know has proposed or even mentioned the fact that we should limit fossil fuels production in some ways.[22] A study[23] from 2015 tries to bring attention to this disparity. The study aims to map how much, where and which fossil fuel we could produce and use and how much should be left underground to have even a remote chance to stay under two degrees. According to the study, we should:

- Leave 82 percent of coal reserves underground (88 % without carbon capture and storage, or CCS)
- Leave 49 percent of natural gas underground (52 % without CCS)
- Leave 33 percent of oil reserves underground (35 % without CCS).

The scale of the challenge this study unveils is staggering. And yet we still use vast sums of money to explore for more fossil fuels and to improve production technologies every year. Fossil fuels are hard to replace, as they are simply so useful.

In the end, the key numbers are quite easy to remember. We need to cut 80 percent of our emissions by 2050. After that we need to proceed towards net negative emissions well before the end of the century. This means that most (two-thirds at least) of our known fossil fuel reserves should remain underground. If we burn even close to all of our reserves, we will exceed our carbon budget by five times, and we will likely face several degrees of warming and risk causing a climate change that is incompatible with the survival of a complex civilization. With the current trajectory, our whole carbon budget will be used by 2030 to 2040, depending on the maximum warming target we have.[24] Building our energy infrastructure anew takes many decades.

The inherited situation simply is what it is: more than 80 percent of our primary energy comes from fossil fuels. Even if we were to build new power plants, vehicles and infrastructure, we would do it with our current infrastructure that uses fossil fuels. In addition, most of the energy produced needs to be consumed in everyday life, not invested in new energy production. We cannot simply stop consuming. It's also often not possible, or economical, to abandon the current infrastructure if it still has usable time left. And when we build a new infrastructure, it is always built at least partly within the frames set by the existing system. This puts serious limits to what we can build and how fast we can build it.

It is, however, rather clear what we need to do. The decarbonisation strategy can be summed up simply: *first, clean up electricity; second, electrify everything.* Electrification can be either direct or indirect. In indirect electrification, we use electricity to make synthetic carbon neutral fuels for uses that are hard to electrify directly. To stop burning fossil fuels, we will need much more electricity and a system that can supplant burning with electricity. No matter how we choose to produce that electricity, this is the only serious decarbonisation strategy we know that could work.

Producing energy is not something that we can simply choose to stop doing. We need vast amounts of energy every day if we are to stay alive and if we want to keep our modern, democratic society with the necessary (and some unnecessary) services and products to which we are accustomed. It is therefore highly unlikely that people and societies would simply choose to consume far less than they do. It is far more likely that people and societies will produce the energy they require somehow, if it is at all physically possible, even if the long-term risks include cooking the planet.

Energy in Society

For millennia, humanity's energy needs were met with photosynthesis. Direct use of photosynthesizing plants in agriculture and forestry, and indirect use through cattle herding provided us with both energy (that is, food and warmth) and power (oxen, horses and the like). Wind and hydropower have been used occasionally for ages, but even at the dawn of the modern era, 95 percent of humanity's energy resources came directly or indirectly from the living environment.[25] As recently as in the middle of the 18th century, the average living standard of people was no higher than it had been in the early Christian era. A major reason for this was that the energy and power needed for more intense economic activity was simply not available on a wide scale.[26] Wind and hydropower resources were utilized wherever they were feasible, but the additions on a per capita level remained miniscule.

The next leap in our energy use happened around 300 years ago, when the use of coal started to grow significantly. Coal had been used since antiquity, but it became an important energy source only after forests diminished in Europe. This move from an energy system that was based largely on photosynthesis to a system that was based on fossil fuels might have actually saved what was still left of the European forests.

Eventually, the demand depleted easily available surface coal mines and people needed to go ever deeper to produce more coal. These mines had a problem of their own, as groundwater started to seep into the mines and made mining ever harder. Various horse-driven pumps were used, but in time even they did not have enough power to get the water out from the mines. Help arrived with the recent innovation of the steam engine, which derived its energy (of course) from coal burning. It was, arguably, the first case of "enhanced coal recovery", where advanced technology was used to increase production and reserves. The steam engine was constantly improved both in efficiency and power, and after sufficient improvements, it also found numerous new uses.

The rest is the story of scientific and technological advance never seen before in the history of our species. This development was, and is, powered first and foremost by fossil fuels. A remarkable part of our technological advances has actually been inventing different ways to reduce the use of human labour by replacing it with machinery and technology that is powered by external energy, either fuels or electricity. Therefore, a significant part of our economic growth and development can be traced back to increases in quantity and efficiency of the ways we use external energy. Unfortunately, almost all this external energy use consisted of fossil fuels, which have some unwanted and cascading side effects.

There has been a strong correlation between increasing living standards and energy consumption throughout history. As a rule, the better access people have had to energy, the higher their living standard and well-being – at least, up to a point. This point has arguably been reached by many rich countries, and our experienced well-being won't significantly increase even if we get access to ever more energy services, or at least the connection between added energy and increased well-being is getting weaker and weaker. In contrast, the same energy resources would increase human well-being much more, if consumed by someone living in poverty.

In fact, more than half of the human population would see enormous gains in their living standards if they only had access to more (modern) energy. Seven of the eight United Nations' Millennium Development Goals[27] require that significantly more energy is made available to the world's poor.[28] Reliable and affordable electricity, for example, makes it possible to obtain enough clean water not only for drinking but also for important hygienic purposes (that is, washing people, clothes and surfaces as easily as we in the rich world have become accustomed to) and to keep perishable food cool, therefore reducing losses and spoilage. This further improves hygiene, nutrition and well-being of the people.

Electrical lighting would permit studying and working after dark, making all activities safer compared to existing solutions such as kerosene lamps. Electrical motors could run both water pumps and light machinery reliably. In short, if our common goal is to help the poor get out of poverty, they will require and deserve reliable, on-demand, affordable and thoroughly modern energy services. It would be all the better if that energy were also produced as cleanly as possible.

According to the UN Human Development Index (HDI), living standards tend to improve greatly at least until people can use around 4,000 kilowatt-hours (kWh) of electricity annually.[29] The living standard continues to improve after this as well, but the correlation between higher energy consumption and higher living standard starts to taper. People benefit from the energy that they consume directly, but they also benefit from the energy that the society and infrastructure around them consumes, for example to provide various services to the people. Currently, the poor try to meet their bare minimum energy requirements by gathering the energy wherever it is available. Using wood and plant residues for energy is particularly harmful as it tends to increase local erosion, destroying valuable soil and making it even harder to make ends meet in the future. What is more, the task of collecting fuels is in many cases left to the women, who often must spend many hours each day trying to find something to burn. A stable energy supply would free them to use this time for more useful activities, including education. In addition to other problems caused by energy poverty, about one million people get sick and die every year due inhalation of particulate indoor air pollution caused by open cooking fires and dirty fuels.[30]

Energy consumption has a clear correlation not only with living standard, but with increased free time, wealth, well-being, and women's education and fertility rates. Fertility rate usually starts to drop when per person income rises to approximately 1,000 – 2,000 USD per year and keeps on dropping until it reaches the level of around 2.1 children per woman with incomes between 4,000 and 10,000 USD annually.[31]

As such, addressing energy poverty greatly helps us to break the vicious cycle of poverty in general, although other measures are also necessary.

Higher energy consumption correlates strongly with higher living standards, but it is not the goal by itself. The benefits it confers are the goal. These benefits – and the drawbacks – that improved energy access might confer to the individuals, society and the environment are determined by how, for what and where this energy is produced and used. The environmental footprint especially varies greatly depending on how the energy is produced in the first place.

Peak Everything?

Besides climate change, another megatrend forces us to reflect on what we want to do with energy and how we produce it. "Peak everything" is an umbrella term for the possible outcome of the current trends in resource extraction: that we need to utilize ever poorer concentrations of energy, minerals and other raw materials. Almost invariably, the problem is *not* about humanity running out of one or another resource. Instead, the problem is that increasing scarcity and the use of poorer and poorer resources are likely to increase the costs of using scarce resources, and these cost increases can have a major impact on our economy and the ability and motivation to cope with other challenges we are facing.

Our increasing use of diminishing natural resources means we also use more energy to produce them. Technological development can slow down or even reverse this trend, and in theory, rising prices encourage us to find other alternatives and ever more efficient production methods. However, in many cases new technology does not make our dependency on one particular resource disappear, but simply shifts it to other resources that are more readily available. For example, renewable energy like wind and solar is often said to require no fuels to produce energy, but this is only true in a narrow sense of the term. Building wind turbines and solar photovoltaic (PV) panels requires significant amounts of energy and minerals, and mining, refining, transporting and even recycling these materials has environmental effects. These materials, sometimes scarce, are the "fuels" of renewable energy production. The core problem is that both wind and solar energy are diffuse, instead of concentrated. For each unit of energy collected, relatively large apparatus needs to be constructed. These demand steel, concrete and glass, as well as many rarer minerals. These demands are highlighted further due to the relatively short lifespans of these facilities, often roughly between 20 and 40 years, although much of them can be recycled.

Relatively little attention has been paid to these resource demands and their inevitable environmental effects, even though major expansion of wind and solar power is likely to demand significant quantities of scarce raw materials. One recent study suggests that if even half of our electricity demand (not total energy) was to be met with renewable energy in 2050, and even after allowing for significant advances in technology and resource efficiency, photovoltaic panels alone could consume almost all of our known silver resources.[32] We would also need much more tellurium and indium that currently exists in known reserves. If this scenario were to be even remotely sustainable, we would also need to recycle the materials much more efficiently than we do today. The study did not reflect on the fact that many of these minerals have other, competing uses, nor did it account for the needs of large-scale energy storage and increased transmission capacity. In this sense, the study can be thought of as rather optimistic. Many much more optimistic studies on renewable energy and its potential leave all material and resource questions largely, or even completely, unanswered.

Also, if we seek to protect the environment, the problems become even harder to solve. While past experiences suggest that we are unlikely to face shortages in basic materials like steel, copper, aluminium and concrete, we would likely need to increase their production

significantly in the near future. Many studies and scenarios that propose all renewable solutions include wind power capacities of 19 – 27
terawatts (TW), which would by itself demand around 37 percent of
the world's current annual steel production.[33] This means that steel
consumption needs to drop radically elsewhere, or that we need to
increase its production significantly. Copper and concrete demand
face similar pressures, at the same time as the consumption of these
resources is growing rapidly as poor countries industrialize. This
message is also abundantly clear in the recent study *"The Growing Role
of Minerals an￭ Metals for a Low Carbon Future"* by the World Bank
(2017[34]), stating that the scenarios leaning on renewable energy sources are significantly more material intensive than the current system.
We might be changing our carbon addiction into a mineral addiction.
 Moving to less concentrated sources will also increase the energy consumed in mining and concentrating the resources. Currently mining
activities and production of metals account for roughly a tenth of our
global energy demand. Increasing these volumes means that we will
need to produce even more energy, which in turn increases pressures
to use ever scarcer energy resources. It is very likely that the increasing demand for all the minerals required will be met by even poorer ores and the use of more questionable mining methods. Assuming
that global oversight can prevent serious environmental damage in
this situation seems hopelessly optimistic at best.
 But could humans reduce their energy demand so much that we could
stop using fossil fuels? What is all that energy used for, and what role
does it play in modern society? What is energy, exactly?

What Is Energy?

 According to one popular definition, energy is the ability to do work.
All life is dependent on getting and using energy. At the basic level,
this means that we need to be fed and we need to stay warm. We use
energy to build houses to shelter us from the elements, and to help

us keep our body temperature in the proper range for survival and comfort. We need energy to move around, and even thinking uses energy. In the end, all activities require energy. In the complex, modern and industrialized world energy plays an especially important role. The whole society, outside of food and energy production, with all its various activities, only exists because said production has a large net surplus.

On the other hand, humans have probably never been so disconnected from the meaning of energy and their ability to use it. Energy production remains largely unseen for most people. For individuals in all except poor nations, gasoline is available in practically unlimited quantities at the local gas station, and electricity flows from the socket on demand. Elevators go up and down, buses and trains transport us from here to there, planes fly and the shelves of various stores are filled with clothing, delicacies, groceries and more or less useful gadgets, as if by magic. But all these activities are dependent on the constant and uninterrupted production and flow of enormous amounts of energy through our society.

Energy exists in many forms. It cannot be created, nor can it be destroyed, but we've become pretty clever in coaxing energy to change form. A rock on top of a slide has potential energy. Set it rolling downhill and the rock's potential energy will be converted into kinetic energy – motion. Everything, including you and me, is made up of molecules that move and vibrate with kinetic energy that we call heat. Lack of heat, or molecular movement, is complete stillness. Hydrocarbons, such as fossil fuels and biomass, contain significant quantities of chemical energy that can be released as heat by inducing the fuels to combine with an oxidizer – that is, by burning them. The nucleus of atoms contains nuclear energy. When the nucleus of an atom breaks, part of its mass gets converted to energy, as per the famous $E = mc^2$ (energy equals mass times the speed of light squared). Mass is, essentially, extremely dense energy.

Energy is therefore everywhere, but only a small portion of it is in a usable form, meaning that it can be used to do work. There are a lot of theoretically interesting sources of energy that remain practically not useful. A bucket of water at 20 °C contains roughly the same amount of heat energy as a coffee cup of gasoline has stored in chemical bonds within its hydrocarbon molecules. However, it is very hard to use the heat energy in the water bucket for any useful work, while the gasoline can be used for multiple useful purposes, from driving a few kilometres on a moped to felling a couple of trees with a chainsaw. The gasoline could also be used in a generator to make electricity, which has even more uses. To put it shortly, the chemical energy in the gasoline is of much higher quality than the energy in the lukewarm water. The term *exergy* is often used to measure and describe the amount of useful work that can be extracted from an energy source.[35]

So what constitutes high quality energy then? One rule of thumb is "the hotter, the better". Nearly all useful processes to turn energy into work – for example from heat to motion directly or by making electricity first – require temperature differences, and the larger the differences, the better. Steam turbines, still the mainstay of electricity production, usually require a temperature differential of least 300 degrees between the "hot" and the "cold" side to be useful, and most modern turbines operate with significantly higher temperature differentials. Even the most advanced thermoelectric Seebeck generators require a temperature difference of at least a hundred degrees centigrade to produce useful quantities of electricity, and just as with turbines, the efficiency increases with the temperature differential. For this reason, power plant designers generally desire very high temperatures whenever that is possible. For example, steam turbines generally use steam that is heated to 500 or 550 degrees centigrade. For other kinds of useful work, such as producing and shaping metals and for various useful chemical reactions, the required temperatures can be much higher.[36]

At this point, it might be beneficial to introduce two central definitions in the energy discussion: primary energy and secondary energy. Secondary energy is high-quality energy that is in a readily usable form, like electricity, liquid fuels or process steam for industrial uses. Secondary energy is made from primary energy sources, which include for example wood fuel, crude oil, coal, natural gas, peat, nuclear energy, solar radiation, wind and the potential energy of water upstream (that is, hydropower).

Biomass, crude oil, coal, natural gas and peat are both sources and storage containers of chemical energy. Solar radiation and wind are both sources of energy, but cannot be stored for later use. Water, on the other hand, can often be stored in reservoirs to store its potential energy, at least up to a point. All of these originally draw their energy from the Sun: directly in case of solar radiation, and indirectly from captured rays of the Sun in the other cases. The source of the Sun's energy is of course the constant fusion reaction happening within the Sun. The intense heat and pressure in the core induces light elements (currently, primarily hydrogen leftovers from the Big Bang) to overcome their differences and join together, releasing massive quantities of energy as a by-product.

On the other hand, fission energy in our current nuclear reactors and geothermal energy that mostly originates from spontaneous decay of unstable atoms in the Earth's crust is essentially energy surplus created and stored in the fiery collapses of long-bygone stars. In our universe, all elements heavier than iron, including our fission fuels uranium and thorium, are produced only during supernova explosions. By splitting the atom, we unlock the energy forged into those elements in the dying moments of a star far, far away. Finally, there is one source of energy that does not originate from fission or fusion: tidal waves are caused by the kinetic energy of Earth's rotation and the gravitational forces of the Moon and the Sun.

Of all the forms of secondary energy, electricity is probably overall the most useful. It is easy to make, transfer, and use. It can be easily transformed to heat or motion, and it can be used to create very high temperatures. With various heat pumps, electricity can even be used to move heat energy from the ground, water (such as a lake) or even winter air way below the freezing point. The biggest drawback of electricity is that it is difficult to store.

Liquid fuels, usually refined from crude oil, are another example of high-quality secondary energy. Crude oil, which took millions of years and just the right geological conditions to form, is an abundant source of energy that can easily be refined to products like gasoline, diesel oil and jet fuel. These fuels, and the crude oil that they are made from, are also relatively easy to store and quite easy to transport even over long distances. Solid fuels such as coal, peat and biomass are a step down in the quality ladder of energy. Biomass fuels and peat in particular have much lower energy density than oil or even coal, and therefore are harder to move around and store. They are also much more inconvenient as sources of motive power, whereas liquid fuels are easily adapted for uses such as internal combustion engines that still power most of the world's transportation.

Finally, there is the residual or waste heat from different power plants (coal, gas, biomass and nuclear). This surplus heat can be used, provided that the plants are so-called combined heat and power (CHP) plants with specialized equipment. It is however only useful for space heating, hot water and perhaps some light industrial processes such as drying or desalination of water, and some of these applications require a separate heat network to be built. However, by combining heat and power, over 90 percent of the primary energy content in a fuel can be used, in contrast to mere 30 to 50 percent achievable in power plants that produce only electricity.

One final but important property of an energy source is the relative amount of energy and resources that need to be used to produce it. With a good energy source, the amount of energy required to use the source is small compared to the amount of useful energy we get. An energy source like this is said to have a high EROEI (Energy Return on Energy Invested). We will go into more detail about EROEI later in the book.

Energy Production

As we wrote earlier, the energy sector is by far the biggest single source of our emissions. Fossil fuels, which are our main energy source with over 80 percent share of the world's primary energy supply, release greenhouse gases when they are burned. Unless we stop the use of fossil fuels almost completely or capture and store the carbon they release, even a heroic effort to conserve energy and cut emissions in other sectors will not be enough to halt dangerous climate change. The project of stopping the emissions from the use of fossil fuels is called *ecarbonisation.*

Energy Production Today

A fact that has merited surprisingly little attention is that globally, the fastest growing energy source in the last decade has been *coal*. During the last ten years, coal burning increased more than in the previous 40 years put together. Even in countries that are hailed as the forerunners of renewable energy, coal is often growing at pace or even faster than other energy sources.

	Solar PV	Wind	Solar + wind	Coal
	Mtoe/a	Mtoe/a	Mtoe/a	Mtoe/a
1990	0.1	0.8	0.9	2,219.9
2018	132.3	287.4	419.7	3,772.1
Growth Mtoe	132.2	286.6	418.8	1,552.2
Growth as %	132,200	35,825	46,533	70

*Table: Annual primary energy pro*uction of *ifferent energy sources, 1990 an* 2018, an* growth rates.*

Despite massive growth rates, solar and wind power were globally barely able to significantly reduce the growth in coal use, let alone reduce the absolute use. The primary energy contents are compared by assuming for the sake of conversion that electricity from wind and solar were to be generated in a coal power plant that converts 38 percent of coal's primary energy content into electricity. Source: BP Statistical Review of World Energy 2019.

Since 1990, wind and solar power have seen astounding growth rates. Between 1990 and 2014, the global production of wind and solar power has increased by a massive 22 203 percent. However, in absolute terms – in terms of energy actually generated – the growth is significant but far more modest. By converting the electricity produced to primary energy (that is, by comparing apples to apples, i.e. the quantity of coal required for the same production), the increase between 1990 and 2018 has been a mere 419 Mtoe (million tons of oil-equivalent) of primary energy generation per year. At the same time, the consumption of coal has increased by 70 percent, or 1,552 Mtoe per year in absolute terms. In other words, the production of solar and wind power combined grew by a bit over one quarter of what the coal consumption has increased during the same period. It needs to be said that almost all the growth in wind and solar power generation has occurred during the last dozen years and the growth rate is still high.

Even this comparison between annual energy generation does not tell the whole truth, as the reliable operation of an electric grid always requires that production and consumption be close to equal. Too much or too little production at any given moment spells trouble such as equipment failures and possible blackouts, and since we cannot control whether wind blows or the Sun shines, the value of wind and solar power to the power grid is less than annual production figures alone would suggest. This value drops further as their share increases. Depending on location and situation, wind and solar start losing their value rapidly after their share of production increases to somewhere between 5 % (solar) to 25 % (wind).

Another comparison might be made with nuclear energy. During an equivalent time period set in the nuclear power's heyday (1968-1990), world's nuclear energy generation grew from about 51.6 TWh (terawatt-hour) to 2002.3 TWh per year.[37] This growth spurt is so far the last time when the share of fossil fuels in the world energy consumption dropped significantly. In 1990, the share of fossil fuels of the world's primary energy supply was about 88 percent, whereas in 2018 the share was around 84 percent.[38]

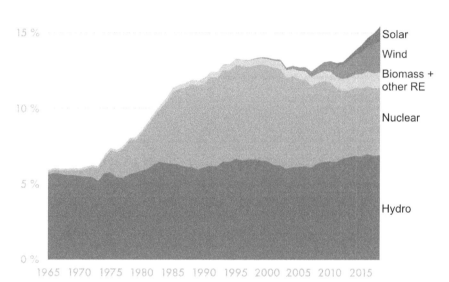

Figure 4: Share of low-carbon energy as a percentage of total primary energy supply, 1965-2018.
Source: BP Statistical Review of World Energy 2019

At the same time, the total use of energy has increased significantly. In 1990, humanity used about 369 exajoules of energy (102,600 TWh), but in 2018, the global energy use was around 580 exajoules (~160,000 TWh). Almost all this growth has been achieved through increasing use of fossil fuels, and our carbon dioxide emissions have grown accordingly.

In short, the world's energy cake is baked from fossil fuels, with some decorative sprinkling from other sources. Despite all the breathless optimism about a renewable energy revolution happening any day now, low-carbon energy is actually in a danger of decline in many parts of the world, chiefly because nuclear plants are being closed while new renewables cannot grow fast enough to even compensate for this loss, let alone cut into fossil fuel use.

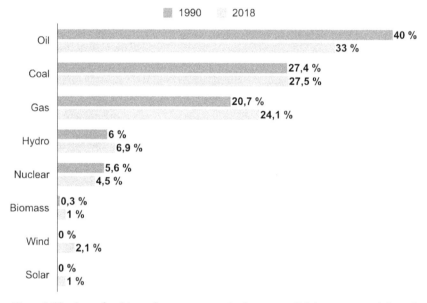

Figure 5: The share of coal in world energy production has grown slightly since 1990, while in absolute terms, coal has grown by 70 percent. Source: BP Statistical Review of World Energy 2019.

Decarbonizing the energy sector

Since the world's energy production accounts for two thirds of global greenhouse gas emissions, taking climate change seriously means that we need to decarbonize the whole energy sector – preferably by 2050. This will mean an increasing rate of electrification (historically we have electrified our energy usage at roughly two percentage points per decade) and finding other ways to clean up those energy uses that are hard or too expensive to electrify.

Generating low-carbon electricity is actually the "easy" part of the plan. We have numerous ways to produce electricity with acceptably low emissions: nuclear power, hydropower, wind and solar radiation can all be harnessed to produce practically emission-free electricity. While it should be noted that there are no true "zero-carbon" energy sources, for practical purposes the aforementioned generally have low enough life cycle emissions to count as "zero carbon" if one wishes to use the term.

The really difficult part only begins when the electricity sector has been decarbonized, as the next necessary step towards zero emissions will be to stop the use of fossil fuels for transportation, industrial process heat, building heating and for chemical feedstocks. There, fossil fuels reign supreme. Despite encouraging progress of electrified transport, it seems very likely that combustion engines will remain important sources of motive power for the foreseeable future – possibly (and hopefully) not in personal transport, but almost certainly in aviation, marine shipping, long-haul road transport and many forms of heavy machinery. The technical difficulties in directly electrifying long-distance aviation are formidable, and electric trucks are likely to be of limited use for decades as well.

Similarly, chemical feedstocks and industrial process heat are often in principle replaceable by ingenious electricity-based solutions, including, for example, making fertilizers directly from atmospheric nitrogen, but these cleaner methods are still much more expensive than deriving heat or feedstocks from fossil sources. Be that as it may, we nevertheless must decarbonize these sectors as well. Arithmetic of our predicament is simple, if ominous: unless decarbonization of non-electricity energy sector succeeds, rich countries are almost certain to miss the required overall target of 80-90 percent decarbonization, and have no hope of achieving net negative emissions that are required by the end of this century.

What all this means in practice is that electricity use and production must grow, as liquid and solid fuels are replaced and supplanted by electricity wherever practical to do so. As well, electricity needs to remain relatively cheap and its steady, predictable 24/7 availability needs to be assured. Neither of these can substitute for the other: successful decarbonization is almost certain to require both cheap and reliable electricity. Otherwise, producing substitutes for fossil fuels will remain too expensive and continuing the use of reliable fossil fuels will remain the easier and cheaper choice. Even zero-cost electricity simply isn't enough to make expensive synthetic fuel factories and refineries competitive with fossil sources, if the variability of electricity supply forces the expensive plants to lay idle for more than very brief periods.[39] Unless the plants can recoup their capital investments, with interest and profit on top, they will not be built, and the world will remain locked in to fossil fuels.

In short, we need enormous amounts of low carbon energy production as fast as possible, certainly much faster than we have been adding it.

At this point, we need to clarify a few terms to make sense of what is often a muddled debate. On one hand, we have goals we want to achieve; on the other, we have means or tools we can use to reach those goals. If we believe the great majority of climate scientists, our goal should be to get our greenhouse gas emissions to near zero as fast as possible. This goal can be achieved by using various tools. Some tools can be more appropriate than others. Some tools can be insidious in that they will take us in the general direction of the goal but can never take us all the way there. At worst, they can lock us on a certain path where progress can be easy at first but become impossible at some point.

Examples of these are often called "bridge fuels", such as natural gas and expanding use of bioenergy. By switching from coal to these bridge fuels, emissions drop fast (at least on paper as the methane leaks from natural gas are not accounted for), but often not nearly low enough. Thus, replacing coal with natural gas can be a good tactic to cut emissions, and especially air pollution, but it might also mean that those gas plants will stay operational for decades, and their owners will be interested in seeing the plants run their whole lifespan. In other words, they will be lobbying hard for their operations, and the more there are such plants, the more lobbying power the owners have as they represent a larger share of wealth and power, and the society is more dependent on their services.

The end results can be troubling, particularly in the rich countries, where we would have other plausible alternatives for producing our energy. However, too strong a reliance on "bridge fuels" and similar solutions that appear to take us somewhere but cannot take us all the way means that a smaller carbon budget is left for the developing world, where poverty translates to fewer real options to decarbonize the energy sector.

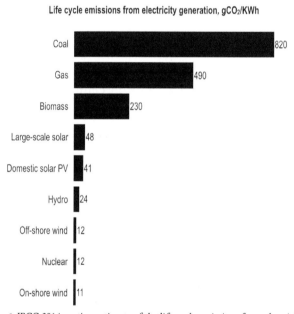

Life cycle emissions from electricity generation, gCO_2/KWh

Figure 6: IPCC 2014 median estimate of the life cycle emissions from electricity generation, $gCO2/kWh$

In practice, all energy sources below 50 gCO2/kWh can be considered low carbon, or "zero carbon", as they only emit something during their construction, which means that were the energy system otherwise clean, these would have close to zero emissions. Even natural gas was once considered low carbon, but that has been changing. Even relatively low leakage rates of 2-4 % in production, transport, storage and usage makes natural gas as bad as coal is for the climate, depending on the timescale observed (methane stays in the atmosphere for much shorter time than CO2, but is a much more potent greenhouse gas). The case for bioenergy is also problematic. Increasing use of bioenergy can lead to land use changes that could lead to emissions equal or even worse than coal, not to mention that dedicated bioenergy production (monocrops) destroys biodiversity and species habitats. Only part of bioenergy can be counted as more or less carbon neutral, and even that part only cuts emissions when it is used to replace fossil fuels.

Our Future Energy Needs

Around 1.2 billion people still live without electricity, and around 2.7 billion still cook their food with traditional fuels such as firewood, dung, charcoal, and agricultural waste.[40] In China alone, around 400 million people are estimated to have used coal for cooking and heating their home just two decades ago.[41] These dirty indoor fires are responsible for roughly four million premature deaths each year[42].

By 2050 world population will be around 10 billion humans. According to recent reports, by the end of the century, this will grow to 11 billion (between 9.5 and 12.5 billion).[43] There is very little we can do about this number, as the trajectory has already been set and locked. Population growth today is mainly the result of longer life spans, not so much of too many children per family. Fertility has actually been on the decline almost everywhere. So we will have more people, but not indefinitely.

These people all want to increase their living standard, and in most cases that means their use of energy will increase. At the same time, we should be replacing fossil fuels with cleaner alternatives, while increased scarcity in many minerals is likely to increase the energy demands of mining activity. Lastly, there is precious little evidence that the rich, democratic western world is willing and able to lower its high-energy lifestyle in any significant measure. These are all powerful trends, and they are mainly pointing in the same direction.

But there is also good news. Energy use seems to have a ceiling in many rich countries, after which it does not grow that much. In many countries, energy use has stayed stable for years, even decades, and in some cases it has even decreased. Some of this might be due to the energy intensive industry moving elsewhere, but some might well be because extra energy use, with the costs implied, simply does not provide that much extra value or happiness after a certain point of material welfare. Efficiency has also been improving at a steady pace.

Global population might grow until the end of this century to reach 11 billion people, but the growth rate is likely to slow down and start an eventual decrease.[44] This would mean that there might not be a fundamental need for ever more growth in material and energy consumption, at least from a population's point of view.

Practically all studies and reports done on future energy demand see that demand growing from our current level of 550+ exajoules (EJ) per year. Estimates for 2050 vary between 480 and 1100 EJ[45] [46] [47] [48]. The lowest numbers are from certain environmental organizations, which typically assume that energy demand in 2050 will be lower than it is today. Most scenarios also assume that energy demand will keep on growing after 2050 at least to 2100. It is however interesting to note that, during the last ten years, the projections of future energy demand have been getting smaller. There might be a bias in the estimates that favours lower estimates for future energy use. As far as we know, none of the studies done have actually asked the developing nations for their future economic development aspirations but have simply more or less assumed that they will remain poor. This is both immoral and dangerous from the risk management perspective, as it would be prudent to also consider the scenarios where most things do not pan out as planned. There might be more people. There might be more growth in energy use in developing nations.

In the graph below we see that most of the growth in per capita energy has been happening in non-OECD countries for several decades. There are 1.3 billion people in OECD countries and 6.3 billion in non-OECD countries.

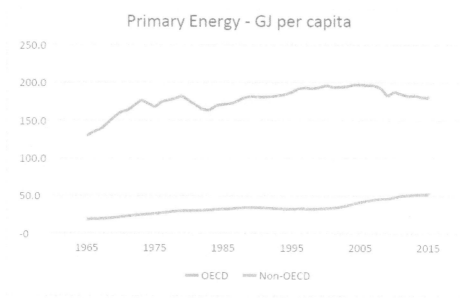

Figure 7: Primary energy use per capita in OECD and NON-OECD countries. Most of the growth for the last decades has been in non-OECD countries. Source: BP 2019.

In the graphs below, we see some of the average energy uses per capita today, and then an estimate of global total energy use if we will have 10 billion people using energy at the average level what a Czech person uses today. The energy demand would grow threefold, and if we would want to supply that energy cleanly, our clean energy demand will grow more than 15-fold.

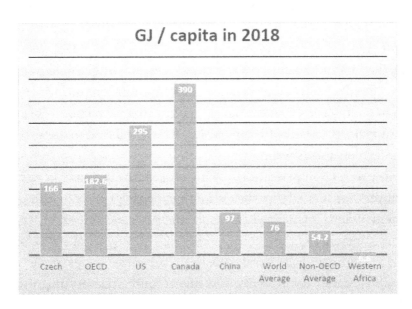

Figure 8: Average primary energy use in a year per capita of different nations or groups of people in 2018. Source: BP 2019

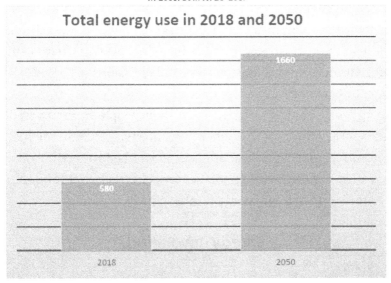

Figure 9: Total energy use in Exajoules for 2018 and by 10 billion people in 2050 on average current consumption of a Czech person. Source BP 2019.

Projected rising energy demand might face some problems however, as in how to meet that demand. Resource scarcities might bump against increasing scarcity of cheaply available fossil fuels, with oil likely the first candidate. This will cause pressures and problems from many sides. If cheap energy is not available in sufficient quantities, the price of energy rises to meet the costs of further extraction. This will in turn make economic growth harder, which will lead to less growth in energy demand as well.

It will also result in a situation in which there are more and more willing buyers for less energy that is more expensive. Nations and governments will feel the need to ensure their citizens and industry get the fuels and energy they need, increasingly by any means necessary. These means include bilateral trade deals, organized coups, trade wars and actual wars over resources. While resource scarcity might lead to less energy demand, it is a double-edged sword. Yes, it will slow down emissions growth. But at the same time, it can send nations into prolonged recessions, constant internal and external restlessness and the inability to invest in alternative energy production. In such a situation, the living standards and well-being of people will likely fall much faster than their energy consumption and emissions.

The main part of future energy demand growth comes from the developing world as they struggle to lift their people from poverty and then towards a productive, high-energy lifestyle. Environmentally, it is of utmost importance how this energy will be produced. And even if we would not increase our total energy use, we would still need to decarbonize our current energy mix as quickly as possible.

Energy Revolution

Currently the so-called new renewables are still a small, if promisingly growing part of our global energy mix. Almost every discussion about energy and climate change eventually turns to the massive and optimistic expectations that renewable energy holds for us. This trend is fueled by the large growth percentages, technological progress and the assumption that price trends will continue downward.

The numbers have been impressive. In 2012 the global solar PV capacity grew by 42 percent from the previous year, while wind power capacity grew by 19 percent. In the decade from 2008 to 2018, solar PV grew by roughly 50 percent per year, and wind by 20 percent.[49]If these growth percentages remain in the double-digits, the absolute growth will also become incrementally impressive. If solar PV would keep its 42 percent growth for the next hundred years or so, we would be producing solar energy at 32,000,000,000,000,000,000 megawatts (3.2×10^{26} W) average power by 2120. One would think that would suffice for most of our needs, given that our own Sun has a similar power level.

Nothing like this will of course happen. Historically every new energy source has grown more or less in a similar manner: slow start, followed by a rapid increase, which then plateaus quite soon. All new energy technologies, from the steam engine to nuclear power, have faced a similar dynamic. Renewable energy will not be different. One of the key questions for humanity is when will this plateauing of growth happen? At least regionally, this seems to already have happened. Wind power capacity increases have been roughly the same for the last 8 years (2012-2018) globally, at roughly 50 GW of added capacity per year. If one assumes a lifetime of 30 years, we will have stabilised at 1,500 GW of wind in 2050, which would produce around 5,000 TWhs of electricity per year. This is less than a quarter of our current electricity use. Annual solar PV installations in Europe have dropped to almost half what they were in their peak year 2010. Europe was amongst the first movers in both these energy technologies, which arguably grew largely due to very favourable policies and incentives. The worry is, can these energy sources grow significantly on a level playing field, without subsidies?

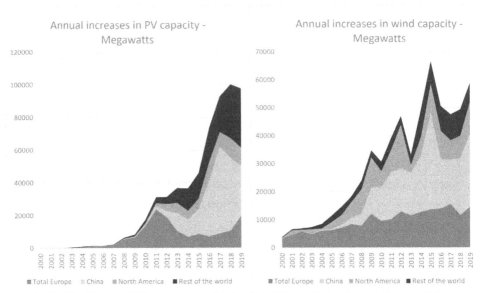

Figure 10: Solar an⟨ Win⟨ capacity a⟨⟨itions in the 2000s. For the last 5 years, solar growth has been outsi⟨e Europe an⟨ North America. Win⟨ installations have stabilise⟨ to aroun⟨ 50 GW per year for almost a ⟨eca⟨e now.

Many renewable proponents seem to think they can. Many projections and studies, both global and regional, have been done on how to reach 100 percent renewable energy (RE100%) supply. The goal seems to be at least technically possible, but unfortunately that does not yet mean it is likely, or even desirable. Most of the projections and studies seem to have severe deficiencies. A recent study "Burden of Proof[50]" evaluates the feasibility of 25 of the most credible global, regional and national studies that project a 100 percent renewable energy future. It scores the studies based on if they take into account the various real-world requirements of building and maintaining a stable electricity grid. These criteria are:

1. applying mainstream energy demand forecasts (considering that energy demand will likely increase from current levels as we wrote above);

2. simulating supply to meet demand reliably at hourly, half-hourly, or five-minute timescales, with resilience to extreme climate events explicitly modelled (each timescale receives a score of its

own);

3. identifying necessary transmission and distribution requirements; and

4. maintaining the provision of essential ancillary grid services.

The results are sobering. With a maximum of 7 points, only three
of the 25 studies scored even half of that, and those were national or
regional studies. None of the global studies (from WWF, Greenpeace
and Jacobson and Delucchi) had addressed even one criterium, with all
scoring a flat zero on their feasibility. While this does not say that the
goal of RE100% is impossible in itself, it implies that we have not yet
done even a single remotely serious study on the matter.

The cost of deep decarbonization of 80 percent of the energy system is another matter. Studies have concluded that it will cost roughly four times as much to decarbonize with mainly renewable energy
than it would with mainly nuclear energy.[51] Another study compared
the required building speeds for decarbonization with RE100% and
technology neutral projections.[52] The conclusion was again sobering.
RE100% scenarios would need to see continuous improvements in energy efficiency that are twice as fast as what we have historically managed in the short term. In addition to that, the world would need to
continuously build new capacity 3 – 11 times faster than what humanity has so far been able to do in the short term. Technology neutral
scenarios were not easy either, but they required only that we roughly
maintain our historical record speeds year after year.

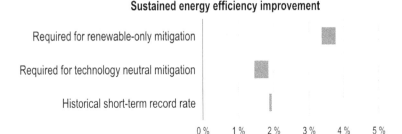

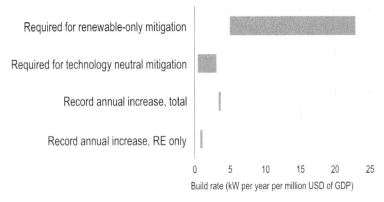

Figure 11: Technology neutral mitigation has been foun• to be much more feasible than mitigation that allows only for renewable energy to be use•. Source: Loftus, P. J., Cohen, A. M., Long, J. C. S., & Jenkins, J. D. (2015).

It seems extremely risky to assume that we can offer ten billion people living in 2050 a decent living standard with renewables alone. The crucial question we need to ask is how likely each of the offered solutions is in meeting our energy needs in 2050. If they are not very likely, people will continue to burn fossil fuels. All serious studies done on the matter, and even common sense, tells us that the likelihood of success is bigger if all options are on the table and used to their maximum potential.

How far will renewables take us?

What we wrote above – that there is not a single serious study done on what it would mean to get to RE100% future and that it seems highly unlikely – flies against what many of us have read in the mainstream media, or even in top-level political statements and targets. Back in 2011 there were big headlines along the lines that the Intergovernmental Panel on Climate Change (IPCC) says we can produce 80 percent of our energy needs with renewables by 2050.

> "The IPCC report shows overwhelming scientific evi-
> ◆ence that renewable energy can also meet the growing
> ◆eman◆ of ◆eveloping countries, where over two billion
> people lack access to basic energy services." – Sven
> Teske, the renewable energy expert at Greenpeace
> commenting on the release of IPCC SRREN
> -report[53]

The press disregarded two important details from the actual SRREN-report (Special Report on Renewable Energy Sources and Climate Change Mitigation). It reviewed 164 energy scenarios. The claim that renewables will be able to provide 80 percent of global energy is based on just one of those scenarios. The data used in this outlier was acquired directly from the renewables industry[54], and it is based on Greenpeace's own Energy Revolution report. Two of the three main authors of this report were lobbyists representing the renewables industry. The main author of the Greenpeace report, Sven Teske, was also one of the main authors of one chapter in SRREN-report.[55]

The scenario in question manages to see renewables producing around 428 EJ (118,890 TWh) of primary energy in 2050. As we mentioned before, humanity used roughly 550 EJ (152,500 TWh) of energy in 2011, when that report was published. So, in 2050, the most optimistic scenario managed to produce 78 percent of our current energy use with renewables.

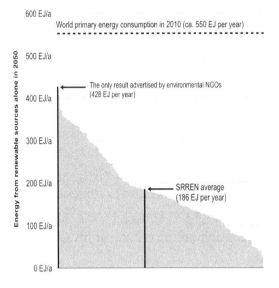

Figure 12: All the results from the IPCC special report on renewable energy.

The popular RE80% claim of the press release and subsequent news articles can be accurate on two conditions: that we will not increase our total energy use from current levels and that 99.4 percent of the scenarios in the SRREN report are wrong. As we wrote above, the energy demand is projected to grow by roughly 50 percent to around 800 exajoules by 2050, and it could easily grow much more if we assume that developing nations will actually develop. Compared to that projection, the outlier of 428 EJ manages to satisfy roughly half of the demand.

The median result of the SRREN is that we would be able to produce 186 EJ (51,660 TWh) in 2050 with renewables. That is about a third of our current use, and less than fourth of the projected 800 EJ. It leaves a gap of 600 EJ to be produced somehow, preferably without emissions, in 2050.

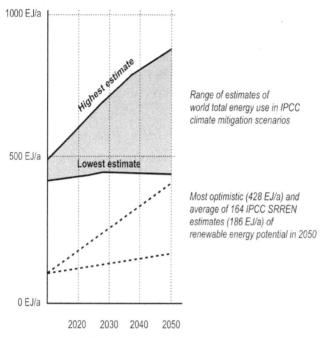

Figure 13: IPCC range of estimates for world energy use by 2050 and the most optimistic and average estimates for renewable energy production at that time.

Even if we managed to achieve double the media result, the situation would still be disastrous for the climate. Mark Lynas, a British environmental activist, had the Greenpeace Energy Revolution scenario modelled with modern climate models.[56] The result was sobering. Even if we had started the project full swing several years ago, and even if everything were to go smoothly with no hiccups along the way, the climate would likely warm by more than 2 °C, and could warm by as much as 4 °C. So even the most optimistic IPCC RE100% scenario fails to mitigate climate change nearly fast enough.

The bad news does not end there. SRREN report was very auspicious towards bioenergy, which often plays a critical role in the renewable energy scenarios. Bioenergy often results in accelerating deforestation but is still accepted as a very low carbon, renewable source of energy. Only three years later IPCC (AR5 that came out in 2014) corrected its median estimate on bioenergy to be over 12 times as carbon intensive as the earlier report assumed. This alone calls into question the SR-REN scenario's ability – limited as it already was – to mitigate climate change, as it basically says that even if something is renewable, it does not mean it is low carbon. Overall the term "renewable energy" is very problematic to use when it comes to climate mitigation or environmental protection.[57]

The more recent IPCC Fifth Assessment Report (AR5) says that to halt dangerous climate change, we need not only large improvements in energy efficiency, but also significant growth in all low carbon energy sources. In addition, we need carbon capture and storage (CCS) for both fossil and bioenergy fuelled power stations. CCS has so far proved to be a disappointment, and commercial scale operations are somewhat scarce. It also entails some technical and economic problems. Even if everything operates smoothly, the CCS process can use up to a third of all the energy produced. Further, storing billions of tons of carbon dioxide is a problem of totally different proportions than is the storing of for example nuclear waste, which is both solid and much, much smaller in quantity.

The IPCC special report on 1.5 °C warming was even clearer. The four main scenarios in it projected an increase of 2 to 6 times for nuclear, as well as even more growth in renewables. Two of the main scenarios that assumed that our energy demand would grow even somewhat modestly, required 5 to 6 times more nuclear energy than we have today.

The fact of the matter is, even if everything goes smoothly, achieving our goal of only 2 °C, let alone the 1.5 °C that was floated in the Paris 2015 agreement, is a very long shot. If one of the mitigation tools fails us, it becomes near impossible. If two or more fail us, the game is more or less over. Even now, all the scenarios that see us staying under 2 °C include capturing carbon from the atmosphere at massive scales with technologies that are mainly still in laboratories, and every year there are more and more assumptions made on future geoengineering possibilities.[58] To put it bluntly, not including all the tools available just because some of them rub some of us the wrong way will increase the risks of climate catastrophe from very likely to a certainty.

Speed of building energy revolution

As noted, both solar PV and wind power capacity has kept growing globally, although the install rate for wind power seems to have stabilized for now. There are several angles or proxies one can use to look at the pace of the "energy revolution". First is the amount of money invested and if it is growing or shrinking. A 2019 UNEP report Global Trends in Renewable Energy Investment[59] finds that the ending decade of 2010 to 2019 will see roughly $2.6 trillion in total invested on renewable energy (excluding large hydro), or 260 billion per year, on average. This is around 14 percent of the total energy investments of $1.85 trillion in 2018.[60] The vast majority, roughly 90 %, went to solar (52 %) and wind (39 %), the rest going mainly to bioenergy and small hydro projects.

The second proxy is how much new capacity we gain with that money. During the ending decade, the "new renewable" (excludes large hydro) capacity climbed from 414 to 1,650 gigawatts, a growth of some 300 % or 1,236 GW. Each added gigawatt of additional capacity cost around $2.1 billion on average. Of this, 638 GW was solar.

In this 10-year period, the cost competitiveness of these technologies has improved spectacularly. The levelized cost of electricity (LCOE, a metric that is useful especially when comparing costs of various projects using similar technologies) of solar PV has decreased by 81% and that of wind by 46%.

The energy generated from new renewables has grown from 754 TWh in 2010 to 2,480 TWh in 2018[61]. 2019 production numbers are not available at the time of writing, but the growth has been roughly 300 TWh / year for the last couple years, so we can estimate that annual production will increase by roughly 2,000 TWh during the decade. This means that each gigawatt has generated roughly 1.6 TWh of electricity on average. The average load factor of the capacity has been roughly 20%. Load factor means the amount of time the energy source runs at "full nameplate capacity" on average during the year. The load factors of wind and solar have been improving with bigger turbines and better PV panels, but they also have natural limits. For example, in the darkness of the night, a solar panel won't produce anything no matter how good it is, and only a part of the Sun's energy can be captured when it hits the panel. So while the capacity added is high relative to other energy sources (nuclear, coal, natural gas), the relative amount of energy produced per capacity is much smaller. The global average load factor of nuclear power plants is around 80%.

Installed capacity is a somewhat problematic metric for variable renewable energy sources (VRE) such as wind and solar. The installed capacity tells how much energy is produced in ideal conditions, but it tells nothing of the annual average (above found to be roughly 20%). Even more importantly, it tells nothing of the fact that the production varies according to weather, time of day and time of year. So the actual production varies between 0 and 100 percent of the peak capacity. With solar PV, the average production (capacity factor) is usually between 8 and 20 percent of the installed capacity, depending on panel type and location. Wind power has an average capacity factor of roughly 25 percent in Europe (180 GW installed capacity and 362 TWh of production in 2018[62]). Wind power capacity factors have been rising in recent years. New, taller and bigger turbines have seen capacity factors of well over 40 percent, even on land.

The most important angle is total emissions. In the previous decade of 2010 to 2019, the total emissions of the power sector are estimated to have grown by roughly 10 %. This is the wrong direction.

Wind and solar have not been the only renewable energy production that has been increasing its production in the 21st century. Globally, hydro has added over 1,500 TWh of annual production between 2000 and 2018. In Europe, bioenergy is the main renewable energy source, although that is not the picture one often gets. As can be seen in the graph below, in 2017, 58.6 % of renewable gross final energy consumption in the EU28 was bioenergy.[63] While in electricity, wind and solar have bigger shares, heating, cooling and transportation have much larger shares of bioenergy.

Gross Final Renewable Energy Consumption EU28 in 2017

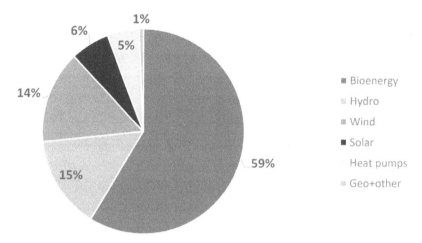

Figure 14: Most of EU's renewable energy comes from biofuels.

Wind turbines and solar panels have a somewhat short operational lifetime, and this poses a further problem. If we assume an average lifetime of 25 years[64], we can calculate how much production we would have if we keep on adding new production at current levels. In 2016-2018, the average annual addition of wind power was 146 TWh. If we assume to add new capacity at 150 TWh per year for 25 years, we will have total production of 3,750 TWh per year, after which we will use all our annual new capacity to replace older facilities. Solar has been growing still. In 2018, a record of 131 TWh of new production was added, growing 6 TWh from previous year. To keep it simple for the calculation, we can assume similar rates as wind power has, 150 TWh per year. In total, wind and solar would have a sustained production of 7,500 TWh per year, after 25 years of construction at current rates. As the current energy consumption is around 160,000 TWh, with a high probability of it rising well above 200,000 TWh by 2040, there is a problem.

So how much faster should we build new wind and solar capacity to meet even the lowest projected energy demand with them? The answer is in the ballpark of several tens of times faster than we have. This is way beyond unprecedented, even if we look at all energy installations combined. A recent study[65] calculated that 100%RE decarbonization would demand up to 25 times faster sustained build rates than we have had historically in the short term, when viewed in relation to levels of wealth. In addition, energy efficiency would need to increase twice as fast as it has done historically.

Technology neutral decarbonization would "only" need to sustain roughly the short-term record speeds on both new capacity and energy efficiency improvements. From these numbers, it would be extremely risky and downright irresponsible to bet our living planet on anything else than a fully technology-inclusive climate project.

Even this is not yet the whole picture, as this macro-level thinking we have been doing above hides a further problem. Wind and solar production are highly variable, and do not match our demand patterns. The rough calculations above assume that we would be able to store electricity and energy with near zero costs and losses as much as we need. It also assumes that electricity can replace fuels everywhere without significant losses, costs or technological challenges. In reality, this is far from the truth. How much more capacity is needed to overcome the problems of variability and overproduction, losses in energy transformation and storage? The best estimates are 2 to 5 times as much.[66] [67] If you do the math, that would require on the order of one hundred times the solar-plus-wind building rate of recent years to be sustained. Maybe a little less, if we are lucky, maybe over 200 times as fast if we are not.

We can decrease the need for energy storage by overbuilding capacity. But then an increasing share of the peak production is lost, making all electricity produced at that time worthless from the market's perspective. This erodes the profitability of all energy production, but especially that of solar and wind. They produce energy when the weather is right, and when the weather is right for one wind farm, it is often right for those in the same general area as well. It is hard to imagine a market-based system where this would happen, as nobody would invest in a project in which most of its product sells at zero or negative costs.

This problem of decreasing value can be mitigated with increases in demand flexibility and energy storage. How does that work, and what does it mean?

Demand flexibility and energy storage

Demand and production must be at balance every second in the electricity grid. Outside the grid, there is more flexibility, but storing and retrieving energy in whatever form always incurs costs and losses. When we increase the amount of variable renewable energy production, we also need to increase our capability to use that energy when it is available or to store it for later use. Most people acknowledge that it is often possible to integrate 20 or 30 percent of intermittent production to the electricity grid without too many problems. Beyond that, the problems start to grow rapidly. This is not nearly enough for deep decarbonization, which means 80 percent or more of our total energy demand (of which electricity is roughly a fifth) is met without emissions. One of the solutions to this problem has been to increase our demand flexibility and energy storage capabilities significantly.

Demand flexibility in practice means that we decrease our energy consumption when it is expensive (when there is not enough) and increase it when it is cheap (when there is too much). Cheap electricity can also be stored as heat, and in more advanced solutions, this heat could be turned back into electricity when prices rise – albeit with significant losses. Another option would be to make hydrogen or synthetic fuels in electrolysers or "Power-to-X" facilities when electricity is cheap.

The feasibility of energy storage and flexibility investments depend on the range between low and high electricity prices, as well as their frequency. Cheap electricity can be bought and stored, and it can be used or sold back to the grid when electricity gets expensive. Water boilers can heat water during low night prices. A smart fridge or freezer can shut down for an hour when electricity prices get high. An electric car can charge its battery mainly when prices are low, and a factory with an energy intensive process might be able to shut it down for a while when prices rise high enough to make it worthwhile.

All of these have a common dynamic: as they become more common, they shrink the margin between high and low prices, making the arbitrage less lucrative for everyone. The more flexibility and storage we have, the less profitable it is, and the less incentive there is for further investments. On the other hand, those further investments are usually more expensive (due to the law of diminishing returns; we have used all the cheap and easy ways first) and therefore would demand higher and more frequent variability to justify the investments. Put shortly, advanced storage and flexibility are dependent on ever higher variability in electricity prices, while they (and the currently used technologies in particular) also decrease this variability, eating their own feasibility. It is a self-regulating system that seeks balance, making solutions outside the boundaries of that balance unfeasible in the long run.

Batteries are the favourite new tech of many energy revolution proponents. They are still much too costly to make sense for the kind of arbitrage where one buys low and sells high. A recent report of a trial by the Californian utility PG&E deserves a glance.[68] The project was not able to pay back its investment in time. The profit from energy arbitrage was largely consumed by the inefficiencies of charging, discharging and other services needed to keep the batteries operational. Frequency regulation of the grid is by far the more lucrative business for batteries, netting around four times as much income as all other services (including energy arbitrage) did. But even this – a much smaller business than actual energy storage – was not enough to pay back the capital investment in time. To sum it up, battery installation prices (per kW) would have to come down roughly 27-fold, from $5,500 / kW in the trial to $200 / kW, to be economically viable, with other things staying the same. In some situations, grid-scale batteries can make sense for some uses, but these are not the norm.

All these solutions and technologies end up achieving one thing that is rarely discussed: they make baseload electricity production more profitable. It is more profitable for a coal or a nuclear plant to operate at full power 24/7 when prices are stable. Increasing the amount of inexpensive flexibility in the current system ends up benefiting the current power stations, especially nuclear power that has very low fuel costs.

Energy storage would need to develop and increase hand in hand with variable energy production. If it does not, this production will cannibalize its own profitability as more and more of its production becomes worthless in the marketplace. One of the key goals of flexibility and storage schemes is to create a floor price for electricity, which would help these energy sources to remain more profitable at higher penetrations. This will not in itself stop us from burning fossil fuels because this would also make them more profitable. The more stable the electricity price, the more profitable most energy production becomes, and the less profitable any energy storage technology becomes. Added cheap flexibility is great news for everyone.

It is also clear that if we find ways to integrate ever larger shares of intermittent production at low costs to our energy system, we will also find ways to make baseload nuclear and intermittent renewables coexist in said system. In short, all the ways which make integrating intermittent energy production to a system that has rather stable, predictably fluctuating demand, are also ways to make it ever easier to have baseload nuclear and variable renewables coexist. This is, of course, excellent news for our climate mitigation project.

Above we have presented very large numbers for future energy demand projections. Can we assume that they have been exaggerated? Maybe energy efficiency and conservation can cut those numbers significantly? This assumption has two inherent problems. First, large increases in energy efficiency and conservation have already been accounted for in those projections. Secondly, there are strong reasons to assume that the effect these will have has been systematically exaggerated.

Energy efficiency and the Rebound effect

Practically in all the energy and climate projections the increase in energy efficiency plays a huge role. It is often the single biggest way we plan to reduce our energy use and therefore emissions. Currently, practically none of these scenarios and projections account for a phenomenon called the rebound effect.

Rebound is not a new phenomenon. James Watt, sometimes called the father of the Industrial Revolution, earned that title by significantly improving the energy efficiency of the steam engine, which was a 40-year old technology by then. Steam engines were built already in the 1730s, but their poor efficiency and therefore need for large amounts of coal limited their use and popularity.

Watt teamed up with Matthew Boulton and in 1775 they founded what could be called the first cleantech company in the world to build more energy efficient steam engines. They were met with huge success, as Watt's engine used only a quarter of the fuel that previous steam engines had used. This makes one think: if gains in energy efficiency are as big a deal as many claim in reducing our energy use, then why, by 1900, had the use of coal grown one hundred-fold from the 18th century, and why has it kept on increasing?

The reason for this is explained by the rebound effect.[69] Rebound means that on one hand, energy saved will lead to those savings being used somewhere else. On the other hand, products and services made with less resources and energy can be sold and used at a lower price, which will increase their market and the incentive to use and buy them, increasing their production volumes. Thirdly, cheaper or otherwise improved technology can find completely new uses, as happened when smaller and more powerful steam engines were adopted to power trains.

A product made with fewer inputs translates to a cheaper product. This means that more people can afford it, so it is possible to increase production. This often results in more absolute consumption of energy and resources, even though it all started by more efficient use of energy. This absolute increase is called a backfire-effect. In practice, the energy saving due to increased efficiency is instead translated to more economic activity (growth). If steam engines would have stayed at the low efficiency of the first models, it would be unlikely that the industrial revolution and the tremendous economic growth that it caused would have happened at all, at least not at the scale they did.

Rebound is hard to measure, as it depends greatly on where and when it is happening, as well as the price of energy. But there is little doubt that it is a real phenomenon. A review of 500 studies[70] concluded that the direct effect is on average at least ten percent (meaning that one tenth of the savings fail to materialize). But it might be much bigger.

A report from International Energy Agency on energy efficiency (2014[71]) said that the direct effects are usually between 10 and 30 percent. In other studies, the indirect rebound has been estimated to vary between 0 and 80 percent. For example, in transportation, gains in fuel efficiency have been found to lead to a rebound of 57-62 percent. Household energy conservation in developed countries leads on average to 20-45 percent rebound. Rebound is usually larger in developing countries. A study on China[72] found that rebound had consumed roughly 74 percent of the improvements in energy efficiency of Chinese industry.

It can even be speculated that if energy efficiency and worker productivity had not constantly improved over the recent history, a significant part of our economic growth would have failed to happen. Many products and services would have stayed too expensive for the mass market, and that mass market would have been unlikely to even exist, as worker productivity and therefore real wages, would have stayed much lower. It is possible that the improvements in energy efficiency have resulted in, indirectly and through various feedbacks, a rebound well over 100 percent.

Despite all this rebounding, increasing efficiency in energy and materials and general conservation are good things. Even if rebound would eat up all the savings, increases in efficiency often increase human well-being.

But the mere existence of this phenomenon means that the capability of energy efficiency to reduce our emissions is likely to be much smaller than is commonly assumed. IPCC notes this in their 2014 report (AR5), saying that we should not disregard or forget rebound, and that accounting for it is critical for an effective climate policy.[73] What this means is that we actually need much more energy efficiency and clean energy production than what the scenarios with optimistic emissions reductions due to energy efficiency assume.

Many of these reports have disregarded rebound completely. A good example of this is when in 2014 IEA corrected its previous assumption from 9 percent to 20-60 percent rebound. Developing countries, where a large part of energy demand increase will happen, often have even larger rebounds because there are many essential and desirable new uses for energy or money that is saved with improved efficiency.

The lack of acknowledgement and discussion of rebound is frustrating because it could be mitigated with smart policies if we were more aware of it. If the price of energy rises along with improved efficiency, direct rebound is much smaller. For example, we could tighten the taxation of dirty energy alongside improving efficiency. Emissions could have a tightening cap, and so forth. But as long as rebound is not discussed openly, it is unlikely we will do anything about it.

Energy conservation also plays a big part in many scenarios. If energy efficiency is about doing the same thing with less energy, conservation is about not doing it in the first place. Energy conservation is a popular topic, but it rarely gets the analytical approach it deserves. Where can we conserve energy, and how much? Who do we mean when we say "we?" What kind of direct and indirect effects could this have? On the other hand, what is the opportunity cost to leave energy unused somewhere? If there is some other cost or a negative effect of conserved energy, how is this measured and taken into account? If tighter rules for building insulation lead to poorer indoor air quality and perhaps to shorter building lifetimes, is it worth it? Or if shutting down streetlights in some areas increases the feeling of insecurity (or even the actual insecurity) for those living nearby, is it really worth it? How is this insecurity measured and valued against the kilowatt-hours used in streetlights? Are we improving people's lives or decreasing our environmental footprint?

These questions are rarely talked about or acknowledged when discussing energy conservation. These opportunity costs rarely make it to the scenarios that present energy conservation as a huge pot of potential savings in energy. In addition to this, a large part of our global population simply does not have anything to conserve from in the first place.

Energy revolution of the poor

There is one more explanation for the low estimates of our global future energy demand we see in some scenarios; that is to keep today's poor people poor also in the future. Energy Revolution 2015 by Greenpeace would give the continent of Africa no more than 28.5 EJ in final energy by 2050, with the UN estimating that there will be almost 2.5 billion people living on the continent by then.[74] Meanwhile the 433 million people living in North America in 2050 would get 41.8 EJ. North Americans would be using more than eight times the energy than their African cousins, per person. According to Greenpeace, they currently use around 6.4 times as much. In effect, the rich would keep getting richer.

IEA, which Greenpeace uses for comparison, would give Africans almost twice the energy, at 47.3 EJ. Even IEA is not overly optimistic on the possibilities of growth in Africa. It is remarkable that the previous Greenpeace's Energy Revolution report (2012) gave Africans more energy than the later report, projecting 30.5 EJ of annual consumption for Africa. So even if renewable energy has progressed immensely, Greenpeace still saw the need to pinch a bit away from the Africans. One cannot ignore the thought that this was done to make their RE100% scenarios look a bit more feasible.

The above numbers are measures of energy end-use, meaning the amount of secondary energy that is used to do useful work. In primary energy the average African would use 7.6 MWhs annually according to IEA, and 4.2 MWhs according to Greenpeace.[75] Back in 2012, Greenpeace had each African using around 6 MWhs annually.

By any western standard, these numbers are horrible. It is not uncommon for a westerner to use up to 100 MWhs[76] of primary energy per year, with electricity alone often being more than 10 MWhs per year per person. The average Chinese person used around 27 MWhs in 2018. [77]We wrote earlier in the book that living standards see significant improvements with increased energy use for at least up to 12 MWhs per person per year. Even with tremendous improvements in the efficiency of energy end-use, we suspect that 6 or 8 megawatt-hours will leave people far below what any of us in the rich world would consider humane.

Is it too much to ask or at least hope that the average African would have, 35 years from now, a similar amount of energy at her disposal as the average Chinese has now? Or is it too much to ask those people and countries what their future aspirations are, instead of inserting numbers into an excel sheet from one's comfy office? One would bet that they are not planning to stay poor. If Africa aims to grow wealthier and increase the living standard of its people, industrialization and increased energy use are the only way of which we are aware. Radical leaps in energy efficiency technology are not forthcoming, as most industrial and construction processes are already relatively close to their theoretical maximums.

Many researchers of development, like Professor Calestous Juma at Harvard University regard[78] "small scale" technology such solar panels capable of charging mobile phones as another huge mistake that the rich countries are making in "helping" the developing world to develop. According to Juma, it will only keep the poor nations poor. A recent study done in Tanzania agrees with Juma: 90 percent of the people who had experience with small scale local solutions would prefer to have grid electricity instead.[79]

The desire and ability of the developing world to develop might have been greatly underestimated in many reports. With rebound alone, there is reason to believe that the projections grossly underestimate the growth of future energy demand. The question remaining is how this energy will be produced. The likely answer is that much of it will come from fossil fuels – the easiest way to add reliable modern energy services. This leaves rich western countries with much more urgency to reduce their own fossil fuel use.

German Energiewende

When talking about energy revolutions, there is no way to avoid talking about Germany. The Germans have decided to give up nuclear power and fossil fuels and build an industrialized society that will run almost exclusively on renewable energy. They call this project Energiewende, energy turn.

The four legs that the Energiewende stands on are:[80]

1. Low-carbon society by 2050, with 80-95 percent less emissions compared to 1990 levels.
2. Economy that runs on renewable energy, with 80 percent renewables by 2050, and fossil energy only as back-up.
3. Closure of the current nuclear fleet by 2022.

4.   Increasing demand flexibility and energy efficiency.

The first and second points are goals. The third is more of a policy act (in this case limiting the toolset on how to meet the first goal), while the fourth is simultaneously a tool to achieve the goals as well as a goal by itself. The closure of the operating nuclear fleet by 2022 is first and foremost a political decision. It should be noted that the stability and security of society's energy supply was not at risk at the time when the decision was made, and neither was its effects on other goals, such as the possibility of reaching low-carbon society by 2050 or even the intermediate goals of reducing emissions 40 percent by 2020.

This decision to close the nuclear fleet was clearly counterproductive towards the low-carbon society goal, yet it was clearly prioritized as more important. Germany has been one of the most coal-dependent countries in Europe. It would have had its hands quite full in just try-ing to replace coal combustion with wind, solar and biomass, even if it had not chosen to start the project by replacing nuclear power first from its energy mix. When the project started, around 80 percent of Germany's clean energy came from nuclear power. In 2018, this had fallen to about a quarter. In absolute terms, nuclear production has fallen from around 170 TWh to 76 TWh by 2018 (38 Mtoe to 17 Mtoe). While coal has also decreased in the 2000s, natural gas usage has increased.

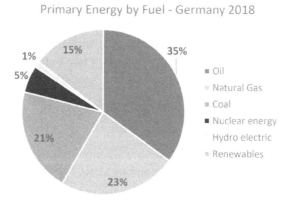

Primary Energy by Fuel - Germany 2018

Figure 15: Primary energy by fuel in Germany, 2018. Around 80% of Germany's primary energy is still based on fossil fuels. Data: BP 2019.

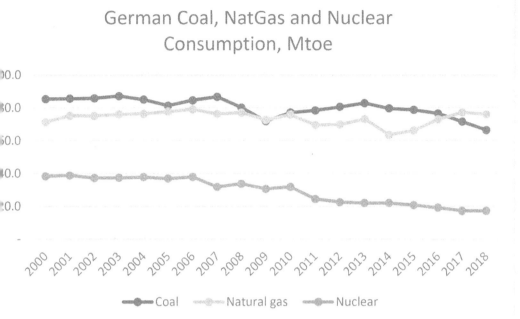

Figure 16: Germany's coal, natural gas and nuclear consumption in Mtoe during the 2000s. Data: BP 2019.

The short history of Energiewende

Energiewende dates as far back as 1998, when the newly elected government coalition of social democrats and greens decided to shut nuclear down by 2010.[81] Several years of negotiations between the government and the nuclear industry led to a deal in 2001. New nuclear power plants were banned, the operational lifetime of the current fleet was limited to 32 years, and various limits were put for electricity produced with nuclear. According to this deal, the last of the nuclear power plants would be shut down in 2022. It was assumed that renewable energy would be able to replace most of the nuclear power. The law that followed in 2000, defining renewable subsidies and support schemes, is one of the most significant events considering renewable energy production in history.

Early on, it was recognized that renewable energy alone might not be able to do the job. Germany's Chancellor Gerhard Schröder lobbied strongly for Nordstream, a natural gas pipeline going under the Baltic Sea. After his career as Chancellor, Schröder was promptly hired by the company which built the pipeline. This pipeline from Russia can import a volume of natural gas that, if used for electricity production, could match the output of the country's whole nuclear fleet. Between 2006 and 2008, Germany also granted permits for 10 large coal-fired power plants. The combined capacity of these plants, 10.7 gigawatts, is comparable to the combined nuclear capacity of Finland and Sweden in 2016.[82] People were surprised by this decision, as it was widely known that coal burning should stop as fast as possible. When James Hansen, one of most well-known climate researchers from NASA, questioned this decision to permit the building of new coal plants, the then environmental minister Sigmar Gabriel replied that since Germany was giving up nuclear, it would be impossible to give up coal at the same time. It was a political decision, and it was not negotiable. [83]

In the 2005 elections, Christian Democrats and Liberals took over the government, with Angela Merkel as the new Chancellor. The new government was more favourable towards nuclear, and in 2010 Merkel cancelled the decision to shut down the nuclear fleet prematurely. This complete U-turn was rationalized especially with meeting emissions reduction targets and improving energy security.[84]

The ink barely had time to dry on the new decision, when in March 2011 the tsunami, caused by the strongest earthquake ever measured in Japan, killed almost 20,000 people and damaged the Fukushima Dai-ichi nuclear power plant beyond repair. Both the international media as well as the rapidly growing social media quickly forgot the tens of thousands of victims the earthquake and tsunami had claimed and started following the events unfolding at the Fukushima plant with unblinking attention.

The huge amount of media attention, along with the fear of the atom planted in the minds of the German population during the cold war[85], led to a sad outcome: even though it is now well-known that radioactive elements that escaped from the nuclear power plant won't have significant health effects to people anywhere, the world was shaken with fear. The polls in Germany showed that the people at large remained against nuclear, and the Christian Democrats, led by Angela Merkel, were facing defeat in the coming state elections, especially to the Greens. So Merkel performed yet another U-turn. The reactors built before 1980 were closed just three days after the Fukushima accident. A bit later Germany informed that it would return to the previous schedule of early shutdowns of all reactors by 2022. Renewable energy was also granted higher subsidies. The environmentalists and Greens around the world cheered Germany's decision, even though it was clear it would lead to much slower reductions of greenhouse gas emissions. Their priorities could not have been clearer.

Costs of the Energiewende

Ever since, the "green energy" project of Germany has been as ambitious as can reasonably be imagined. German consumers are paying roughly 25 billion euros more each year just to pay for the feed-in-tariffs (as the EEG in their utility bill). In addition to these tariffs, there are the investments to actually build the plants and the needed infrastructure. Despite massive spending, Germany's emissions from energy production and fuel use (coal, oil, natural gas) has decreased less than one percent per year in the 2000s, slower than EU on average.

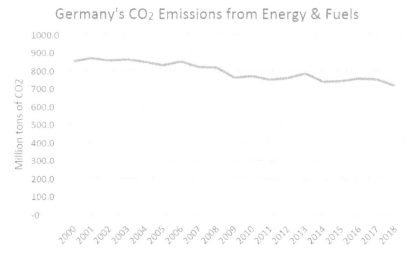

Figure 17: German CO2 emissions from energy pro♦uction an♦ other fuels use have ♦ecrease♦ at less than one percent per year ♦uring the Energiewen♦e. Data BP 2019.

What will happen when the rest of the nuclear plants are closed by 2022? It is absolutely certain that it will be much harder to close down the fleet of coal plants that still (in 2018) produced 35 percent of Germany's electricity – more than renewable sources put together.[86] From a climate perspective, Germany has used hundreds of billions of euros and almost two decades going nowhere. The current EEG surcharges levied to pay for the current fleet of renewable energy installed is roughly 25 billion euros each year, or ~300 € / year / person. In 2018, the renewable energy surcharge (EEG) was 67.1 € / MWh for the consumer, roughly 23 % of the total cost of electricity for consumers. In 2018, renewables (excluding hydro) produced roughly a third of German electricity, so the EEG charge per MWh of renewable energy produced was around 210 € / MWh. The average total cost of electricity for consumers in EU-28 countries is at a similar level.[87]

Another cost of the Energiewende nuclear phase-out policy is the social cost. A recent study found that this cost is roughly 12 billion € per year, or 150 € / person / year, as half of the nuclear fleet has closed. So it might double to 24 billion € per year in 2023 when the whole fleet is shut down. Most of this (70 %) is health costs from increased mortality due to air pollution, as most of the nuclear that was closed was replaced with coal combustion and imports, the study found. To put that sum into social perspective, it corresponds to roughly 1,100 additional premature deaths each year.

This is all highly interesting, and no doubt a controversial and difficult thing for the German people to accept, as the implied social costs of nuclear energy were the primary arguments used to justify the phase-out. As these risks were never properly quantified or compared to the likely alternatives, the result is that people are paying a much higher price for a decision they took while trying to avoid that very cost.

For the sake of comparison, if the annual EEG money were used to build nuclear power plants, even assuming no learning from the current expensive pilot plants being built in Europe, it would add 4 to 5 gigawatts (30 to 40 TWh of energy annually) of new capacity every year.[88] The Germans' electricity demand is around 60 GW in daytime, so the whole grid would be clean in 10 to 15 years. This is, of course, precisely what happened in France, Sweden and other places already in the 1970s to 1990s.

The current status of Energiewende

The Energiewende has been tremendously successful in one thing: it has added wind and solar energy at a very significant rate and created a meaningful initial market for these technologies. This helped to eventually bring costs of production down, with mass production and learning effect. In 2000, renewable electricity consumption – excluding hydro power – in Germany was 14.3 TWh in primary energy. In 2018 it was 209.2 TWh.[89] Yet with the closures of nuclear energy, the total emissions from the energy sector have decreased slower than in the EU on average during the 21st century. From 2000 to 2018, Germany's energy sector emissions decreased by 15.8 percent, less than one percent per year.

By 2020, Germany has promised to cut emissions by 40 percent from 1990 levels. Much of this reduction was already achieved by shuttering inefficient power plants and factories in former East Germany in the early 1990s. According to some studies[90], Germany will be unable to reach its ambitious climate goals it has set for 2020, even though it has built more renewables than it originally planned. The German environmental minister said in 2014 that Germany would only be able to reduce its emissions by 33 percent instead of 40 percent. Critics, such as the WWF chapter of Germany, have said that even this amount is way too optimistic.[91]

Reaching their stated emission goals now would need closures of all its lignite-burning power plants by 2020, including the brand-new ones that have technical operational lifetimes reaching to at least 2050. Nothing like this is happening. In June 2014, the State of Brandenburg gave Vattenfall the permission to mine 200 million tons of lignite from 2026 forward. The prime minister of the state, Dietmar Woidke, defended the decision by saying that "brown coal is indispensable as a bridge into the era of renewable energy" [92]. When burned, 200 million tons of lignite will release as much emissions as the whole of Sweden does in four years. Somewhat ironically, the mining project faced the risk of cancellation by Vattenfall, a Swedish energy company fully owned by Swedish state. The absurdity of this all is boiled down with Sigmar Gabriel's letter to Swedish prime minister Stefan Löfven, in which he pleads for Vattenfall to continue investments in its huge lignite mines and exploration. Sigmar says the matter as it is:

> *"However, we also strongly believe that we cannot simultaneously quit nuclear energy and coal-based power generation"*[93].

Subsequently in 2016, Vattenfall decided to sell the mines to Czech energy company EPH, so the lignite production is not in danger of shutting down any time soon.[94]

McKinsey prepared a report which follows the same, clear message: As Germany will lose roughly 100 TWhs of annual clean production due to nuclear closures, it will have to lower its emission reduction goals to less ambitious levels. As news blog Carbon Brief asked a representative of Germany's energy ministry (BMWi) about quitting coal burning in 2014, the answer was as clear as it was unforgiving:

> "A simultaneous exit from nuclear energy an⏧ coal
> is not possible in a highly in⏧ustrialize⏧ country like
> Germany."[95]

Britain's energy and climate ministry DECC answered the same question by saying that most coal plants are so old that they will be shut down, and building new ones is only possible if they are equipped with carbon capture and storage, which is currently uneconomical and therefore unlikely to happen. Britain aims to stop coal burning by 2025. This forms a sad contrast with Brandenburg's permission for lignite mining from 2026 forward.

According to a study from Greenpeace[96], Germany faces odds that could well be described as impossible. To reach the goals for the Paris COP21 agreement (which Germany and most other countries have signed), Germany will need to cut emissions by 95 percent from 1990 levels by 2050. Yet a recent government document prepared for Chancellor Angela Merkel is backpedalling, saying that the country should postpone any firm decisions for mapping out coal closures.[97]

To achieve the goal it signed for in Paris, Germany needs to electrify most of its current burning (natural gas for hot water, liquid fuels for transportation, coal and lignite for electricity) and clean up its electricity production in just a few decades (coal needs to phase out by 2030). This would mean that electricity demand would increase manifold (three to five times over) from the current 600 TWhs annually.

In early 2020, some interesting news regarding Germany's emissions was published.[98] During 2019, Germany had managed a significant

6% reduction in emissions, largely thanks to higher emissions prices in the ETS. This, in turn, made coal less competitive and natural gas more competitive, and significant additions of renewable energy production that year. Switching from coal to natural gas roughly halves the emissions, but it can only be done once, and natural gas emissions are roughly ten times too high to be compatible with the emissions reduction targets. The methane leakages of natural gas usage can also have a significant effect on its total climate forcing – something that is usually disregarded in emissions accounting.

In 2019, a German government-appointed commission proposed that the country would close its coal fleet by 2038. The proposal still needs to be accepted and implemented by the states and the government, which remains to be seen.[99] But even if Germany is likely to fail its 2020 climate targets, it has not deterred them from setting out ambitious plans for 2030. In their new Climate Action Programme 2030[100], a 55% emissions reduction from 1990 levels is planned (in line with EU targets), with the help of many progressive and sensible-seeming policies such as having a national emissions trading system for heating buildings (natural gas, fuel oil etc) and for transportation fuels.

Discussing the Energiewende

It is believed amongst academics studying the Energiewende[101] that it will stand or fall with its ability to reduce emissions in the longer term. Even if year-by-year emissions fluctuate and some reasons for optimism have come up every now and then, it seems more and more clear that Energiewende is failing its most important goal. The government officials and high-level politicians, quoted above, have been saying this again and again when they have stated the impossibility of leaving nuclear and coal power at the same time. The recent decisions to limit increases in renewable energy production to around 1.2 percentage points annually for the next decade, and especially the persistence of closing down the rest of the nuclear fleet by 2022, which produced 14 percent of German electricity, seem to cement the fact that emissions will not decrease nearly fast enough.

This latest reform of the Renewable Energy Act (EEG) has already earned criticism. According to DW, Hubert Weiger, chairman of environmental organization Bund für Umwelt und Naturschutz Deutschland (Bund), slammed the plans as a "bag-full of lazy compromises at the expense of climate conservation."[102] This criticism forgets that one of the key elements of Energiewende, getting rid of nuclear power, is also at the expense of climate conservation. It is like blaming the government for not running fast enough, while at the same time strictly forbidding the use of both legs. And this is one of the fundamental problems in the German energy discussion: climate is seen as an important thing, but it is forbidden to even mention that with the current nuclear fleet fully operational, achieving those climate goals would be far faster and more realistic.

Spain, which is rarely mentioned, also had its energy-turn, which failed miserably.[103] Spain offered generous subsidies for renewable energy in the early 2000s. The arguments used to justify them are the same arguments we all have heard many times: more jobs and the huge export potential of new technologies. Between 2006 and 2012 renewable energy grew five-fold. Meanwhile, the subsidies paid grew 18-fold, and the total bill for supporting renewable energy surpassed 30 billion euros in 2012. With economic problems growing for other reasons as well, this was too much. Subsidies and tariffs that had already been agreed on got cut afterwards, and investor trust on investing on renewable energy in Spain fell sharply.

Even though the Energiewende is cited as a "power to the people" project, the tariffs often end up in the pockets of wealthy companies, trust funds and investors who have the ability to invest in large-scale projects. The bill is paid by regular energy users, and disproportionately by the poor. In rich households, energy bills are not a big portion of the monthly budget, and the well-off also have the possibility to buy new energy efficient appliances or do energy efficiency renovations for their property. Poorer households already use a large chunk of their available income for energy and other necessities, and larger bills push them further into energy poverty. This real-world phenomenon has been largely ignored by the global progressive left, which usually is interested in the welfare of those less fortunate. These topics are important, and they need to be discussed along with the successes, especially if we aim to have a sustainable, fact-based and just energy policy.

From the climate's point of view, it is hard to come up with rational explanations for why the Germans are proceeding the way they are. Replacing nuclear power might have been political realism in nuclear-critical Germany. But it can also be seen as irresponsible short-sightedness where politicians were looking to score spare votes from the people at the expense of the environment. Even if Germany were to continue building renewable energy production at a significant scale, most of that production would replace nuclear instead of fossil fuels for years to come. Any emissions goals they have would be reached at a slower pace and with greater absolute emissions than would have been the case if Germany had started the closures with fossil fuels.

History offers some examples of successful rapid emission reductions. The energy turn that France took in the 1970s and 1980s cleaned up their electricity emissions in two decades, while at the same time energy consumption and the economy were growing rapidly. This project, incited largely by the 1970s oil crisis, managed to cut emissions far faster, even though that was not even a stated goal for the project. For decades, the French people have been avoiding the release of massive amounts of emissions and breathing cleaner air.

Summary

The first part of the book presented the reasoning behind why this book was written. The urgency of mitigating climate change and the massive size of the project is one side of the story. The challenges, bottlenecks and risks inherent in proposed solutions is the other side. These range from the addition of variable energy sources that will get progressively harder and harder, to the bottlenecks and environmental impacts of manufacturing and raw materials production that these energy sources will face. Thirdly, there is future energy demand, which will likely increase a lot from today, and be further compounded by the unspoken issue of rebound that could negate a large part of the emissions reductions we are currently planning to do with improved efficiency.

Finally, the German Energiewende was discussed as an illustrative project on what will happen with emissions when an advanced industrial nation throws everything it has to develop renewable energy and decides to phase out nuclear at the same time. The answer: not much. It is clear that we need faster progress on climate change mitigation, and it is clear that this progress should include nuclear power as one of the tools. Next, we discuss the role of nuclear power in more depth.

PART 2

Nuclear Power

What is Nuclear Power?

The second part of the book explains what nuclear power actually is, and on the other hand, what is often said about it. We compare nuclear power with other energy sources from most, if not all, relevant perspectives. The most important perspective is its potential to help mitigate climate change. We also ask and offer our views (which we base on solid scientific and historical evidence) on other nuclear related things. Is nuclear power dangerous? Does it lead to nuclear weapons proliferation? Is it too slow and expensive to build to help with climate change? Is it a yesterday's technology that we should leave behind as we move on to other alternatives? Or is it essential in our fight to stop climate change and offer billions of people the living standards and energy services they want and deserve?

During the last couple years, most credible organizations, from IPCC to IEA[104], have stated that nuclear is not only part of the needed toolbox to solving climate change, but an essential part that we should have much more of to make climate mitigation faster, cheaper and less risky. For example, the recent (2018[105]) IPCC Special Report on Global Warming of 1.5 °C sees nuclear grow 2 to 6-fold from current levels by 2050. The more likely scenarios that allow energy demand to grow as population and economies grow, see a 5 to 6-fold increase by 2050.

To start, nuclear power is low carbon, even if we account for all the emissions from constructing, mining, fuel production and disposal, decommissioning and so forth. The US National Renewable Energy Laboratory (NREL) did one of the most comprehensive analyses on the matter recently, based on studies released between 1980 and 2010.[106] The study concluded that nuclear was even more low carbon than we had previously thought. Depending on the type of reactor, the emissions were 12-13 gCO2/kWh. This was based on what is called life cycle analysis that accounts for the whole energy chain from construction to decommissioning to disposing of the spent fuel.

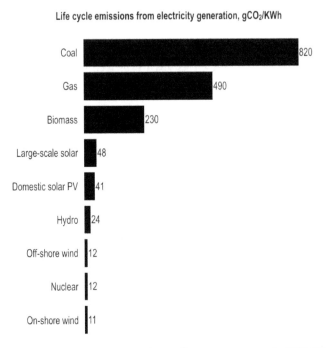

Life cycle emissions from electricity generation, gCO₂/KWh

Figure 18: The median estimates of life cycle emissions from different energy sources by IPCC 2014.

According to NREL, IPCC and many other sources nuclear has emissions comparable to wind, and actually lower than solar PV and new large hydro projects. All these energy sources have less than one-tenth the emissions that come from burning coal. These sources are called low-carbon or zero-carbon energy sources in this book, even though in reality nothing is totally zero-carbon. The emissions come from the construction and mining and such activities, but they do not burn any fuels that emit CO2 when energy is produced. Therefore, even these low emissions will largely go away if we decarbonize the rest of the energy system.[107]

Nuclear is not any more dependent on other fossil fuel use than any other energy technologies. Given its relatively high net energy (EROEI, which will be discussed more later), it is less dependent on fossil fuels and other natural resources than other low carbon options.

There is one more self-evident fact that needs to be said. Decarbonizing our whole energy system will require vast amounts of clean electricity, and all sources are needed. Everything has its bottlenecks, be them physical, social, regulatory, political, psychological or whatever. With these bottlenecks in mind, it is irresponsible to claim that we only need wind and solar to fight climate change, and it is equally irresponsible to claim that all our climate problems could be solved by nuclear power. Everything has its place and limitations, and the most important thing is to concentrate on replacing fossil fuels where-ever they are used, as efficiently as possible.

Nuclear and Climate

There are just a handful of countries in the world that have managed to decarbonize their electricity production at even close to the speed now required, apart from special places like Norway which has splendid hydropower resources. These countries include Sweden, France and Belgium. All three of them did it mainly with nuclear power. And all three did it by accident, with no policies to curtail greenhouse gas emissions. Further, all these countries saw their economies and energy demand growing rapidly during the decarbonization. Both France and Sweden produced over 80 percent of their electricity without emissions by 1990. Even if it was not intentional (or perhaps especially because it was not), it deserves to be mentioned that this was 60 years sooner than what Germany's energy and climate policy, often touted as the most progressive in the world, plans on achieving. Today, there are other examples as well, such as Ontario in Canada, Switzerland and Finland which all have emissions under 100 gCO2/kWh on average, and all of them have significant fleets of nuclear.

Nuclear is currently our single most important low-carbon energy technology, producing around 10% of our electricity and 4.5% of our primary energy. Even though hydropower currently produces more energy, it has much more limited possibilities to increase its production, as most of the good hydro sites have already been developed, especially in OECD countries. All clean energy sources combined accounted for roughly 15% of primary energy in 2018.

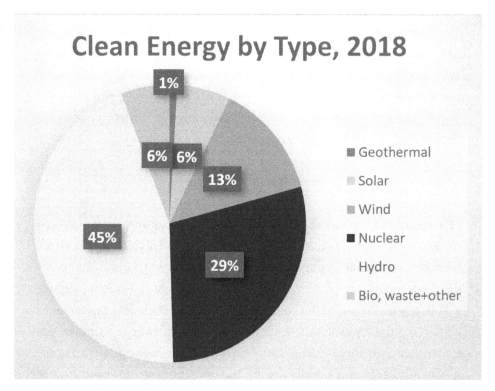

Figure 19: Clean energy shares globally per type in 2018. Source: BP 2019

Considering that the world has had somewhat of a priority in mitigating climate change since 1990, for three decades already, the clean energy percentages are not very encouraging. The rate of adding wind and solar have been much slower than the rate of adding nuclear was during a similar period from 1967-1990. And this even as we are now much wealthier than we were back then. Further, nuclear was built without any active climate policy. The aim was to build non-oil dependent energy production, and still many countries managed to reduce their emissions significantly around the 1980s.

How significantly? Several times faster than what the most ambitious climate policy of Germany has been able to achieve. There is no fundamental reason to believe we could not manage a similar transition today. There is even less reason to believe the task would be easier if nuclear power is not used as one of the proven tools.

Of course there are obstacles for nuclear power that will make progress slower than it should be. These include tight (and ever-changing) regulation for building and operating nuclear power plants, long, expensive and risky licensing procedures, political uncertainty and anti-nuclear activism. These obstacles are mainly man-made: political and regulatory. Both increase economic costs (capital investment cost and cost of capital) and risks. A lot of that regulation is there for a good reason, but we have never had a serious discussion whether all of the regulation is absolutely necessary or if it could be streamlined, given that nuclear has already proven itself to be our overall safest energy source. Indeed, from a public and environmental health perspective, any regulation that leads us to choose a mix of other energy technologies instead of a modern nuclear reactor is a loss. Especially with new reactor types currently on the drawing board, the regulatory framework of 20th century reactors means that it is unnecessarily hard for these new reactor types – regardless of their merits – to enter the market. Yet not many people seem to have political courage to suggest we should have a thorough look at current regulation with the aim of making it easier, faster and cheaper to license and build nuclear power.

In many countries, the politicization of nuclear power has also led to risks and costs increasing, and in some cases the political volatility is such that it is impossible to even propose building nuclear, even if it is not already forbidden in law. Politicization leads to more lobbying, and at worst, political games of "I scratch your back if you scratch mine." As nuclear is deeply political, these games become a necessity, but they also erode the public trust in both nuclear power and the political system overall. Some countries have also banned nuclear altogether, such as Germany, Austria, Australia and many states in North America.

Those obstacles mentioned above were probably less of a problem when France decarbonized its electricity between 1975 and 1990, lowering its carbon emissions roughly two percent annually for ten years. Currently France has emissions of roughly six tons per capita per year, with Germans having between nine and ten tons, depending on year.

France is not an isolated exception. Swedes have emissions under 5 tons per capita, with the biggest sources being industry and transportation. Sweden did not have any climate policy in place, but they still managed to cut emissions by 3.1 percent annually for a decade during their nuclear buildout.

The whole of the Nordic countries (Sweden, Norway, Finland, Denmark and Iceland) have an electricity grid that has roughly 60 gCO2/kWh of emissions – a level the rest of the world needs to achieve in the coming decades to meet climate targets. The Scandinavian grid consists mainly of hydro, nuclear, wind and biomass. Other examples of fast decarbonization and clean electricity grids include Belgium, which managed to cut its emissions at a rate of 2.7 percent for a decade, and Switzerland, which has one of the cleanest grids in the world, due to hydro and nuclear. All of these countries would be in a prime position to deepen their decarbonization efforts to industry and transportation, but in a very worrying sign of the times, they are struggling and actually mainly discussing if they should rebuild their already clean electricity grids to replace nuclear power with renewable energy.

History shows us that there are no technological barriers to scale up nuclear power fast enough to have a serious impact on climate change. One would think that with modern knowledge and tools we could even do better if we really applied ourselves. While solar and wind have been scaling up fast, there is still no evidence that they would be able to scale all the way in a timely manner.

Best increase in electricity generation per capita over 15-year period

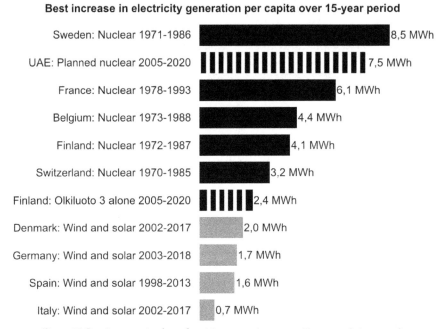

Sweden: Nuclear 1971-1986	8,5 MWh
UAE: Planned nuclear 2005-2020	7,5 MWh
France: Nuclear 1978-1993	6,1 MWh
Belgium: Nuclear 1973-1988	4,4 MWh
Finland: Nuclear 1972-1987	4,1 MWh
Switzerland: Nuclear 1970-1985	3,2 MWh
Finland: Olkiluoto 3 alone 2005-2020	2,4 MWh
Denmark: Wind and solar 2002-2017	2,0 MWh
Germany: Wind and solar 2003-2018	1,7 MWh
Spain: Wind and solar 1998-2013	1,6 MWh
Italy: Wind and solar 2002-2017	0,7 MWh

Figure 21: Best increases in clean electricity generation over a 15-year perio, per capita.*

It would be best if we built all low-carbon energy sources at the same time and use them to replace fossil fuels.

In addition to the obstacles mentioned above, there is a further cause for worry in many western countries. We stopped building nuclear for roughly two decades after 1990. This sort of hiatus means that we lost much of our know-how, supply chains and the advantages of serial production with nuclear, both in construction and in regulatory bodies. As we have learned with the catastrophic Olkiluoto 3 and Flamanville EPR-projects, it is hard, slow work to start from scratch.

This is an often overlooked subject in a broader sense as well: it is important to not lose expertise in the long run, and policies that have banned building new nuclear plants or set a closure-date for the current ones (like done in Sweden in the 1980s) are sort of one-way streets with no easy turning back. Any industry that has a set date of expiry (even if it turns out to be imaginary as in the case of Sweden), starts to slowly die as soon as the date is set, as fewer and fewer young people see any opportunities in the industry and the mentality turns from innovative and progressive to regressive and defeatist.

Olkiluoto 3 and Flamanville, along with other new, often troubled projects in western countries, have another quality that helps explain their problems. We are building new reactors-types – and not just that, but a new generation of reactors (Gen III+) – that have never been built before. There are not many examples of large prototypes, inside or outside the nuclear industry, that have gone as planned and stayed on budget.

Does closing nuclear power increase emissions?

Whenever one sees opposition to new nuclear or demands for closing operating plants, the offered alternatives are always the same: more energy efficiency, more renewables, more energy conservation. All these propositions seem to forget one basic fact: if these tools are used to replace nuclear power, they cannot be used to replace fossil fuels. Their potential, which is always limited, is used to replace other clean sources of energy, and environmentally the net result is, at best, zero.

Often it is negative, as it is very hard to replace nuclear that provides continuous baseload power that our society is dependent upon, with intermittently producing renewable energy. This leads to more burning of natural gas, biomass or even coal, to help keep the electricity grid stable when wind and solar are not producing enough. The key is, if there are fossil fuels used, one should be replacing them first.

But if we use nuclear power to provide baseload and flexible production and renewables to their best abilities, the grid will be cleaner sooner, and more affordably. No matter how much efficiency and conservation and demand flexibility we have at any given moment, this remains a fact. We will always be able to close down fossil fuel plants sooner if nuclear is allowed to play its role.

There are concrete examples of this available. When San Onofre Nuclear Generating Station (SONGS) in California closed down in 2012, it was replaced mainly by natural gas.[108] Experts agree that despite rosy promises of increases in efficiency and renewable energy, the possible closure of Diablo Canyon, California's last operating nuclear power plant, will also see emissions rising significantly.

After the Fukushima nuclear accident, Japan closed most of its nuclear reactors, bringing nuclear share of electricity down from 30 percent to around two percent. Japan implemented very aggressive plans of conservation and efficiency and many waited for a huge roll-out of renewable energy, following government subsidies. But despite all of this, the biggest increases have been in burning of oil and liquefied natural gas (LNG). Local utilities had plans to add coal power capacity by a fifth in the following decade.[109] Japan's emissions rose by 17 percent in 2012. In 2013, Japan announced that it is cancelling its target of 25 percent emissions reductions by 2020. The new goal is to have emissions increasing "only" by three percent, and this in a situation where Japan is already one of the biggest emitters in the world. The share of fossil fuels in Japanese energy mix rose from 62 percent to 88 percent in just few years, and the cost of those fossil fuels has been estimated to be roughly USD40 billion annually[110].

Greenpeace calculated that Japan could achieve its previous emission reduction target even without nuclear, if only it would build enough renewable energy production. But what if Japan would build those renewables, start up most of its nuclear fleet and build new reactors, as it had planned to do prior to Fukushima? The emission reductions would not only be met, but met with flying colours, demonstrating a huge win for climate.

Luckily, the Japanese situation has been progressing, albeit slowly. The government is trying hard to win public support to restart the nuclear fleet[111], and nine reactors have already been restarted, with some 17 in the process of restart approval.[112]

The fear of the atom is, for understandable reasons, deep in the Japanese psyche, and this makes restarting reactors politically hard. Many anti-nuclear activists say that nuclear should not be used because people fear it. Yet they themselves have been instrumental in creating and planting much of that fear in the first place.

It remains a fact that from the perspective of climate change, closing nuclear power plants prematurely is, without exception, bad news. In the current situation, it will always be replaced at least in part by combustion. In addition, any efficiency measures and new renewable capacity that is built, should be used to replace fossil fuels instead of other clean energy sources.

Nuclear Technology Overview

Nuclear is often portrayed as yesterday's technology that we should not waste any more resources on. This argument is as false as it is silly, and its main point seems to use cheap rhetoric to add certain images and values to something, without said images having any basis in reality. First, the age of any given technology is not an argument for or against it, as it says absolutely nothing about the value or usefulness of said technology. Second, even if age were used as some kind of qualification for any technology, nuclear energy would actually come on top, since it is the most recent of our major energy technologies. A few of the most important researchers that came up with the key concepts are still alive, while the inventors of the solar PV effect (in late 19th century) are long gone (not to mention wind power from 13th century). Further, the nuclear industry is still evolving strongly. New reactor designs are being developed and built around the world.

What is nuclear energy based on?

In simple terms, producing nuclear power is based on the energy that gets released when certain atoms split (fission, our current way of producing nuclear power) or get combined (fusion, as happens in the sun). This energy, released as heat, is then used to boil water (usually) which in turn is used to spin steam turbines and generators, which generate electricity.

What makes nuclear power exceptional is the enormous energy density of the fuel. Even the current generation of light water reactors (LWR), which use only a small part of the energy available in uranium, can produce roughly 16,000 – 20,000 times the amount of energy from uranium than is produced from the same amount of coal. There are also reactors that use most of the available energy in uranium, or thorium, which is another possible nuclear fuel. These reactors can produce in the order of millions of times the energy from nuclear fuel than is produced from a comparable amount of coal. All the energy used by a person living a high-energy lifestyle could be produced from the amount of nuclear fuel roughly the size of a golf ball. In comparison, if this energy were produced by burning fossil fuels, it would take a huge pile of coal and 5 to 10 tank trucks of oil.

On the atomic level, nuclear reaction is based on neutrons that get released from the core of the atom. When a fissile (fissile means it is able to be split) core splits, it releases heat and one or more neutrons. Some of these neutrons will hit another core, splitting it as well, causing more heat and neutrons to be released. A chain reaction is created. If the rate of neutrons hitting other cores is increasing, the reaction is called supercritical. Some materials act as neutron catchers, so they can be used to slow down and control the reactions. When a proper amount of fissile material and neutron catchers are used, a stable nuclear reaction can be sustained, which continues to release energy.

Another way to control the nuclear reactions is by the density and shape of the fuel (fissile material). First, the share of fissile uranium-235 is crucial for the chain reaction. While only about 0.7 percent of natural uranium is U-235, this amount is increased (called enriching) to about 3-5 percent for use in current reactors. The farther the fissile atoms are from each other, the less likely the neutrons are to hit other atoms. This means that thermal expansion and the shape of the fuel can be used to control the reaction. If the fuel expands when it gets hotter (when more reactions are happening), this naturally slows down the reaction, making it impossible to go supercritical in an un-controlled way. This is a so-called passive safety mechanism, and it is used for example in reactors that have the fuel in a liquid form, such as a molten salt reactor (MSR).

Water slows down and reflects neutrons. Both these properties in-crease the likelihood that the neutrons will hit another core and keep the reaction going. Therefore, removing the water will also stop the reaction, which is an important safety mechanism. Water can also used to transfer the heat from the reactions to the turbines. Most cur-rent reactors use water for neutron moderation and heat transfer.

Breeding reactors and fast neutrons

There are just a handful of atoms that are fissile, meaning that they can split when a neutron hits them. The only one available in any sufficient quantity in nature is uranium-235 (U235). Another one is plutonium-239, but it is not present in nature. Different isotopes, for example U235 and U238, are chemically identical, but they have a dif-ferent number of neutrons in their core. U235 is the most common nuclear fuel in today's reactors. We can also make fissile isotopes from fertile isotopes. A fertile isotope is by itself not able to sustain a chain reaction, but when it is bombarded with neutrons, it can catch one of these, which results in a fissile isotope, which can then be used as nuclear fuel. This is called breeding.

The most common example is Plutonium-239. It starts with urani-um-238 catching a neutron, becoming uranium-239. This isotope is unstable, so it quickly loses a beta particle and becomes neptuni-um-239, which then loses another beta particle and becomes pluto-nium-239, which is fissile. A similar process can be done with tho-rium-232. It is first turned into (unstable) thorium-233, which turns into protactinium-233, which then turns into fissile uranium-233.

A reactor that can make more fuel that it uses in this way is called a breeder. But breeding happens in today's reactors as well. In fact, with

typical fuel cycling of three years, around one third of the energy created in a light water reactor comes from plutonium, which gets created in the reactor from the uranium-238 present, as normally, over 95
percent of nuclear fuel pellets is actually U-238. [113]

It is noteworthy that uranium-238 is more than a hundred times
more common than uranium-235, and thorium is three to four times
as common as uranium. With reactors able to breed their fuel from
these abundant isotopes, our nuclear fuel reserves grow to what can
only be regarded as infinite (more on this later). Brundtland commission (WCED), which originally coined the term sustainable development, classified breeder reactors as renewable energy already back in
1987.[114]

Short history of the nuclear industry

As so many technological breakthroughs and major projects before
and since, nuclear energy saw its birth in the cradle of military research.[115] The potential to use nuclear energy as a weapon was seen
early on, and during the Second World War, the race to harness the
power of the atom for killing and destruction started in earnest. Most
of the participants were at least somewhat aware of the possibility to
build a nuclear weapon, and most assumed that the other side was
working on it. The race was won by the United States when it forced
Japan to surrender and ended the war by dropping nuclear bombs
at Hiroshima and Nagasaki. Nazi Germany also had its own nuclear
weapons program, but it lacked in support and funding from the leaders and therefore made less progress.

The nuclear reactors that were operated during the war were used to
produce weapons-grade plutonium (Pu239). Soon after the war, the
interest to harness the power of the atom for civilian purposes started
growing as well. The first reactor to produce electricity to light a light
bulb was EBR-I (Experimental Breeder Reactor-I), a prototype fast
breeder reactor that was built in the U.S in the early 1950s. EBR-II

was a subsequent scaled-up version, which managed to run and produce both heat and electricity for thirty years for the Argonne West
National Laboratory, up until 1994, when it was shut down.[116] The
EBR-II was also remarkably safe: in an experiment, it shut down safely
without operator intervention, even with a total loss of cooling and
control room power.

Back in the early days of the nuclear era, uranium resources were
thought to be quite scarce. This led to some urgency to develop breeding reactors that could breed nuclear fuel from the much more abundant U238 isotope.

As Bill Clinton got elected as president, his new administration shut
down the next phase of the breeder reactor program, which was aimed
at building the first commercial scale version of the reactor with integrated fuel reprocessing, called the IFR (Integrated Fast Reactor).
Some say the program was shut down as a "thank you" for the anti-nuclear environmentalists that had supported Clinton's election,
but there might also be other reasons for the closure.[117] Meanwhile,
the liberalization of the electricity market, cheap oil and gas, new dis-
coveries of uranium resources and prevalent anti-nuclear sentiment
amongst many western populations led to shutting down most other
fast reactor projects around the world. There was one program that
did survive. Russian BN-600, a fast spectrum sodium-cooled breeder
reactor, started operating in 1980 and has operated ever since, being
one of the most reliable reactors in the Russian fleet. Its bigger sib-
ling, BN-800 started up in 2014, and in August 2016 it reached its full
power.[118]

The IFR project was restarted by GE-Hitachi some years ago as
S-PRISM, which they have since offered to the British government
to help get rid of their plutonium stockpile. A few years ago, the
S-PRISM and ARC-100 reactor concepts, both based on the IFR/
EBR-II, combined their efforts, and in late 2019, the ARC-100 passed
the first phase of Canadian vendor design review.[119] Both India and
China are also planning their own fast/breeder technologies.

Another interesting project was the Molten Salt Reactor Experiment (MSRE), built in 1964. This type of reactor was planned to breed uranium-233 from a thorium blanket and then use that as a fuel. The fuel would be in a molten, liquid form, so it would be impossible for the reactor to "melt down". This offers some inherent safety advantages. Even though the 7.4 MW MSRE ran successfully from 1965 to 1969, the project was cancelled in early 1970s, as other uses were found for the money and research concentrated on sodium-cooled breeders.[120]

The interest in molten salt reactors has since sparked up again. For example, the Chinese have found interest in the technology.[121] In 2014, there was news that China aims to have a working MSR in 10 years instead of their previous aim of 25 years. This sparked worry among many that Chinese will use technology that was designed and researched in the U.S. to leapfrog the U.S. nuclear industry. Only a few months later, Transatomic Power in the U.S. published their plans for an advanced MSR.[122] Canadian company Terrestrial Energy is developing their IMSR (Integral Molten Salt Reactor) and they are currently farthest along the path to a first-of-a-kind in North America. A broadly similar reactor is being planned also by ThorCon, among many others.

The winning technology of the civilian nuclear reactor race proved to be the light water reactor. PWR (Pressurized Water Reactor), which was originally designed for nuclear submarines and scaled up from there, became the most common reactor type in the world. A simpler modification of the PWR, called the BWR (Boiling Water Reactor), has taken second place in popularity. Both reactors are light water reactors, which means that they use regular water for both cooling the reactor and for slowing down (moderating) the neutrons. This means that if the coolant (water) is removed, then also the moderator is removed, and the chain reaction stops. This will not stop the production of heat, however, as the fissioning of various radioactive materials continues, generating heat. This heat production is significant especially right after the reactor shuts down but diminishes rapidly.

Another reactor type, the heavy water reactor called the CANDU, was developed in Canada during the 1950s and 1960s. A heavy water reactor uses heavy water (deuterium) for moderating the neutrons, but normal water for cooling. As heavy deuterium water already has caught an extra neutron, it is much less likely to catch another neutron compared to normal water. This makes heavy water reactors much more flexible about their fuel than light water reactors. While LWR uses enriched fuel, with the U235 content increased from the natural 0.7 % to 3-5 %, heavy water reactors can use natural uranium or lower enrichment uranium as fuel.

Yet another design was the RBMK, designed in the Soviet Union. The RBMK uses graphite for neutron moderation and light water for cooling. This combines the weaknesses of water and graphite, as we learned in the Chernobyl nuclear accident, where an RBMK suffered a catastrophic melt-down. When the coolant (water) is removed, it still leaves the moderator (graphite, which makes the chain reaction possible) in place. But if the water is removed, there is nothing taking the heat away from the reactor, which leads to problems.

Britain also developed its own Advanced Gas-Cooled Reactor (AGR), which uses carbon dioxide for cooling. Despite the ambitious plans to export the technology, it remains a niche product at the global scale. As 14 out of 15 of Britain's nuclear reactors are AGR's, it forms the backbone of the UK nuclear production. The fleet is aging, and will be closed by roughly 2030, leading to an urgent need of new capacity. Due to technological and materials-related matters, prolonging the operative lifetimes of AGR's seems to be harder and more expensive than those of light water reactors.

Nuclear reactors can be crudely divided into four generations. First generation includes mainly research reactors and the early reactors that were used to manufacture plutonium for the nuclear weapons programs various governments had. Second generation reactors were the first ones widely used for civilian electricity production, and they were built roughly between 1960 and 1990. They form the backbone of the current global nuclear fleet. Third generation reactors, which are the evolutionary version of the second generation, have been built since 1990.

Nuclear industry today

A further evolution of the third generation is the 3+ generation now being built around the world. These include Westinghouse's AP1000 which is being built in the U.S. and in China, AREVA's EPR being built in Finland, France and China, and Rosatom's AES-2006/VVER-1200. The first VVER-1200 was connected to the Russian grid in August 2016. China managed to start both the first EPR and the first AP1000 reactors built in the world almost simultaneously in mid-2018. The "plus" in the 3+ tells that it is a further improvement on the third generation, including passive safety features. These reactors are often capable of passive cooling for safe removal of shutdown decay heat for several days, without any power or outside intervention.

Fourth generation reactors include many revolutionary designs compared to the current common types. Many of these are breeding and/or based on non-water technologies such as molten salt or lead. The Generation IV International Forum was founded to develop these reactor designs in the early 2000s.[123] A lot has changed since then, with a lot of R&D being done by private companies, often smaller start-ups.

This "waking up" of the nuclear industry in western countries has come after decades of hibernation. It is no wonder that many people still think that the current designs, mainly PWR and BWR, are the only ways to produce nuclear energy, and that the nuclear industry itself is slowly withering away. PWR and BWR ended up as the dominant designs at least partly by accident, through their first application to power the submarines, which then led to them being more familiar and available as a technology.

As is the case with many technologies, different ways of doing things have different pros and cons. Light water reactors do have their advantages, but they also have their weaknesses, compared to other reactor types. Currently they enjoy by far the most mature supply chains, suitable regulations, experience and expertise. Their safety record has shown them to be excellent in this regard. Water as a heat transfer material puts one limitation for their use: outlet temperature. It is hard to get high temperatures with water, as the pressure needs to increase exponentially to get higher temperature steam. Higher pressure means thicker, more expensive pressure vessels and perhaps increases the need for additional safety measures. Other designs that rely on non-water coolants can provide higher temperatures without high pressures, which is useful for different purposes, such as industrial processes or making hydrogen.

The current R&D on nuclear reactors is diversified. There are both large and small reactor designs, and cost reduction has become one of the main goals, along with passive safety features. Many designs are modular, with components made in factory assembly lines to minimize on-site fabrication. Flexible production of heat, electricity and water desalination are some design features being considered, as they have significant market applications. In short, the industry has started to develop reactors more from the perspective of what the market needs. The next steps are to get the market to realise these solutions exist, then create the regulatory and legislative framework for them.

Nuclear energy tomorrow – New reactors for new uses

For the last couple years, nuclear innovation has found a new gear. That gear is towards commercial small reactors of many different types aimed for a multitude of potential new uses. Most of these reactors do generate electricity, but that is not their only trick. Some are designed to be very flexible in their operation and can offer services for power grids that struggle with increasing amounts of variable wind and solar production. Some are even adding local energy storage systems, which will allow them to "load-follow" the grid demand even more affordably and flexibly. Two examples are the molten salt reactors from Terrestrial Energy and Moltex. They have planned on adding an optional molten salt storage unit for their reactor, which can store some of the high temperature heat from the reactor for days with only small losses. The system would also have some extra turbine capacity so that this heat can then be used to produce more electricity for the grid when it is needed.

 A recent analysis of such a "flexible nuclear" system was done by LucidCatalyst. In the graphs below, we can see that adding a relatively small amount, around 10 % of total production capacity, of this kind of advanced nuclear with short term storage to a grid that has a high amount of wind and solar can help immensely with balancing the grid. Under the default scenario, natural gas is used to back up the variable production from the renewables. In the advanced nuclear scenario, the natural gas gets mostly replaced with the advanced nuclear+storage system, while the levels of wind and solar production stay the same. Needless to say, this cuts emissions significantly. This option is also likely to be much more affordable than a system relying on batteries, as it uses molten salt or other similarly inexpensive methods to store the energy as high-grade heat instead of electricity.

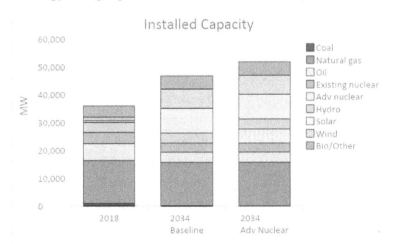

Figure 22: This image depicts production capacities of different technologies. Around 5 GW of Adv Nuclear with storage was added to the high renewables, low cost natural gas-scenario from NREL. Image Credit: Lucid Catalyst Ltd

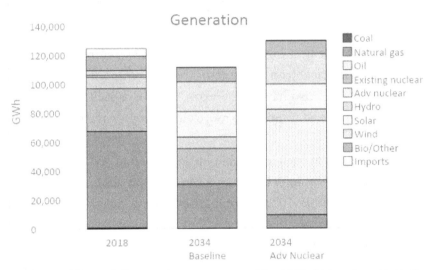

Figure 23: This graph illustrates the energy generate♦. That 5 GW of A♦v nuclear a♦♦e♦ to the system replaces most of the natural gas as the flexible backup for variable renewables. Image Cre♦it: Luci♦ Catalyst Lt♦

Other uses for new nuclear energy are in the heating and industrial process heat sectors. Around half of global energy is used as heat, and most of that is done by combusting fossil fuels. In the higher temperatures required by various industrial processes, over 95% of energy is provided by combustion, mostly of fossil fuels, and the rest is done with electricity (which is also made mostly by combustion of fuels).

There is a limited number of ways to produce high grade heat reliably and affordably without emissions. Using carbon capture and storage with coal or gas is one, but it is more expensive and less effective than current methods. Burning sustainable biofuels might be another, but there is a very limited quantity of sustainable biofuels available – indeed, some argue that we are already taking too much from our ecosystems for our own use, causing biodiversity loss and habitat fragmentation. We can also use direct electricity, but that is often more expensive than using fuels, and if we need reliable electricity for industry, then wind and solar are of limited use. We can also make hydrogen or other synthetic fuels and burn them, but that is even more expensive, as the process has many losses on the way. And lastly, we can use direct nuclear heat/steam to supply the heat, since this is what the reactors produce already anyway.

The industrial heat market is one that many of the new reactor vendors are eyeing with increasing curiosity for the reasons mentioned above. Small reactors could supply the steam and electricity used in an industrial park or large facility reliably, affordably and without emissions. One of the more obvious low-hanging fruits here is petroleum refineries, which currently use a lot of oil and petroleum gases to produce the heat and hydrogen their processes need. Of course, oil refining might not be the business of the future in the ideal world we want to see, but one must start somewhere. Eventually, large-scale production of synthetic fuels that are carbon-neutral is essential if we are to completely decarbonize the transportation sector. Emission-free nuclear can power the entire synthetic fuel process, and the petroleum industry likely has the best expertise in synthetic/biofuels production and the processes involved.

For industrial purposes, even nuclear has its limitations and obstacles to overcome. The current generation of light water reactors is not well-suited for most applications due to their large size and relatively low outlet temperature (around 300 C). Various high temperature reactors that can provide industrial heat in the range between 600 to 900 degrees are being designed, but in many countries these would require a fundamental change in how nuclear power is perceived and treated in society. Instead of a few large and centralized power stations we would need to have dozens, even hundreds, of small, fit-to-purpose reactors at industrial sites. In many countries the licensing and regulatory framework for nuclear plants alone practically forbids this kind of activity.

For heating of buildings, the situation is again a bit different. If there is a district heating infrastructure in place, then any small to medium size reactor operating in combined heat and power mode can supply much of the city's heat very cost-effectively. In combined heat and power (CHP) production, some of the electricity production is lost, while a larger amount of heat energy (at roughly 80 to 100 °C) is gained. For one unit (e.g. MWh) of electricity lost, 5-10 units of heat is gained, depending on the case. Nuclear district heating has been done for decades in Switzerland, Hungary, Bulgaria, Czech Republic, Slovakia and Russia.[124] According to most studies, nuclear is among the most cost-effective ways to produce district heat, either through CHP or dedicated heating reactors.

District heating can also be done with dedicated district heating reactors that only produce hot water for the network. They can be designed as low-pressure and therefore do not need expensive pressure vessels or turbine generators for electricity production. China is already building a commercial-scale first-of-a-kind district heating reactor, the DHR-400. There are others being designed as well, such as Finland which announced such a design project in early 2020.[125]

But most of space heating is done by burning fuels locally, in gas or oil boilers, sometimes even using solid fuels such as coal or wood pellets. Many areas, like Europe, have a comprehensive gas delivery network already in place, and gas is also used for cooking. Renovating millions and millions of houses and apartment buildings with heat pumps and electric stoves or district heating networks is unlikely to happen quickly, if at all.

First, the costs per household would be prohibitive, in the thousands of euros. District heating only makes sense if most of the area buildings are connected to it, and it is still a big investment – plus it will need a central power plant to provide the heat. Second, people are accustomed to certain things, such as gas stoves and boilers. Any significant change in their habits is often met with resistance. Even if this resistance could eventually be overcome by tax incentives, subsidies or promises of lower heating bills in the future (or higher, if they insist on burning fuels locally), it might take years or decades to do it, and it would need to be done in many places simultaneously. This would, in turn, perhaps lead to overheating of the heat pump / electric stove market and lack of skilled workforce to do all the installations and so forth. The electric grid would likely also need strengthening as each household adds a dozen or so kilowatts of peak demand. A city of just 50,000 households switching from gas to electricity would increase peak demand by hundreds of megawatts in a relatively small area.

Another solution would be to replace the natural gas with a carbon-neutral alternative, such as hydrogen or synthetic methane made of hydrogen, or a mixture of the two. The problem here is that this hydrogen or synthetic methane needs to be made first, and that requires (clean) energy, much more than what ends up in the product, as the conversion processes always have losses. Here advanced nuclear reactors can again help. With high temperature reactors and high temperature electrolysis, the efficiency of hydrogen production can be increased compared to using regular electrolysis. And as we learned above, even with regular electrolysis, the facilities often need to run nearly all the time to get the costs down.

Clean Liquid Fuels and Replacing Crude Oil

Replacing oil faces two central problems: the unique beneficial properties of oil and the scale at which we use oil. Crude oil supplies roughly one third of our primary energy and is hence our largest single source of energy. Replacing something at that scale is a huge undertaking. But replacing oil is not impossible, just very difficult. We use oil for transportation for very good reasons: it is easy and safe to use, easy to store, it packs a lot of energy per volume and weight and is relatively cheap. Oil and natural gas are also used as feedstock for many useful things like pesticides, fertilizers, medicine, plastics and synthetic fibres.

Providing cost-competitive, clean drop-in replacements for current gas and liquid fuels is the Holy Grail of climate mitigation. We are very unlikely to be able to electrify our energy use fast enough and biofuels are too limited to scale. In many use cases, electrifying doesn't even make sense, at least with current or foreseeable technologies. We will need all available tools, from electric vehicles to public transportation to reducing our need to move around and finally to being able to synthesize liquid fuels at massive scale.

Synthetic fuels may be the best drop-in solution for both today's infrastructure and people's habits. This also makes it much more scalable – we only need to scale the fuels production, not the whole infrastructure replacement-program or changing of people's habits indoctrination. Synthetic fuels will need hydrogen as the key feedstock, and it needs to be clean, affordable and produced at massive scale.

Clean hydrogen has been gaining attention in the last couple of years. Europe came up with a Hydrogen Roadmap[126] and IEA publishing a report The Future of Hydrogen[127], both in 2019. In early 2020, the Hydrogen Council published their "Path to Hydrogen Competitiveness: A Cost Perspective[128]" and eighteen U.S.-based companies released their "Road Map to a U.S. Hydrogen Economy."[129] While these reports mainly discuss hydrogen made with renewable energy, nuclear hydrogen is also a very attractive option, especially with mass-produced advanced reactors that are well-suited for the task. The key parameter is cost. The lower the cost of hydrogen, the sooner it replaces fossil hydrogen in its current uses, and the sooner it can start replacing fossil-based fuels with carbon-neutral alternatives. According to the IEA report above, roughly three-quarters of dedicated hydrogen production is done from natural gas, which accounts for 6% of global natural gas use. The rest is mostly made from coal (2% of global coal use), and a couple percent is made from oil by electrolysis. Hydrogen production emits 830 million tons of CO_2 annually.

Today most hydrogen is used to make ammonia for fertilizers and in petroleum refining, both to hydrocrack oil molecules into smaller ones that are more useful and valuable, and to reduce the sulphur content in the oil. Making methanol is another large use of hydrogen today. These are the first ones that need to be replaced with clean hydrogen. Hydrogen can be used directly in other places as well, such as transportation, if suitable infrastructure and vehicles are in place.

So far, they are somewhat limited – only a few hydrogen-fuelled car models are available, and the refilling network is limited.

The more interesting solutions lie in the other things that can be made from hydrogen. It can be combined with carbon to make synthetic fuels like gasoline, kerosene (Jet-A) or diesel. If the carbon does not come from fossil fuels, these fuels can be carbon neutral.

If we are to produce clean liquid and gaseous fuels at massive scale, we will need clean and very cheap hydrogen to produce them. Electrification of transportation is still in its infancy, although progress has been promising. Even with the most optimistic scenarios, we will have close to a billion combustion engines on the roads by mid-century. The problem is that while EV's are growing, so is the annual sales of new vehicles, and it seems people are preferring bigger and hence more gas-guzzling vehicles. Trucks and other large machinery also use a significant share of our liquid fuels and might be hard to electrify at scale. EV production is already bottlenecked by battery availability, and that situation is likely to get worse.[130]

Then there is marine transport. We basically have two options to decarbonize marine transport, of which only one is really a choice. We can either refit or build an entirely new fleet of ships that are powered by small nuclear reactors, or we can use clean energy to make drop-in fuels for those ships. Ammonia, made from hydrogen and nitrogen, is a good bet, as it can be used in today's diesel engines with minimal modifications, and it can be manufactured more easily than synthetic hydrocarbons. In addition, ammonia is carbon-free, and emits no carbon dioxide during combustion.

Aviation is another sector that will need high-quality liquid fuels, in this case hydrocarbons. JET-A, the commonly used fuel in modern aeroplanes, needs to be replaced with something very similar, as the fuel is highly regulated.

To make affordable synthetic replacements for any of these uses, we will need very affordable hydrogen as a starting point. The cost needs to be well below $2/kg, preferably around $1/kg. To get very affordable hydrogen, we will need to have low-cost and highly efficient electrolysers, low-cost energy (electricity or heat or combination depending on process) and very high capacity factors. And it needs to be highly scalable. A nuclear-based system is the only one that even theoretically meets all these demands, provided we can find ways to bring down the costs.

How much clean energy would we need? It takes a lot of energy to make hydrogen with electrolysis and transform it into other fuels or methane; much more than ends up stored in the fuels themselves. As a rule of thumb, around half of electric energy can be transformed into methane, and a third into liquid fuels.[131] To replace our current oil use completely with clean "e-fuels" made from electricity, we would need to increase our electricity production perhaps four-fold from today, depending.

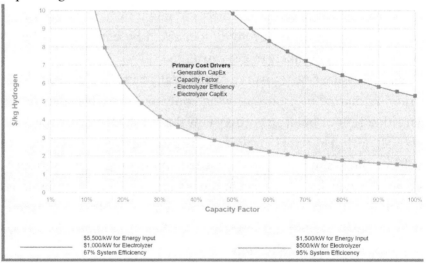

Figure 24: A graph on how the costs of different components affect the cost of hydrogen. Image credit: Lucid Catalyst Ltd[132]

Luckily, that won't need to happen, but even if we replace just a quarter of our oil use, we might need to double our electricity production. If nuclear is among the only even theoretically feasible options to make clean hydrogen at low enough costs, it would need to make up most of that increase. This means growing our nuclear production around tenfold just for this.[133] It is clear we cannot do this given how we build nuclear today. If we truly want to replace oil use in different sectors, the competing fuels or technologies need to be cost-competitive.

Nuclear Fuel – Supply and Environmental Consequences

There are a lot of worries presented on the availability of nuclear fuel, especially in the case of expanding our use of it. Ugo Bardi wrote a book, Extracted: How the Quest for Mineral Wealth Is Plundering the Planet (2014), for the Club of Rome. It includes a chapter by Michael Dittmar with the title *The End of Cheap Uranium*, which includes most of the modern-day arguments about the perceived supply problems of nuclear fuel and the evidence used to justify them. These include:

1. There is only 80 years' worth (formerly 50 years) of uranium deposits at current level of use.
2. The best uranium deposits have already been depleted, so we need to mine uranium from increasingly poor deposits in the future.
3. The peak of uranium production was in the 1980s and/or increasing production of uranium is expensive.[134]
4. Uranium production in Europe has fallen to negligible levels much before Europe extracted its known reserves.
5. Current uranium production is less than our use (hinting at scarcity).
6. Breeder reactors have not been built (in significant amounts) during the last decades.

Most of these arguments are based on facts and evidence. The conclusions that are drawn are, however, hasty and superficial, as not even the most basic arguments are used to check their validity. What follows is our superficial peer review on the solidity and logic of Michael Dittmar's conclusions.

Dittmar's conclusions on the uranium situation are as dark as they are desolate. For example, he takes European uranium production as a starting point (argument 4), and proceeds to model and conclude that the rest of the world will follow in Europe's footsteps. He sees no reason to ask why Europe's uranium production has fallen (at least political and regulatory reasons seem possible, along with economic ones). He simply assumes that nothing will happen, and nobody will do anything as the situation (uranium production) slowly deteriorates and uranium prices rise.

The narrative sees no new uranium deposits being found (argument 1), because, according to Dittmar, we have not found significant deposits for decades. What is overlooked is that the uranium resource, along with many other minerals, is more of an economic concept than a geologic one (argument 2). When uranium prices started rising in the early 2000s, it created, for the first time in years, an incentive to go prospecting for new deposits. In just a few years, known reserves grew by 17 percent (which was something Dittmar forgot to mention). Between 2011 and 2013 alone, known reserves increased by seven percent.[135] Dittmar draws a straight, declining line for the currently operating uranium mines (argument 3 and 1) but fails to mention that every time we have gone out looking for more uranium, we have also found it. Uranium is available in limited, finite quantities, surely. But the important question is how limited, and at what price and level of technology.

Dittmar also overlooks another important detail, the 20-year Megatons to Megawatts-deal[136], which ended in 2013. According to that agreement, Russian highly-enriched uranium (HEU) was first made to reactor grade (low-enriched, LEU) nuclear fuel which was then bought by the U. S. and used as fuel in U.S. nuclear reactors. For two decades, this accounted between 13 and 19 percent of global nuclear fuel use, so it is no wonder that we have been mining and producing less nuclear fuel than we have been using (argument 5). With the agreement in place, the lower need for new uranium was easy to foresee. Further, the global use of uranium is relatively easy to predict for years ahead (argument 1, 2, 3, 4, 5 and 6). We know the (maximum) number of operating nuclear reactors we will have for the next five, even ten years quite accurately. With that knowledge, we also know how much demand for nuclear fuel there will be. As we know, new reactors, let alone new advanced breeder reactors, do not pop up overnight.

Dittmar does not ask, nor does he answer, the rather obvious question: why on earth would uranium prospectors and producers invest, go exploring and dig for uranium for a market that does not have a need for it? And to pay dearly for stockpiling it? Or to dump it into the market, crash the price of uranium and drive their companies to bankruptcy? Exploration and production investments follow the long-term prices of the global uranium market, and a large portion of uranium is sold with long-term contracts. It is only natural that the production of uranium has not grown (argument 3), because the prices have stayed low and the demand has not been increasing significantly. This logic goes for all minerals, and it would actually be strange if something else had been happening. It seems that the sole purpose of Dittmar's text is to mislead the non-expert reader rather than educate them.

Price and resources of Uranium

When compared to its energy content, uranium is dirt cheap. Even if only the naturally fissile isotope, uranium-235, which accounts for 0.7 percent of all uranium, were used as fuel, it is still cheap. One kilogram of uranium releases roughly 20,000 times the energy (in current light water reactors) than a kilogram of coal does.

The price of uranium oxide (of which ~85 percent is uranium) has been falling from its peaks in 2007 (over $300/kg on spot market) and 2011 (over $150/kg). For the last three years (since 2017), the long-term price of uranium has been hovering around $70/kg. For comparison's sake, the price of coal was around $50 per ton (1,000 kg). That fall in price was mainly due to surplus uranium in the market, which in turn was the result of the nuclear closures following the Fukushima nuclear accident in 2011 in Japan and elsewhere, and the political uncertainty if the reactors in Japan will be restarted and when.[137]

A significant part (roughly half) of the uranium fuel cost comes from enrichment and fuel fabrication. Yet still uranium enjoys a price difference of more than 10 times less than coal, on a per energy basis. The end of cheap uranium, currently absent from the market data, would mean that breeder reactors and other ways to increase fuel availability (higher burn rates, recycling, secondary uranium resources) would become more competitive. This would lead to available reserves multiplying many times over (arguments 1 and 2).

Globally, the nuclear reactors use roughly 68,000 tons of uranium per year.[138] This can be compared with the

- 4,529,331,451 tons of oil,
- 3,309,421,395 tons of oil equivalent of natural gas or the
- 8,012,769,663 tons of coal we also use every year. [139]

The identified resources recoverable and costs below $130/kg have been estimated by the IAEA/NEA "Red Book" to be around 6.1 million tons. This equals about 80 years of use at the current rate. This is actually a rather long time for most minerals. For example, the current R/P ratio (reserves / production) for silver indicates our known silver deposits may last only for about 30 years. When the price is doubled to max $260 per kg, the reserves increase to around 8 million tons, or around 120 years of use.[140] If the price goes considerably over $260, the conventional reserves see a doubling (argument 1).

The amount of uranium in the top 1.6 kilometres of earth is estimated to be around 25,000,000 million tons. By improved enriching, recycling and reprocessing, the uranium use of current reactors can be cut roughly in half. This would double the R/P ratio of our reserves.[141]

Uranium reserves are more of an economic concept than a geological one. The reason is that uranium is everywhere in smaller or larger amounts. Rising price increases the reserves in many ways: it catalyses more exploration and advanced production technologies, it makes some already known deposits economically viable and it leads to more careful use of uranium fuel.

A long-term maximum price for uranium can be set at roughly $300 kg. This is the price at which we are already able to collect uranium from seawater[142], and that price will likely come down with further research.[143] The world's oceans have 3.2 parts per billion of uranium[144], making a total resource of roughly 4,500 million tons (compared to 6.1 million tons current known reserves of terrestrial uranium). What is more, this uranium is constantly being replaced by erosion.

Before we hit this maximum price, it will likely become viable to get uranium from certain secondary sources. These include phosphate rocks and coal ash. Somewhat ironically, the uranium and thorium contained in coal ash contains more nuclear energy than what was in the coal that was burned to ash.[145] A price of $300 / kg would show in the cost of nuclear energy production, but not significantly (argument 1 and 2).

Ugo Bardi despairs in his book about the gigantic investments that would be needed to grow the global uranium production to match a bigger fleet of nuclear reactors. But he forgets to do any comparisons, nor does he "dig deeper" into the matter. As we said before, we use coal in vastly larger amounts than we use uranium, yet we seem to find the money and resources to invest in coal production, along with oil and gas and other minerals that have seen rapid rates of growth in their historical production. The material needs for wind and solar power are much bigger than nuclear power, so if we follow Bardi's logic, those energy technologies are doomed as well.

Uranium mining and the environment

Mining is often a messy and destructive business for the environment. Whether we like it or not, our world is completely dependent on many sorts of mining activities, and this is unlikely to change in the near future. This dependency includes renewable energy, energy efficiency improvements and practically any sort of manufacturing or making of things with modern materials. Mining for uranium is no exception, save for in the scale of the needed operation. With superior energy density compared to other energy sources, much less fuel needs to be mined for any given amount of energy produced. Compared with other mining activities, uranium has the following advantages:

- Uranium mining is minuscule compared to other fuels, such as coal.
- Fewer mines mean easier environmental control, observance of regulations and lower risks for mining accidents.
- Because of its high energy density, it is often possible to produce uranium as a by-product of other mining activities.
- Uranium's relatively high price per kg and chemical attributes allow it to also be produced without major surface mining operations (low-impact in-situ leaching).

So even as all human activities, including mining, are not without environmental harms or risks, it is essential to compare those harms and risks, and control them in cost-effective ways. Around half of global uranium is produced by in-situ leaching, while less than half is produced by more traditional mining. Less than one tenth is produced as by-products of other mining activities. Two-thirds of uranium comes from three countries: Canada, Kazakhstan and Australia.[146]

Will breeder reactors radically change the nuclear fuel markets?

In the long term, the modern nuclear fuel business might face a new threat: breeder reactors.[147] Ever since the dawn of civilian nuclear power it has been clear that fast breeder reactors are the way of the future. But this future might still lie decades away. A 1 GW breeder reactor uses roughly one ton of uranium or thorium and generates 7–8 TWh of electricity. The uranium or thorium can be used at least 50 times more efficiently than uranium is used in current light water reactors. This efficiency also opens many secondary sources of uranium and thorium, as well as depleted uranium currently left over from enrichment, as viable fuels.

Breeder reactors are explained in more detail elsewhere in the book as well, but from the perspective of nuclear fuel supply and prices, they offer several important points for consideration:

1. Breeders make their own fuel from uranium-238, which is about 140 times as common as uranium-235, the fissile fuel used in light water reactors. Another way is to breed fuel from thorium, which is 3–4 times more common than uranium.

2. We already have significant amounts of U238 stockpiled:
    *   Around 370,000 tons of heavy metal from civilian nuclear reactors, of which most is U238.[148] It should be enough to provide global electricity for around a century.
    *   Around 1,200,000 tons of depleted uranium (mainly U238), left over from enrichment activities. There aren't many commercial uses for this mineral, but in a breeder reactor, the stockpile would be enough to provide the current level of global electricity use for 450 years.

3. Extraction of uranium from seawater would become more viable, providing us with a practically endless supply of nuclear fuel.

4. Some breeder designs can use thorium. There is roughly 2,800,000 tons of thorium, which is a by-product of other mining activities with little uses for itself, lying around. It would be enough to produce our current level of electricity use for a thousand years.

As spent nuclear fuel – now considered waste – turns into a useful, valuable resource, it will see its status changed. The annoying political problem nobody wanted to deal with might turn into a valuable source of clean energy. While there will still be high-level nuclear waste, the amount will be smaller, and it will lose its activity faster. Most of the dangerous isotopes have half-lives of a couple decades and would all but disappear in a couple centuries. Even these radioactive elements, if reprocessed and separated, can find many valuable uses in medicine and industry.

There are some conclusions that we can make about uranium resources. First, in the timescale relevant for climate change mitigation, uranium supply won't become a major issue even if we grow our nuclear fleet many times over and use the less efficient but readily available light water reactors. The price of uranium can increase significantly before it becomes an issue for the overall cost of nuclear electricity. With increasing prices, the uranium supply will multiply until we hit a level at which seawater extraction becomes viable. Yet it is prudent to start seriously designing, licensing and building commercial breeder reactors and other advanced designs, such as high temperature reactors for industrial heat uses.

The staggering amount of clean energy available through breeder reactors, via spent fuel, depleted uranium, natural uranium and thorium, is a physical fact that humanity simply cannot afford to ignore. With the combination of seawater extraction and breeder reactors, the nuclear fuel supply becomes essentially limitless.

Is Nuclear Power Safe, or Dangerous?

No other energy source receives as much talk about risks as nuclear power. Yet, it is the safest energy source we have.

Nuclear is our safest way to produce energy

Decades of media messaging have convinced many people that nuclear power is uniquely dangerous. This is difficult to rectify, as most people are very reluctant to change their minds, no matter how many facts, data and evidence are presented. We tend to feel threatened when exposed to ideas or information inconsistent with our world view, making us double-down on our convictions with even more resolve. To make matters worse, this normal response is complicated by our poor ability to assess risks in the first place.

There are a few ways to compare the risks of different energy sources. One is to calculate the amount of premature fatalities any given energy source causes per unit energy produced. This somewhat morbid metric goes by the name deaths per terawatt hour, or D/TWh. Sickness and other harms to health can also be estimated and compared on national and international levels. Many of these hazards are what are called stochastic, meaning it is often impossible to show a direct cause and effect in single cases, but statistics of larger groups show the big picture.

For example, if someone gets cancer, it is often impossible to say with certainty what was the cause for that cancer. Cancer might be due to diet or lifestyle, inheritance, environmental toxins, background or man-made radiation or just bad luck. Cancer cases have been increasing historically, and in a way, that is a positive thing. As most cancers take a long time to develop and therefore come at old age, this means that more people are living longer lives instead of dying of something else sooner.

These stochastic effects can be estimated statistically. Smoking makes it much more likely one will get lung cancer, and it is seen as the biggest cause for it, even though not all smokers get lung cancer.

But what about comparing the health hazards of different energy sources? As stated before, nuclear power is one of the safest ways to produce energy. A big reason for the disparity between the fact and the image in people's minds can be found from availability bias. Even a small problem in a nuclear power plant is reported by the media, even though it would present no danger or risk to anyone. This reporting creates an image of danger and risks in people's minds – after all, why else would the media be reporting it, if it is not dangerous? Well, the media reports it because everything with nuclear in it sells papers and gets clicks on the internet, even more so if some sort of connection to potential risk or danger can be made in the headline. Yet small particulate matter in the air we breathe, due to combustion of fuels, causes thousands of times of more deaths, without much reporting or interest from anyone.

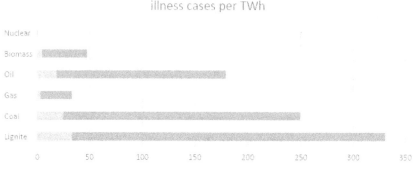

Figure 25: Deaths or illnesses per terawatt hours of electricity generation in Europe. Source: Lancet 2007 [149]

The huge difference between statistical facts and the perceptions people have is astonishing. Take the worst nuclear accident in history, Chernobyl in 1986. It is "common knowledge" that it has caused much suffering and health impacts in countries that got a big portion of the fallout, like Finland. But then on the other hand, careful studies of those health hazards say that no additional cancers were detectable from the Chernobyl fallout in Finland.[150] None. This means that for practical purposes, nobody in Finland has died due to civilian nuclear use, including all the accidents, ever. That is a phenomenal health record. Yet when you ask people about nuclear power, they always mention the risks and dangers.

What about the risks if we expand nuclear use? A paper had studied what the additional radiation dose would be on average, if we produced all our electricity (20,000 TWh/year) with French nuclear technology from the 1990s. The added dose rate they came up with was 0.15% of the average background radiation we get today.[151] That has practically zero observable health effects (see more in the chapter on radiation). New nuclear plants have even smaller radiation releases.

What about combustion of fuels? There are some recent studies done on the health effects and costs of burning in general and burning coal in Europe in particular. The effects of European coal burning were studied by various environmental organizations which released a report "Europe's Dark Cloud" in 2016.[152] According to the report, more than 22,000 premature deaths were caused by coal burning in the EU in 2013. The largest share comes from Europe's "coal belt", namely Poland and Germany, causing roughly 5,800 and 4,300 annual fatalities, respectively.

The other significant sources of coal-related deaths are presented in the figure below.

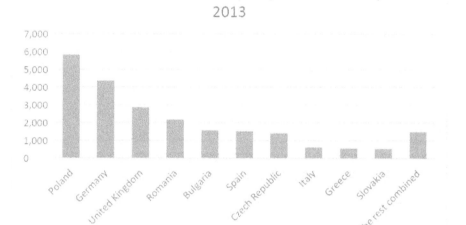

Figure 26: Deaths caused by coal combustion in Europe in 2013 by country. Source: Europe's Dark Cloud (2016).

Many of these deaths are exported to neighbouring countries, as air pollution does not respect national borders. The coal plants in France caused the death of 50 French citizens each year, plus 340 outside French borders. On the whole, French people still suffered a total of 1,380 annual coal related deaths, with 490 of these being imported from Germany. French coal, on the other hand, resulted in 90 premature fatalities in Germany.

The total annual health cost in the report is put at 32 to 62 billion euros per year. Given that the study ignores many of the other harms caused by air pollution, that value is probably a low estimate. This is an external cost that is not included in the price of coal burning. If it were, it would equal roughly 3–6 cents per kWh.[153]

Another report by OECD examines the global costs of outdoor pollution today and up to 2060[154]. The annual health care costs alone (excluding the value of lost work or lives) will increase from current $21 billion to $176 billion by 2060. Global fatalities due to outdoor pollution will increase from $3 million to $6–9 million in 2060.

And we worry about nuclear power? Why? Nuclear fears are often connected to radiation. What is it radiation, and exactly how does it affect us?

Radiation

There are lots of different sorts of radiation. Radiation is energy that can move around space and go through materials. Radio waves, visible light and infrared are examples of non-ionizing radiation. When we are interested in possible health effects of radiation, we talk about ionizing radiation. This kind of radiation has a lot of energy in it and can ionize atoms and molecules. When this happens, an electron is removed from the atom and its chemical reactivity is changed. This is how radioactivity causes biological effects such as cancer or genetic damage.

Ionizing radiation can be caused by unstable atoms, which are therefore called radioactive. These atoms have extra energy or mass, which makes them unstable. When an atom like this decays, extra energy is released as radiation. Ionizing radiation can be electromagnetic (gamma and x-rays, part of the ultraviolet spectrum), or subatomic particles (beta and alpha particles). These are discussed in more detail later.

Short history of radiation and its uses

The German Wilhelm Röntgen discovered roentgen rays (by accident) in November 1895. As he did not know what he had found, he gave them the temporary name X-rays. A couple weeks after, he took the first X-ray picture of his wife's, Anna Bertha's, hand. After seeing her skeleton, Anna exclaimed, "I have seen my death!" In 1901, Wilhelm got the Nobel prize in physics for his discovery.

Only a few months later, the French Henri Becquerel discovered (again, by accident) radioactivity. After many experiments, he concluded that uranium salts radiated their own radioactivity, different from the X-rays discovered by Röntgen. He named them Becquerel.

It was Marie Curie who got to name radioactivity, as she started researching Becquerel's radioactivity for her PhD. She discovered that some uranium and thorium salts had stronger radioactivity than uranium, so there was something else in them as well. Together with her husband Pierre Curie, she managed to separate radium, which radiates over a million times more powerfully than uranium. She also discovered radium's daughter product, which she named polonium, after her homeland Poland. Marie and Pierre Curie shared a Nobel in physics with Becquerel in 1903, and Marie also received a Nobel in chemistry for her discovery of polonium and radium in 1911.

Meanwhile, in 1899 and 1900, Ernest Rutherford discovered alpha and beta radiation in Montreal. The French physicist Paul Villard discovered gamma rays, which Rutherford later (in 1914) proved to be similar but shorter wavelength to röntgen rays. In 1900 the English Frederick Soddy discovered isotopes.

At first, the dangers of ionizing radiation were not known. Perhaps the most famous example of this is the "radium girls." They painted watches with self-illuminating radium paint. The brushes were thin, and the work demanded precision, so they licked the bristles to keep a sharp point. The result was multiple cases of jawbone cancers, malformations and deaths, as radium attaches itself to bone tissue similarly to calcium. Five of the sickened employees sued the company, and they eventually won. This was a precedent for the workers' right to sue their employers for dangerous or harmful working conditions.[155]

Radioactivity proved to be a big boon in the early 20th century health product market. Radium or radon was added to bottled water, which was then sold (and bought) as a health drink. Many such products were (luckily) frauds that didn't contain the promised radioactive elements in significant quantities. But Radithor, sold by one William Bailey, was the real thing. It was also a commercial success, as he sold over 400,000 bottles of it in five years. The product was very dangerous to one's health, but the sales tactic was genius. He promised doctors who recommended his product 17% of the sales revenue. A box of 24 bottles cost $30, which was a very significant sum back in the 1920s.

Eben Byers[156], a successful and wealthy man, had a problem. His broken arm wasn't healing properly, which hurt his golf game, and even his libido. His doctor prescribed Radithor for it, and when he started to feel much better right after he drank some, he became an evangelist and an avid consumer of the miracle product. He drank three bottles of Radithor per day. He made his family drink it, as well as his friends and even his horses. By 1931 he had consumed some 1,400 bottles of Radithor, and with it, a dose of radiation three times what is now considered to be a deadly dose.

In the beginning, he felt absolutely radiant (excuse the pun), but then his health quickly deteriorated. He lost weight and experienced pain everywhere, especially his head and teeth. A little later his teeth started to fall out, and eventually most of his jaw was removed. Holes started to form in his skull as his bones started to simply break down and disintegrate. In early 1932, a few months after the officials had banned the sale of Radithor, Byers died. Wall Street Journal apparently had this front-page headline at the time "The Radium Water Worked Fine until His Jaw Came Off."

Measuring radiation and its health impacts

The three basic units for radiation measurement are Becquerel (atom decays per second), Gray (the amount of radiation energy received per kilogram of tissue) and Sievert (the estimated equivalent health effect of a given dose, considering the absorbed dose per type of tissue, the multiplier of the organ that receives the radiation considering how vulnerable it is to radiation and the type of radiation received). It is not a scientifically exact value as it requires many assumptions to be made. From the public discussion and public health point of view, the last one, Sievert (or Rem in some parts of the world, one Sievert equals 100 Rems), is by far the most relevant one, as it directly tells us the potential health consequences. Becquerel, on the other hand, offers impressively large numbers, which is probably why it is widely used by click-bait journals and anti-nuclear campaigners. However, Becquerel tells us little about potential health effects.

The effects of small radioactive doses have been researched for decades, but there is no conclusive evidence on the quality or quantity of these effects. The primary reason for this lack of evidence is that the effects of small doses are so small. Any potential harmful effects are so hard to detect, that even the possibility of small radiation doses being beneficial to health has not been ruled out. In practice, for example, lifestyle choices such as diet are known to cause much bigger health impacts than even relatively large variations in individual doses of radiation received. It is however widely regarded that radiation can cause what are called stochastic health effects. This means that while the majority of recipients experience no effects, the statistical risk for some individuals to develop a cancer, for example, grows.

As long as evidence of the effects of small radiation doses is inconclusive, a linear no-threshold (LNT[157]) model is used in assessing the effects of radiation, in accord with the precautionary principle. The LNT model is based principally on the health statistics of people who have received large radiation doses. Another reason for its use is said to be Herman Muller's fruit fly radiation experiments, which extrapolated the high-dose results linearly down to zero.[158] The model assumes that the health impacts grow linearly with the growing radiation dose. It also assumes that there will always be some statistical health impacts, no matter how small the dose. For example, if a health study finds that 50 units of radiation causes a cancer at 50 percent likelihood, and that 100 units causes a cancer at 100 percent likelihood, the model assumes that one unit of radiation causes a cancer at one percent likelihood. This means that if one hundred people are each given one unit of radiation, then one of them will develop cancer because of it. The often heard comment "all radiation is harmful" is mainly based on the assumptions made with the LNT model.

Studies that involved the victims of Hiroshima and Nagasaki nuclear bombs tell us that this model works reasonably well with larger radiation doses. What remains unclear is if it also works with smaller doses of less than 100 millisieverts (mSv). Just for scale, the global average dose is 2.5 mSv per year. It is quite difficult to study the effects of small doses, since the effects themselves are by definition small, and confirming them through statistical noise is next to impossible. Studies require decades of follow-ups on populations, so they are expensive and lengthy. It is also likely that people have variable susceptibility to radiation effects. Various organs and body parts vary in how harmful radiation is to them. Kids and foetuses are more susceptible, and elder people less.

It is also possible that the LNT model does not account for all the health effects of radiation. One Swedish study found that small radiation doses might have had a larger impact than was thought on the neurological development of those who were foetuses when that dose was received. Even so those effects were very small. On the other hand, the model also ignores the potential health effects that small radiation doses might have in stimulating our body's defence mechanisms that can then also defend against other harms. Finally, the LNT model fails to explain why those regions that have a naturally high level of background radiation do not have a corresponding level of health effects.

The wider research suggests that the LNT model is roughly in the right direction. It might underestimate some effects, but it might also overestimate others. Because there is no definitive evidence one way or the other, most radiation safety regulators and research institutions go by the precautionary principle and recommend the use of LNT. This has also led to some overshoot.[159] The Sun's UV radiation is not strictly ionizing, but it has been shown to increase skin cancer. According to the LNT model, all sunlight (yes, even that reflected from the moon) is therefore seen as hazardous to one's health, because it always causes some risk for cancer.

There are arguably good reasons to believe that the mechanisms of the human body are more efficient in repairing small damages. One unit of radioactivity each year for ten years is likely less damaging than one dose of 10 units at one time. For this reason, a Dose-Dose Rate Effectiveness Factor (DDREF) is often used with LNT when small doses are in question.

LNT has also been widely criticized, from both sides. One group of researchers thinks it underestimates the harms of radiation, mainly criticizing the use or emphasis of DDREF, and another group thinks that small doses are practically harmless and says that LNT overestimates them. Another subgroup of the latter think that small doses are beneficial. This is called the hormesis theory. According to it, small doses of radiation activate the defence and repair mechanisms in our bodies. When activated, these mechanisms also fix damages from other sources, leading to a net-positive result for small radiation doses (even if there were also some harmful effects, there would be more positive ones). There is some evidence supporting hormesis, but there is also some evidence against it, so it has not acquired mainstream status. But it should be noted that it has also not been credibly falsified.

In 2005 both the Science Academy and the National Academy of Medicine of France gave a joint statement where they criticized the use of LNT and its assumption that all radiation is harmful as "not based on known biological concepts".[160]

Even if experiments do not always correspond with reality, some studies on human cells[161] have found mechanisms that could repair damages from small doses without noticeable harms. Some further studies are under way, so we might know more about very low-level radiation and its potential harm in the future. These studies place test animals deep underground, where there is minimal amount of background radiation. Somewhat ironically, the site chosen is a tunnel dug from the WIPP repository for nuclear waste in the United States, as the surrounding salt layer gives very little radiation. We will also know more about the radiation effects from nuclear accidents, as the massive follow-up studies from Fukushima get their results in during the next 20 years. So far, there has been little evidence of harmful effects from the radiation itself.

The current consensus seems to be that LNT does not underestimate the harms of radiation. It is also a straightforward model that is easy to use in estimating health effects of radiation in large groups of people. Most mainstream studies done on nuclear accidents, like those done after Fukushima, apply the LNT model. It is therefore safe to assume that the results from these studies do not underestimate the health effects.

The International Commission on Radiological Protection (ICRP[162]) as well as the United Nations Committee on the Effects of Atomic Radiation (UNSCEAR[163]) advise not to use LNT in estimating effects from small doses or for epidemiological studies. The assumption that one unit of radiation divided to hundred persons would cause one cancer is too simplifying and misleading with low radiation doses. This advice is of course ignored in studies done by anti-nuclear organizations and people.

While it is true in principle, that it may be possible that all radiation is harmful, it is not by any means certain. The million dollar follow-up question is "how harmful?" and "what are the doses and dose rates we should worry about?" And, in the context of whether we should use nuclear energy to mitigate climate change more effectively, "how much does the use of nuclear energy increase our dose?" Even with nuclear accidents, this increase in the risk is practically always tiny (more on this later). What the radiation debate seems to miss is the scale and comparison. There is no practical difference in everyday life if some of the many risks we face turn from infinitely small to slightly less infinitely small.

 We get our daily radiation dose from both natural background radiation and from man-made sources. The average annual dose is 2.5 millisieverts (mSv), but depending on where one lives, this can be tens of times larger as well. For example, people living in Pispala, a popular neighbourhood in southern Finland, get an average annual dose of 35 mSv[164], mainly from indoor radon (we will use this dose in the book, along with mSv, for comparison of different radiation doses). Here are a few samples of radiation doses both in Pispala and mSv:

- A person living in Ramsar, Iran can get an annual dose of three to four Pispalas, or 90-130 mSv, mostly from radon.
- In the popular tourist resort Guarapar, Brazil, the background radiation levels are among the highest on the planet. One can get up to five Pispalas or 175 mSv per year by living there.[165]
- Prypjat was a town near Chernobyl that was evacuated after the nuclear accident in 1986 (more on that later). In 1992 measurements found radiation levels of roughly 0.7 Pispalas, or 25 mSv per year, although there were some pockets that had much higher levels as well. During the accident, the evacuees received doses of roughly 1 Pispala (30 mSv). The liquidators who cleaned up after the accident received average doses of 3.5 Pispalas (120 mSv).[166]
- Finland got a lot of Chernobyl's radioactive fallout. The lifelong additional dose from that fallout to each Finn is roughly 2 mSv (a few weeks in Pispala). This radiation has not caused any additional cancers according to research. Aircraft crews get a similar annual dose from cosmic rays.[167]
- Around 170 of the frontline emergency workers at the Fukushima accident got a dose that could slightly increase their chances of developing cancer later in life. The limit for this is a dose of three Pispalas, or 100 mSv[168].

- A medical PET+CT scan gives one a dose of 0.6-0.8 Pispalas, 20-25 mSv.
- Hiroshima bomb survivors who were in the area got a dose of six Pispalas, around 200 mSv.
- A nuclear power plant worker is allowed a maximum dose of 1.5 Pispalas or 50 mSv during one year and no more than 100 mSv in a period of consecutive five years.

Dangers of Radiation

There are several factors that affect the level of harm caused by exposure to radiation. When these are added up, we get the total dose and how harmful that potentially is. In addition to the quantity of the substance, at least the following factors should be noted:
- Total dose received.
- Duration of exposure.
- Dose rate (the speed at which radiation was received).
- Half-life (activity).
- Type of radiation (alpha, beta or gamma).
- If ingested, what is the chemical reactivity of the radioactive material in the body?

With other factors staying the same, materials that have long half-lives give out less radiation than those with short half-lives. This means roughly that the more dangerous a radioactive material is, the sooner it is gone. Many isotopes go from one to another in a long chain of decays until they become stable atoms such as lead or iron. Some isotopes in this chain are more radioactive than others, so the decrease in radioactivity is not linear. This explains the phenomenon we see with uranium ore, which has large concentrations of radon and radium (uranium's decay products) which are more radioactive than pure uranium.

Alpha radiation is heavy particle radiation and does not travel for long distances. A few centimetres of air will stop alpha particles, as will a sheet of paper. Alpha particles do not usually penetrate skin, and regular clothing is adequate protection. Most harm is done if alpha particles end up inside our bodies, by swallowing or breathing. Among others, uranium, radium, radon and thorium give off alpha radiation.

Beta radiation is light particle radiation (electrons) that travels for a few meters through air. Beta particles can partly penetrate skin, and larger doses will harm the skin. Clothing offers some protection from beta radiation. Beta is also is more harmful when it gets inside our bodies. Some sources of beta radiation are strontium-90, carbon-14, sulphur-35, cesium-137 and iodine-131.

Gamma radiation and X-rays are highly penetrating electromagnetic radiation. They can travel longer distances and can penetrate human tissue for many centimetres. Basic clothing offers no protection. To stop this kind of radiation, dense materials such as water or lead are required. Gamma radiation is easy to detect with a radiation detector. Gamma is often released alongside alpha or beta radiation. Some sources of gamma radiation include iodine-131, cesium-137, cobalt-60 and radium-226.[169]

Radiation also comes in different intensities, which means that the energy content of radiation varies. This has a large effect on the potential for harm that radiation causes. For comparison, one type of fuel will burn much hotter than another (the energy content of the heat varies), and that has a big effect on how dangerous a flame is.

External radioactive sources rarely pose any relevant harm or danger. The greater risk is radioactive materials that get inside our bodies, although even those are a small risk in relation to many other everyday things. Therefore, it is important to understand how various substances react in and with our bodies to understand the harm from radiation. Let's consider radioactive Xenon-133. As a noble gas, it does not react chemically with anything in our bodies, and quickly passes through. Xenon-133 is quite radioactive, but the harm it causes to humans is next to zero. And with a half-life of just 5 days it also disappears quite quickly. Radium, strontium and cesium on the other hand easily end up in our bones, as they resemble calcium, which is the building block of our bones. They can stay in our bones for our lifetimes, slowly decaying and giving off radioactivity to the neighbouring tissue. The biggest worry after nuclear accidents is iodine-131, which finds its way to our thyroid gland and can deliver a significant radioactive dose to the gland, which might then develop a cancer. Iodine-131 has a half-life of only eight days. While it can quickly give humans a significant dose, we can prevent that dose by saturating our thyroid glands with normal iodine (eating iodine pills), which prevents the radioactive iodine from accumulating.

The harm done by radiation is also affected by the time frame in which the radiation was received. A dose of one Sievert (1,000 mSv or 30 Pispalas) received in a short period of time can cause radiation sickness but is not lethal. Five Sieverts is lethal for around half of the population in a few weeks. Eight Sieverts is considered lethal despite being given medical attention. But if similar doses are received during a longer period of time, there are no acute effects such as radiation sickness. Our body constantly repairs any minor damage caused by radiation. If this were not the case, many people who have received radiation treatment for cancer would actually have died because of the radiation. A record in radiation dose received is probably held by Albert Stevens, who was injected with plutonium (in an experiment) in 1945, and subsequently got a dose estimated at 64 Sieverts during the next 20 years.[170] Despite receiving a dose eight times what is considered lethal, Stevens died of unrelated heart condition at the age of 79. This means that the LNT model (linear no-threshold) must be flawed, as according to it, Stevens should have died roughly eight times over because of radiation.

Do nuclear power plants increase surrounding radioactivity?

Overall, the nuclear industry is a rounding error in our radiation dose. The graph below[171] shows the shares of ionizing radiation we get from different sources on average. Less than 0.001 % of the average global radioactive dose of 2.5 mSv comes from the civilian nuclear fuel cycle. That includes high level nuclear waste, mining and everything else imaginable. Add the Chernobyl (0.01% of average radiation dose) accident, and it's still a rounding error.

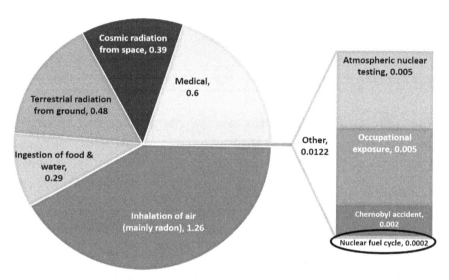

GLOBAL AVERAGE RADIATION SOURCES, MILLISIEVERTS / YEAR

Figure 27: The sources of radiation for people on average. Source: UNSCEAR 2008

The nuclear industry dose corresponds to a few minutes visit to Pispala. In a study named "How much is clean air worth[172]" the authors look at the dose per person that would result if the nuclear technology of France of the 1990s were used to provide electricity at a rate equal to the entire electricity production of the world in 2010 (20,000 TWh/yr) for the next 100 years. Such a scenario would increase the dose rate by only about 0.15 % beyond the background level of 2.5 mSv/yr.

Given these ridiculously small amounts of radiation that nuclear reactors release, and how much attention is given to this radiation in the public, it is educational to make a comparison. Coal plants, with coal ash and other pollution, can actually release a hundred times more radiation to the surroundings compared with a similar sized nuclear power plant.[173] This is due to the small amounts of uranium and thorium and their decay products present in all coal deposits. Even if most of them are caught in filters, some get released into the air people breathe. If similar ash came from a nuclear power plant, it would often be classified as low-level radioactive waste. It goes without saying that if coal plants would need to follow similar rules for radiation releases than nuclear plants do, they would need to shut down immediately. This also goes for biomass burning, although biomass has smaller concentrations of uranium and thorium in it than coal.

Beneficial uses of radiation

Radiation has many beneficial uses. Most medical imaging technologies are based on radiation. Radioactive substances are so easy to detect that minuscule amounts can be injected to patients' bodies as markers. Radiation therapy is used to treat many cancers. It involves precisely the same kind of radiation as is all other ionizing radiation (electromagnetic x-rays and gamma rays as well as particle radiation). The radioactive isotopes that are used in medical treatment usually come from nuclear reactors, often from research reactors built just for this purpose, but these isotopes can also be found and separated from spent nuclear fuel. When cancer is treated with radiation therapy, a high radiation dose is delivered to the tumour so that it will destroy cancerous cells and/or stop them from dividing. Radiation therapy given from outside the body is done from multiple angles and with time between sessions to give maximum dose at the tumour to destroy it, but a minimal dose to surrounding tissue (for example the tissue between the skin and the tumour inside). Another treatment is to plant a source of radioactivity in or beside the tumour.

The total doses received in radiation therapy can be as high as tens of Sieverts (thousands of Pispalas), and this poses risks of its own. These risks are weighed against the option of not doing the radiation therapy at all.

Radiation is also used in industry, such as detecting microscopic cracks in pipes and joints and performing quality control on welding seams. Radioactive isotopes are also present in fire detectors, and radiation can be used to kill pathogens in foods, which enhances food safety and lengthens shelf life. It should be noted that the food being sterilized this way does not become radioactive itself. Radiation is also used in plant breeding to produce beneficial mutations (incidentally, it is one of the methods allowed in "ecological" agriculture).

Radiation is a controversial, even scary, subject for many. It cannot be seen, heard, smelled, tasted or even felt. Yet it is very easy to detect with relatively simple equipment. Depending on the dose and dose rate, the effects of radiation can be almost instantaneous or manifest only decades after exposure, if at all. There are a lot of different types of radiation, and some types are more harmful in some conditions, while other types are harmful in other conditions.

But it is safe to say that radiation is nowhere nearly as dangerous as is commonly thought. While radiation can have harmful effects, these effects need to be put into context. Burning of solid fuels, and the indoor and outdoor pollution from it, causes millions of premature fatalities and sickness each year. Around half of our radiation dose is man-made, mostly from medical diagnosis and treatments which have helped save millions of lives. Only a miniscule part of our dose is due to the use of civilian nuclear power, waste and accidents included. As nuclear power plants often replace other more harmful energy sources, they also help save lives indirectly.

Nuclear accidents are the largest cause of premature deaths from nuclear power, but even there the situation is not as straightforward as it seems. Research shows that our fear of radiation, along with the stress and other factors, is much more dangerous than the radiation released from an accident itself. This fear, stress and uncertainty, while being very real for the people experiencing it, is not an inherent quality of radiation as such. It is a result of poor level of knowledge combined with common fearmongering and stigmatizing behaviour in societies, supported by bad policies and myopic regulation that only aims to minimize our radiation doses at all costs[174]. All too often that cost is lost human lives.

Nuclear Waste

Nuclear waste is another controversial topic, often one of the primary reasons for people to be against nuclear power. The mere phrase "nuclear waste" summons an image of barrels leaking radioactive, glowing green goo in some dark cave, just waiting for the unsuspecting future generations. This image has been planted for most of us from the popular TV series The Simpsons. But what is nuclear waste really? To get the short answer, you can look up the graph a couple pages ago that shows the sources of our radiation doses. Nuclear fuel cycle, which includes the waste as well, represents less than 0.001 % of our overall dose on average.

Most of the waste is what is called low-level radioactive waste (LLW). It includes materials and supplies that have been exposed to radiation in various situations in the nuclear fuel cycle, industry and hospitals. There is quite a lot of this waste, but it is usually not dangerous, at least not due to radioactivity. Another part of the waste is called intermediate-level waste (ILW). It often needs some radiation shielding, but no cooling, and it needs to be disposed of with due care. It includes items like water filters from nuclear plants or materials from decommissioned nuclear plants.

The final category is high-level waste (HLW), mainly spent fuel from nuclear reactors. Spent fuel from a light water reactor, depending a bit on design and use, consists of:

- ~95.6 percent uranium, mostly uranium-238
- ~0.9 percent of plutonium (reactor-grade, not weapons-grade)
- ~0.5 percent of radioactive nuclides[175]
- around 2.9 percent of non-radioactive fission products

There are basically three types of radioactive materials in spent fuel:

1. Slowly decaying material. These represent well over 95 percent of the material and include uranium and plutonium. These isotopes have half-lives in the thousands, even millions of years. They are not very radioactive (because they decay slowly), but they are the main source for the "nuclear waste is highly dangerous for hundreds of thousands of years" myth (more on this later).

2. Quickly decaying materials. These isotopes often have half-lives of some hours or a few days. They are often dangerous, but they also disappear quickly. One example is iodine-131, which has a half-life of 8 days. As a rule of thumb, after 10 half-lives, a substance has disappeared for practical purposes.

3. Between the isotopes mentioned above are the most problematic ones. These isotopes have half-lives of several decades. This means that they are rather highly radioactive, but it still takes several hundred years for them to disappear. These include strontium-90 and cesium-137, which both have half-lives around 30 years.

The waste from breeder reactors is very different from the waste produced in light water reactors. Breeder reactors can "burn" (transmute) most of the long-lasting isotopes and radioactive nuclides, and their waste has much higher concentrations of strontium-90 and cesium-137. Indeed, breeders can use spent fuel from light water reactors as their fuel, utilizing the uranium-238, plutonium and some of the radioactive nuclides.

The volume of high-level waste needing long-term storage can be greatly reduced by reprocessing the fuel and separating the various isotopes. Uranium-238 is not dangerous (slightly radioactive and mildly toxic, comparable to many other heavy metals), and yet over 95 percent of spent fuel is U238. Separating the isotopes can also allow us to collect isotopes that can be used in medicine and industry.

Spent fuel can also be reprocessed and recycled to be used again. This is being done in France, Japan and Russia. While this is often economically challenging compared to just using a once-through fuel cycle, it does reduce the amount of long-term waste and uranium mining needed.

Long-term waste storage

Around 40 kilometres (26 miles) east from the small town of Carlsbad in the middle of a desert in New Mexico, there is a nondescript reddish-grey building resembling a warehouse and surrounded by a fence and various other buildings. Inside this building is a mine shaft that goes down 660 meters below ground level, into a 250 million years old and 660 metres (2,000 feet) thick salt bed. In that salt bed, WIPP, or Waste Isolation Pilot Plant, has been used since 1999 to store transuranic (TRU) waste from the U.S. nuclear weapons program.

Even if the facility has had its problems, the main one seems to be pretty much solved: given the age of 250 million years, the salt bed is likely to stay put for long enough to have the unstoppable radioactive decay run its course and render the waste practically harmless.

Solutions of various kinds are being planned in many of the countries that utilize nuclear power. The first one to start storing waste (in mid 2020s) from civilian reactors is likely Onkalo, situated in Finland and built by Posiva. Another project a few years behind the Finnish one is in Sweden, run by SKB.

The nuclear industry is one of the few industries that collects, manages and stores its waste products. In relation to our many other industries and endeavours, the waste "problem" of the nuclear industry seems a rather insignificant one, and already quite well resolved. Even without an operating long-term storage, the waste has caused no harm to the public or the environment and is unlikely to do so. A geological underground repository will be passively safe and won't require any active monitoring, which will make it more cost-effective than the current intermediate solutions to storing the waste.

Usually, humanity's solution to pollution has been dilution, spreading it into the atmosphere and environment. Coal power plants and factories have often just built higher smokestacks to spread their pollution more widely and in lower concentrations if someone has complained. Exhaust pipes from cars push their pollution into the air, to spread and dilute. In the countryside this is often not a big problem, but cities and their inhabitants suffer from this waste stream tremendously.

While the nuclear industry is held accountable to take care of their waste, this has been made almost impossible in many countries with unrealistic demands and/or political decisions (or, often "non-decisions") and legislation. If similar demands were applied to any other human activity, our society would stop and collapse in a few days. For example, in Sweden, the final repository is allowed to increase people's annual radiation dose by roughly similar amount one gets by sleeping next to another person for a year. Even this limit is far from reached according to the studies made on the repository.[176]

Posiva has been doing years of research on Onkalo, including different leakage scenarios and the worst effects they could have for humans in the future. Amongst the 40 scenarios, the worst case for people 10,000 years in the future includes the following assumptions[177]:

1. A waste storage canister would corrode through in 1,000 years, 100 times faster than assumed), AND
2. The bentonite shielding around the canister would disappear suddenly, AND
3. Groundwater would move upwards, AND
4. A city would be built on top of the repository, AND
5. A person would live her whole life on the most contaminated square meter of land, AND
6. She would eat only food grown on that most contaminated square meter of land, AND
7. She would only drink the most contaminated water.

The radioactive contamination would peak at roughly the year 12,000 AD. The person fulfilling all the criteria above would receive an annual extra dose of 0.00018 mSv, corresponding to staying a few minutes in Pispala or eating a few bananas.[178] The safety case of Onkalo is roughly a million times on the safe side from causing any significant harm, ever, even locally.

The whole framing of the nuclear waste discussion is completely distorted, and this distortion is as much the fault of the nuclear industry as anyone else. It basically states that even the extremely remote possibility of any harm caused, ever, from nuclear waste is intolerable and that any other risk to our planet is preferable to that, no matter how severe and how likely that risk.

Why is it the nuclear industry's doing? For example, it is useless to say that spent nuclear fuel is actually not that dangerous after a while (which is true), if the industry then packs the waste in several layers of different protective materials, digs a hole that is half-a-kilometre deep for the waste and fills it with concrete afterwards. Who in their right mind would believe that the waste is anything but the most dangerous and deadly stuff on the planet? Another aspect is the nuclear regulators and their mandate. Nuclear regulators regulate only the nuclear industry, not the energy industry in general nor the overall public safety – even if this might be what many of us assume. The outcome of this is that something seen as "not safe enough" by our regulators can still be a thousand times better for the public health than the next alternative, but the regulator's mandate, know-how and resources do not include this analysis and conclusion. Their job description is only to be interested in the nuclear part of the public safety, not the overall public safety.

We need to move away from this black and white thinking, where any possibility for a leak of any size is seen as unacceptable, to a discussion where different risks and gains are weighed pragmatically and calmly. Saying that the risks from nuclear waste are unacceptable while accepting other risks that are many orders of magnitude greater and more likely to materialize is intellectually dishonest. It will lead us to wrong conclusions on what are the best ways to fight climate change, biodiversity loss and energy poverty – just to mention a few of the biggest problems we currently face.

Nuclear Power Plant Accidents

It is next to impossible to discuss nuclear power without also discussing nuclear accidents. While there is a risk for such accidents as long as plants are built and operated, this risk is rarely compared with the risks of other forms of energy production. We often discuss how likely or unlikely future nuclear accidents are, but rarely discuss how dangerous or destructive those accidents actually are, especially compared to other energy sources. The common image people have in their mind of a nuclear accident is a catastrophe of biblical proportions: massive destruction, thousands of dead, and eternally radioactive wastelands and ghost towns. Media reporting supports this view, often simply because catastrophe sells, nuclear sells and nuclear catastrophes sell unlike anything else. Media outlets have little incentive to control the spreading fear by telling facts, but every incentive to keep fearmongering.

There will always be a non-zero risk of some type of accident with nuclear power. What matters is the actual impacts of accidents that already occurred, and what we may have learned from them. According to evidence (the accidents that should not have happened but still did), surprises can pile up in surprising ways, leading to even more surprising outcomes. It should be noted that each nuclear accident so far has led to significant improvements in safety through learning. The essential point is that the actual effects of the accidents have been relatively small. As discussed earlier, nuclear power is one of our safest ways to produce energy, even with accidents included. When this is weighed against the fact that giving up nuclear power will mean that climate catastrophe will get worse, it is quite clear that not using nuclear power in our climate fight is a bad idea from a risk perspective.

INES scale of nuclear accidents

Nuclear accidents are classified with the INES-scale (International Nuclear Event Scale) with numbers between 0 to 7.

Incidents INES 0–3

- INES 0 – Deviation
- INES 1 – Anomaly
- INES 2 – Incident
- INES 3 – Serious incident

Accidents INES 4–7

- INES 4 – Accident with local consequences
- INES 5 – Accident with wider consequences
- INES 6 – Serious accident
- INES 7 – Major accident

We use different models, risk analysis and calculations to estimate the likelihood of a nuclear accident for any given reactor type. These analyses deserve a healthy dose of scepticism, as according to them, none of the accidents that we have experienced should have happened. On the other hand, none of the accidents that have happened have been those horrible catastrophes we imagined. But how did the three most famous civilian nuclear accidents happen, and with what consequences?

Three Mile Island (INES 5)

Three Mile Island (TMI) ranks as the third most famous and serious civilian nuclear power plant accident. It happened 28th March in Harrisburg, Pennsylvania. Nobody died, and no significant amounts of harmful radioactivity were released into the surrounding areas. Reactor number two had a partial meltdown, and the cost of clean-up was around one billion US dollars. Public communication about the accident was a horrible failure. This caused panic, mistrust and the strengthening of the nascent anti-nuclear movement. Three Mile Island is commonly seen as one of the key reasons for the almost total shutdown of building new reactors anywhere in the western countries during the next 30 years.

The TMI pressurized reactors designed by Babcock & Wilcox had their quirks. The bigger problems were probably the lack of proper training and expertise of many nuclear operators in the fast-growing industry. People who had operated far smaller nuclear reactors in Navy submarines for a couple of years found well-paying jobs in the civilian nuclear industry. Those submarine reactors were sized in the ballpark of 12 MW, which made them much easier to handle than the civilian reactors that were dozens of times larger. For example, a full day after shutdown, a 1.2 gigawatt PWR still produces around 15 MW of residual heat.

The chain of events that led to the partial meltdown started around eleven hours before the accident.[179] Plant operators were trying to clean up some sophisticated water filters of the secondary water loop. The blockage was stuck, so instead of using pressurized air, the operators forced some water through to remove the resin. A small amount of the pressurized water got past a valve and ended up in the wrong place (instrument airline). Later this water caused the feedwater pumps to turn off, cutting off feedwater to the steam generators. This in turn caused increases in pressure and temperature in the reactor cooling system, which eventually led to an automatic emergency shutdown (SCRAM[180]). As the turbines were offline, decay heat started gathering in the primary water loop.

Three auxiliary pumps were automatically activated, but they offered little help, since some valves were closed due to maintenance. This effectively cut off all primary and auxiliary cooling from the core. This closure of the valves was a violation of Nuclear Regulatory Commission (NRC) rules and was later found to be one of the key reasons for the partial meltdown.

As pressure in the primary system kept increasing, it automatically opened the pressure release valve. Normally this valve closes after pressure goes down, but due to a mechanical failure, it remained open. In addition to pressure, cooling fluid also started leaving the system. This mechanical failure of the valve was found to be one of the key factors that led to the accident. The stuck valve went unnoticed by the operators, mainly due to a badly designed status indicator light.[181] The operator read the indicator as the valve being closed (as it should be), while in reality it was stuck open. This caused a lot of confusion amongst the operators, since other indicators were acting strange considering that the valve was supposed to be closed. Only the next work shift, seeing the situation with fresh eyes, realized what was happening. By then, it was much too late: 120,000 litres of coolant fluid had leaked from the cooling system, and the damage had been done.

The accident revealed severe shortcomings in communications between officials and the public. Responsibilities were found to be unclear. The public received a constant barrage of conflicting information, which increased panic and caused unnecessary evacuations.

The accident was a result of many unlikely technical problems occurring at the same time. Combined with somewhat lacking operator skills, the result was a partial core meltdown. Nobody got hurt and no significant radioactivity was released to the surroundings. What was released was mainly harmless Xenon-gas, although a small amount of radioactive iodine was also released.

Chernobyl (INES 7)

By far the most serious nuclear power plant accident happened on 26th of April, 1986, in Chernobyl nuclear power station, in what is currently Ukraine. The hydrogen/steam explosion in the core and the fire that followed spread large amounts of radioactive matter to the immediate surroundings as well as farther away. Some emergency workers received radiation doses so high that they died due to acute radiation poisoning and its later complications during the next few years. The raging fire in the core lifted the lighter radioactive particles high into the air and during the following days, winds blew them across Europe, where they fell with rainfall.

The fallout was so severe in the nearby areas that people had to be evacuated. Officials should have distributed iodine pills to the public and advised them not to eat vegetables or drink milk produced in the area, since they were contaminated with iodine-131. But Soviet officials dropped the ball. Without their paranoid secrecy on all things nuclear, the health effects would have been much lower.

As it is with all things, nuclear reactors can be designed well, or less well. They can also be designed horribly. This category is reserved for the RBMK, which was the type of reactor in Chernobyl. It was designed in the 1950s, and all the Soviet scientists had to work with were the small "graphite piles" that were used to produce plutonium for the weapons program. The main goals for the RBMK were low costs and flexible operation. Low cost was achieved by making the reactor very large and allowing it to use uranium fuel that did not have to be enriched to similar levels as the fuel for western reactors. Flexible operation meant that the reactor could be refuelled without shutting it down. This had two goals: the primary goal was to minimize interruptions to power production. The secondary goal was to make it easier to use the reactor for weapons grade plutonium production, should the need arise.

These parameters led to using graphite as the moderator for the nuclear reaction instead of heavy water, which was four times as expensive. The reactor ended up being very large, so it would have been very expensive to build a containment building around it. Some have estimated it would have doubled the cost of the reactor. So containment was left out. Costs were also cut by leaving additional safety systems to a minimum. The prevailing Soviet doctrine concluded that containment buildings and safety systems were unnecessary, since in principle the RBMK was completely safe, provided it was operated exactly according to the instruction manual.

However, even that manual omitted some important weaknesses of the RBMK, which were never told to the operators. The design choices combined with the use of low-enriched uranium fuel meant that the reactor could become unstable in certain conditions. Most reactors are designed in a way that if the coolant (often water) is removed, the reactor shuts down. With RBMK, the opposite happens. If the cooling water turns to steam and the cooling system dries up even partially, the chain reaction in the core accelerates. If reaction controls do not operate fast enough or if they are turned off, this will lead to even more water turning to steam, accelerating the chain reaction further, which will eventually lead to a meltdown. This was especially likely when the reactor was operating at lower power, during which the coolant pressure and boiling point were lower.

Finally, the control rods of the reactor were badly designed. The tip of the rod was made of graphite, which accelerates the reaction. When inserting a completely removed rod into the reactor, the fission reaction accelerates for about five seconds before starting to slow down. This was not a big problem when a single rod was inserted. But inserting all 211 control rods at the same time to the reactor operating at full power had catastrophic effects. To top it all off, the mechanism of inserting the control rods was slow even by 1980s standards. Western designs of similar age inserted control rods in three seconds, while the same operation took RBMK some 20 seconds.

The people at the Kurchatov Institute who designed the reactor were not stupid, and they were well aware of the inherent problems in their design. The Soviet officials did not want to hear of any problems, however. Everything nuclear was by definition top secret in the Soviet Union, and the operating principles of the RBMK were no exception. Reactor operators were forbidden to discuss any possible problems with each other. So when the operators at the Ignalina nuclear power plant discovered the problem with the control rods in 1983, they told no one about it. Nobody imagined that someone would manually turn off all the safety features and then run the reactor at dangerously low power.

Chernobyl – What happened?

A safety experiment was scheduled for reactor 4 in the Chernobyl nuclear power station in April 1986. The goal of the experiment was to ensure that the reactor could be cooled if there was a power loss during a shutdown. Previous experiments had failed, and the politically appointed management, who had only superficial knowledge of nuclear power, were hard-pressed to make certain that this time the experiment would succeed. Partly due to the embarrassing former failures, and partly due to the low perceived risk, Soviet nuclear safety officials were not notified of the experiment.

The plan was to run the reactor at a low power level of 700 MW (thermal), and then cut the flow of steam to the generator. The generator, running at full tilt, would keep on spinning, and its behaviour would be monitored and measured. This would help ensure that the power it generated would be enough to keep the coolant pumps running long enough for the diesel-powered backup generators to start up.

It was planned that the reactor would be powered down slowly to the desired level during the early morning hours of 25th April. From there, the dayshift, who had been familiarized with the experiment, would be able to take over and start the experiment. As the day shift came in, another power station got dropped from the grid, and the grid operator in the area asked Chernobyl operators to postpone the experiment. This was agreed on, but the preparations were kept underway, and even some of the safety features were turned offline in advance. The grid operator gave permission only late that night, at 23:04, to continue with the powering down. The day shift was long gone, and even the evening shift was starting to leave. The night shift that had just arrived got orders to go ahead with the experiment as soon as possible. The reactor power level was promptly lowered. Here one of the operators made a mistake: he pushed the control rods in too deep, and the reactor was practically shut down.

The experiment could not be carried out with a reactor that was shut down, and the operator managing the experiment demanded swift action. The automatic system that moved the control rods in the core was turned off (an essential safety feature in the RBMK). Most of the rods were then pulled out from the core manually. The chain reaction kicked in, and in a few minutes the power level increased to 160-200 megawatts thermal. This was not enough for the experiment, and the automatic warnings were bypassed, more rods were pulled out and preparations for the experiment were continued. Numerous warnings came on, but the operators did not realise that the momentary shut down and other preparations had caused the reactor to go unstable and unsafe for the experiment, which could only be remedied by letting the reactor run for a while on a higher power level.

The experiment was then started by cutting the steam flow to the generators. The generator slowed down and the power to the pumps responsible for the pressure and circulation of coolant water went down. As the pressure went down, the boiling point of the circulating water lowered. As the water started to boil and turn to steam, the chain reaction in the RBMK accelerated – which is the opposite of what happens in most other reactors. Apparently, nobody had told the operators of this critical "feature" of the RBMK.

As the chain reaction accelerated, the automatic safety system started lowering control rods into the reactor to keep the power more stable. But only 12 rods had been left to be controlled by the automatic system, while the other 199 rods were on manual control and drawn completely out of the reactor. 36 seconds after the experiment was started, the 12 rods were fully inserted, but the power level kept increasing. At this point, someone decided to initiate emergency shut-down.

Emergency shutdown started pushing all the remaining rods into the reactor at once. Due to the bad design of the control rods we mentioned earlier, this accelerated the nuclear reaction for a few seconds before it would slow down, especially with many rods being pushed in at the same time. Although this "feature" had been noted three years earlier in the Ignalina power plant, nobody had shared the information with Chernobyl operators. The reaction accelerated so fast that at least part of the rods overheated and got stuck before the part of the rod that would slow down the reaction got inserted into the reactor.

During the next few seconds, the chain reaction went hypercritical and totally out of control. The power level indicators showed 33,000 megawatts, while the reactor's designed operational power was 3,200 megawatts. It is impossible to reconstruct what happened next, but the best guess is that the tremendous heat energy produced caused a massive steam explosion, which popped the 2,000-ton top of the reactor vessel through the roof of the reactor building. This explosion wrecked the rest of the cooling systems in place, and the RBMK pulled one last trick from its sleeve: With all cooling gone, nothing held back the chain reaction. Another, even more massive explosion destroyed the reactor core and sent the highly radioactive fuel and graphite pieces around the compound. As air was drawn into the torn reactor core, the red-hot graphite started burning. Despite heroic and quite literally self-sacrificing actions of the emergency workers, the graphite burned for two weeks, sending most of the remaining radioactive materials high into the atmosphere and surroundings.

The following morning, Soviet leaders woke up, knowing nothing of what had happened and at what scale. It was not unusual in the Soviet Union that environmental destruction or accidents went unreported, and the nuclear program was especially sensitive. The scale of what occurred started unwinding when Finnish border control officials noticed abnormally high radioactivity levels. This information was forwarded to the prime minister Kalevi Sorsa, who decided not to publicize the matter, as it would probably only antagonize Soviet Union.

The following morning, 27th of April, the radiation alarms in the Swedish Forsmark nuclear power station went off. The source was found to be the dirt from one employee's boots, which carried radioactive fallout from Chernobyl brought to ground by rain. In cooperation with Finland, the Swedes located the likely source to be a nuclear power plant accident in western Soviet Union. The fallout spread all over Europe, and the cesium-137 can still be measured in many places. As denial finally became impossible, Soviet officials had to admit to the world that the accident had happened.

Pripyat, a town near the Chernobyl nuclear power station, was evacuated in the afternoon of 27th April. Kiev, which was 90 kilometres (55 miles) away from Chernobyl, went on preparing their parade for the 1st of May. Nobody was giving the public iodine tablets, even though it was clear that the destroyed reactor had leaked large amounts of iodine-131. Iodine-131 is a radioactive isotope that is often the most dangerous radiological consequence of nuclear accidents, but also easily prevented from causing harm by giving the population iodine tablets. It also disappears in a few weeks. A short notification about the accident was finally read in the evening news of 28th April, but there still was no mention about any dietary restrictions.

It is common to see the Chernobyl accident referred to as a typical example of how dangerous nuclear reactors can be. This has little to do with facts and a lot to do with perceptions. This type of reactor, with the unique properties that led to the accident, has not been built in decades, and was only built in the Soviet Union. While there are still a few such reactors operating, they have all been retrofitted with improved safety measures. One rather surprising and even scary fact remains less discussed: Chernobyl reactors 1, 2 and 3 remained in operation even after the accident. Reactor 3 was the last to shut down, in December 2000. It would be wise to replace the remaining operating RBMK's with safer designs as soon as possible.

Recently, many people have seen or heard of the HBO mini-series about the Chernobyl accident. While highly entertaining, it is also fictitious in some important ways. Jaakko Leppänen, a research professor of nuclear technology at VTT Technical Research Centre of Finland Ltd, wrote a simultaneous blog as the original episodes were aired, fact-checking the events as they unfolded in the mini-series. The blog can be read here: https://fissioreaktori.wordpress.com/hbos-mini-series-chernobyl/.

Health impacts of Chernobyl

Chernobyl has claimed a few dozen lives, according to the World Health Organization and United Nations Scientific Committee on the Effects of Atomic Radiation (UNSCEAR). According to UNSCEAR's latest, most comprehensive report[182] to date on Chernobyl:

- 134 plant staff and emergency workers suffered acute radiation syndrome (ARS) from high doses of radiation.
- In the first few months after the accident 28 of them died.
- Although another 19 ARS survivors had died by 2006, those deaths had different causes not usually associated with radiation exposure.
- Further, some 6,000 thyroid cancer cases were reported in the three most affected countries of Belarus, Ukraine and four most affected regions in the Russian Federation. 15 of them had proven fatal, although very likely not all of them were caused by the Chernobyl fallout.

At most, there are 62 confirmed fatalities from the worst nuclear accident in our history. Statistically, there might be some 4,000 extra fatalities all in all due to the low doses of radiation spread around, according to some LNT models. However, these models have what the UNSCEAR calls unacceptable uncertainties at these low doses and has recommended that they are not used for epidemiological purposes[183],[184].

The cleaning up afterward was done by roughly 600,000 "liquidators", of whom only a small number received significant amounts of radiation. Iodine-131 was the largest health hazard for those living in the surrounding area. As we know, iodine-131 has a short half-life so it was essentially gone in two months. The risk on the longer time frame is from fission products such as cesium-137 which has a half-life of 30 years and caesium-134 with a half-life of two years.

Luckily, these health risks are proving to be less serious than many have thought. Around 6,000 thyroid cancers have been diagnosed (up to 2005) in the group most at risk (mainly children living in nearby areas), with 15 fatalities. Even as most thyroid cancers were treated successfully, almost all cancers could have been avoided with prompt actions by the government to distribute iodine pills.

Very small doses were delivered to a larger population of around 5 million; the LNT model suggests 5,000 could die prematurely. Even smaller lifetime doses, in the neighbourhood of 1 mSv or less (a week or so in Pispala), are estimated to have been delivered to hundreds of millions of people living in Europe and the rest of the world. The Union of Concerned Scientists has done their own calculations and point out that (according to LNT model) the final death toll would be somewhat higher (at 27,000 total fatalities) than that mentioned above, due to these very small doses.

These doses, however, are well within the variation of background radiation, and similar or even much smaller than doses routinely received from medical imaging and such. As discussed earlier, there is little evidence that small doses have the linear health consequences that LNT suggests, and the major expert organizations on radiation and its health effects have concluded that LNT model should not be used for epidemiological purposes. For example, conclusive studies have found that no additional cancer cases have been caused by Chernobyl fallout in Finland (2 mSv lifetime dose).

Some groups have not been content with the relatively low mortality estimates of the World Health Organization and other agencies that comprised the Chernobyl Forum.[185] They have proceeded to make their own, non-peer reviewed studies on the matter, resulting in tens, even hundreds of times more estimated fatalities.

European Greens were among those disappointed by the Chernobyl Forum's results, so they commissioned and published their own TORCH-report[186] (The Other Report on Chernobyl). It again made good use of the LNT model and stuck to it on a purely theoretical level, whereas the Chernobyl Forum had searched for actual empirical evidence of harm to people's health. TORCH managed to report 30,000 to 60,000 extra cancer deaths in the whole of Europe.

Next was Greenpeace[187], who calculated that Chernobyl would eventually cause around 93,000 premature extra fatalities. The method was rather curious: any area that had any amount of fallout was included. If there were any increased fatalities in that area after 1986, these were counted as being due to Chernobyl. This dubious method meant that the increased fatalities that were due to liver cirrhosis in the area of the recently dissolved Soviet Union were promptly attributed to Chernobyl. The report did not question whether there could have been other reasons for liver cirrhosis than radiation from Chernobyl. Perhaps alarms should have gone off, as there are no studies showing that radiation causes liver cirrhosis.

Even this estimate, 10 times higher than that of the Chernobyl Forum, was not enough for everybody. Alexei V. Yablokov, one of the authors involved in the Greenpeace report, a former member of Russian Academy of Science and one of the founders of Greenpeace Russia, wrote a book Chernobyl: Consequences of the Catastrophe for People and the Environment (2007). It is based mainly on a wide variety of materials written in the Slavic languages. The book claims that around a million humans have died or will die due to the Chernobyl accident, growing the official estimates a hundred-fold and Greenpeace's estimates ten-fold. Experts who have reviewed the book (and who know Russian language and can check some of the sources used) have noted that as a scientific study, the book has negative value. [188] It uses fictional novels as sources, and scientific literature receives scant attention.

In addition to blaming liver cirrhosis and other diseases that have no known connection with radiation, the book resorts to fabrication and lying when scientific reality does not concur with the author's preconceptions. For example, in the chapter dealing with Finland, a study concerning the area of Tampere concluded that birth defects had decreased after the Chernobyl accident. Yablokov, on the other hand, first generalized the study to cover the whole of Finland, and then promptly changed "decreased" to "increased".

These kinds of problems have not stopped some anti-nuclear people from using Yablokov's book as the definitive proof on the destructiveness of nuclear accidents.[189]

Indeed, the common strategy for many anti-nuclear advocates seems to be ever-more imaginative and ridiculous claims that are poured on the unsuspecting public, as it is a well-known psychological fact that people often think, despite the actual evidence, that the truth is to be found somewhere in between the extreme claims made. This same tactic is used with Fukushima, as we will learn later in this book.

The disproportion between the actual evidence and the amount of public worry is enormous, especially if it is compared with common, everyday risks our society accepts to ensure everyday access to energy services. Coal is probably the most glaring of these. Coal mining accidents alone kill thousands every year, with tens of thousands getting sick and permanently disabled due to coal dust and other hazards. [190] Air pollution kills roughly seven million each year, according to WHO.[191] Catastrophic climate change, which might end up being the biggest risk associated with coal burning, is not even included in these numbers.[192] Greenpeace has done a study on the matter a few years back, as have other environmental NGOs more recently. These studies find that around 20,000 people are killed each year in Europe alone as a result of coal burning. In addition, coal burning distributes heavy metals and other toxins which have no half-lives to the environment.

The scale of this gap between reality and perception is so enormous that it makes it difficult for many to believe. Even if we take Greenpeace's numbers at face value – for which there is no good reason – it could be said that a Chernobyl accident every few years would be an acceptable price for giving up coal burning from a public health perspective. Sadly, we would soon run out of Chernobyl-type reactors and would have to content ourselves with less harmful accidents.

Fukushima

The most recent, and our second-worst nuclear accident is likely the one which currently affects our public nuclear discussion the most. A giant tsunami, which resulted from a record-breaking earthquake near the eastern Japanese coast, destroyed the back-up power sources of Fukushima Dai-ichi nuclear power stations. As a result, three reactors that were online at the time were badly damaged and released large amounts of radioactive matter to the surroundings. As is often the case with large-scale accidents, the reasons for the accident can be traced back to actions that were or were not taken long before the tsunami rolled over the insufficient sea walls and hit the plant.

It is hard to imagine a more challenging place to build nuclear power plants than the Pacific coast of Japan. The whole region is geologically unstable and is under a constant threat of earthquakes and tsunamis. But there are 127 million people living in the densely populated and wealthy Japan, and the country has an enormous appetite for energy. When this is combined with almost non-existent fossil energy reserves and the dense population (making renewable energy sources challenging as well), most of that energy has been imported. Japan is the world's largest LNG (Liquefied Natural Gas) importer, second largest coal importer and third largest oil importer. Japan also remembers that during the Second World War, the allied forces cut most energy imports to the country with dire results.

If safety is given proper attention, it is not in itself that dangerous to build nuclear power plants even in geologically unstable areas such as Japan. The NRC (Nuclear Regulatory Commission of the U.S.) pointed out risks regarding earthquakes and tsunamis back in 1991.[193] The

NRC study concluded that if a nuclear power plant lost its backup power during a massive power failure, the reactors could overheat.[194]

The Fukushima Dai-Ichi nuclear power station had six reactors with a total capacity of 4.7 gigawatts. All of them used sea water for cooling and had no independent cooling towers. Since the accident, this type of "extra" cooling towers have been built on the Loviisa nuclear power plant in Finland, for example. Since there is little chance for tsunamis in the Baltic sea, this is mainly in preparation for a major oil accident. The first of the Fukushima reactors was brought online in 1971. The Mark I containment building it had was criticized as too weak in the 1970s, so the designer, General Electric, made some design improvements for them in the 1980s. Their operation required that the decay heat from shut down reactors could be removed with active back-up cooling systems using water-circulating pumps. In the U.S. the NRC required that back-up generators would be placed in earthquake and tsunami-proof locations at least one hundred meters away from other buildings. It also required extra mobile generators to be placed nearby. IAEA (International Atomic Energy Agency) had recognized NRC's recommendations as reasonable already in the early 1990s and recommended implementing them for its member states. But IAEA does not have power over national nuclear safety agencies.

The Japanese government had ensured everyone, including itself, that Japanese reactors were already completely safe. This led to the perverse situation in which the government would lose face if, despite claims of safety, additional safety improvements were implemented. The country had at least five different organizations that had their hand at least somewhat in civilian nuclear power, but before 2001, none of them had the power to mandate safety improvements to be made on nuclear power plants. This multitude of overlapping officials and agencies also caused inner struggles and paralyzed quick decision-making. To top it all, NISA (Nuclear and Industrial Safety Agency), which was the empowered agency in 2001, was not an independent actor as is the NRC. It was a subsidiary of the Japanese ministry of industry and commerce.

As the IAEA tsunami recommendation landed on their desk in the early 2000s, NISA had to compare it with another, cheaper recommendation seen as good enough by their parent organization. Perhaps unsurprisingly, the latter won on the basis that the nuclear safety commission had already reviewed how Japanese reactors would handle total power failure and the destruction of back-up generators. The study concluded that such an event was so unlikely that it was not worth the effort of preparation.

If Japan had followed the recommendations of the NRC 20 years earlier, the Fukushima accident would most likely have been avoided, or at least it would have been limited to a much smaller scale, similar to Three Mile Island. But even this negligence did not ensure that the accident would happen. The last straw was likely the order that evacuations from two-kilometre radius need be completed before any emergency pressure release could be done. This order was well-meaning, since pressure release like this always releases radioisotopes into the surroundings which would be higher than the limits normally allowed. But releasing the pressure could also prevent much larger damages and consequences.

Fukushima - What happened?

On March 11th in 2011, the seabed near the east coast of Japan shook like never before, during measured history at least.[195] During the following three minutes, the east coast of Japan moved over two metres closer to California and sank almost a metre. Global daytime shortened by 1.8 microseconds and the rotational axis shifted by roughly 25 centimetres (10 inches).

All Japanese reactors did what they were supposed to do in such a situation: they shut down immediately. In Fukushima Dai-Ichi, the three operating reactors also went to a shut down and back-up generators started up, running the water pumps for cooling as planned. One of the operators of reactor 1 thought that its isolation condenser[196] was working even too efficiently, as the temperature was dropping fast. He decided to bypass the automatic system and shut down this passive cooling mechanism. According to some sources[197], this was one of the key mistakes that later led to the accident.

The earthquake, which happened on the sea floor around 100 km to the east of Miyagi prefecture, had sent a massive tsunami on its way. Around one hour after the earthquake (15:35), the tsunami, which was in some places as high as 15 metres, hit the east coast of Japan. It flooded and flushed whole towns to the sea and entered deep inland. In just a few minutes, 21,377 people died or went missing in the rubble and the sea. More than 6,000 people were injured, and hundreds of thousands were left homeless. Some 250,000 buildings were destroyed wholly or partially, and a further 750,000 buildings were damaged.[198]

Another nuclear power station in Fukushima prefecture, Fukushima Dai-ni, survived the tsunami with relatively small damages. In fact, it was used as shelter for local folks, because it is such a robust, safe structure. In Fukushima Dai-ichi, the destruction was much heavier. The tsunami ripped apart the diesel fuel tanks of the generators and flooded the turbine halls, which had the back-up generators running in their basements, producing the essential electricity to keep the cooling pumps and control rooms running. Only one of the generators, which was placed at a higher location and which was cooling reactors 5 and 6, survived intact. Both these reactors, along with number 4, were offline due to fuel loading.

Reactors 3 and 4 shifted from generators to battery power. Control rooms still had power, so the operator's job was to make sure that all valves and electrical devices that had to do with cooling reactor 3 down were left in optimal position when the batteries would run out of power.

Reactors 1 and 2 had shared batteries, which had been flooded and had lost most of their charge. They were emptied in a few minutes, and total darkness took over the reactor building and the control rooms. There was no way to control emergency cooling any more, and it was impossible to know how much water was left in the reactor pressure vessel. When the accident occurred, there had been 4.5 metres of cooling water mixed with steam above the fuel assemblies. If the fuel assemblies were to surface above the water level so early after the shutdown, they would overheat and eventually melt.

Reactors 1, 2 and 3, which were running when the accident happened, were the most immediate threat. Of these, reactor 1 was the biggest worry, as its fuel had been in the reactor the longest, which meant that it would also produce the most decay heat. In addition, its isolation condenser had been manually switched off a few minutes earlier. Reactor 2 had its emergency cooling (RCIC) on, so that would help at least for some time. Back-up power to reactor 3 had been cut off, but it still had batteries feeding power to the most critical systems.[199] TEPCO, the operator, notified the Japanese government that reactor 1 had an emergency.

The cooling water circulating in reactors 2 and 3 kept getting hotter, and at some point it would boil and turn to steam. All electrical connections between the reactors had been destroyed. All roads leading to the site had been flooded and were filled with debris, collapsed buildings and people running away, so it was hard to get to the site. Big enough generators were too heavy for helicopters. Electrical cables needed to be hooked up to the reactor buildings but moving cables 10 cm (4 inches) thick and weighing a ton amidst fallen buildings and rubble was not easy to do with manpower only.

Eventually, the operators working with flashlights managed to get some of the emergency cooling systems back online, at least partly. Fire trucks were driven beside the reactor buildings, and by hooking up their hoses to the emergency cooling system, the pressure increased, and more water was pumped to the reactor pressure vessels. But the pumps in the fire trucks were not strong enough to push much water into the over-pressurized vessels which were getting hotter. There would need to be a pressure release, which would also release radioactivity to the surroundings.

Reactor 1 was completely dark, so it was impossible to get any information on what was going on in the reactor. A few hours after the tsunami (8:49 PM), operators managed to get some electricity back to the control rooms of reactors 1 and 2. The indicators showed that the situation in reactor 1 was serious, and the operators notified the local authorities that evacuation plans must be started immediately as there might be need for emergency pressure release directly to the atmosphere. This was only done as a precaution, and preparations for the pressure release were not started.

A bit later, at 9:30 PM, the prime minister of Japan announced that the evacuation zone was to be expanded from two to three kilometres, which effectively doubled the number of people that needed to be evacuated. In hindsight, this was a serious mistake, as this new plan was not properly communicated to all local officials due to the general chaos.

Around midnight, the radiation levels in reactor 1 rose as a sign that the water level had fallen to the level of the fuel assemblies and preparations for the emergency pressure release were finally started. Releasing pressure without electricity was something that had not been practiced, so the preparations proceeded slowly.

What happened inside reactor 1 during this time? In three hours, the cooling water had boiled away. An hour and a half later the zirconium cladding of the fuel rods had become so hot that steam dissociated into hydrogen and oxygen. The fuel started to melt, and the pressure inside the reactor vessel increased rapidly. Without pressure release valves (which needed electricity), this pressure was hard to release. The containment vessel, made of inch-thick steel, ruptured and the hydrogen along with some radioactive fission products inside the reactor leaked into the reactor building. If passive hydrogen removal systems – a safety feature required in many countries – had been installed to the reactor building, this hydrogen would have been burned back into water, and nothing more serious would probably have happened. These systems were not a requirement in Japan, and had not been installed, so the reactor building started to turn into a bomb, just waiting for a spark.

The preparations for the pressure release continued through the night and morning, as did the evacuations which needed to be finished before permission for the pressure release would be granted. Damage inside the reactors kept getting worse, and around 5 AM radiation detectors noticed that radioactivity was leaking from the reactor buildings. Evacuation was still underway. Finally, around 9 AM, information was received that the evacuations had been finished. One of the operators went into the reactor building to manually open the pressure release valve. He only had time to open it partially when his dosimeter told him that the maximum allowed dose of 100 mSv had been received and he had to return. This limit was increased to 250 mSv a few days later, but then it was too late. At 10:40 AM pressure was finally released, but it was much too late.

At 15:36, with the pressure release still underway, reactor 1 ran out of time. A huge hydrogen explosion blew the top of the reactor building off, sending debris and pieces high into the air and around the compound. This debris broke the power connection, which had been established just a few minutes earlier, between the reactor buildings and the newly arrived high-voltage generators. The explosion also spread the radioactive fission products that had been gathering in the reactor building all over the area, slowing down any further repairs. Five emergency workers were injured.

On the next day, 13th March, the emergency cooling of reactor 3 finally stopped. It had been operating on the steam produced by the decay heat from the reactor, but eventually the pressure had decreased too much. The preparations for emergency pressure release were started, but it was already too late. A couple hours later, the fuel started melting and the red-hot zirconium started splitting steam into hydrogen and oxygen. A fire truck arrived a few hours later and started to pump seawater into the reactor, and by some miracle, the pressure was lowered by releasing some steam and gases to the atmosphere, along with radioactive elements. But the designers of the pressure release systems had forgotten the possible hydrogen problem. A day later at 11:01 AM, there was an explosion in reactor 3 building.

Just an hour later, 70 hours after power was cut, the emergency cooling of reactor 2 overheated and the turbine which had been powering it stopped. The water boiled away, and in under four hours the fuel started melting and flowing to the bottom of the reactor vessel. Hydrogen started forming there as well, but someone had opened a panel on the wall to let the hydrogen and lighter radioactive elements out from the reactor building.

Reactor 4 had been in shut-down during the accident, so there was no immediate danger even though there was no power. But it shared a ventilation duct with reactor 3, and with no electricity available, the valves had been left open. Part of the hydrogen forming in reactor 3 found its way to the reactor 4 building and started gathering there, waiting for a spark. On 15th March, to everyone's surprise, there was an explosion in reactor 4 building. The reason for it was confirmed only six months later, and so fear and rumours spread far and wide that the spent fuel that had been removed from the reactor had overheated and was the cause for the explosion.

All three of the operating reactors had melted down. Yet nobody died in this nuclear accident. Further studies by WHO and UNSCEAR have concluded that it is unlikely that anyone involved in the emergency work would die prematurely due to the radiation doses they received. Reactor 4 was basically still fixable, but it would be hard and expensive due to the radioactivity in the area. Reactors 5 and 6 did not suffer damages.

Significant amounts of radioactive elements were released to the surroundings during those few days. Mainly this consisted of iodine-131 and isotopes of cesium. Some radioactive isotopes also dissolved into the overflowing cooling water, and some of these ended up leaking into the Pacific Ocean. Small leaks have continued for a long time. None of these leaks will have significant health impacts or impacts on the environment.

If preparations for the emergency pressure release had been started right after operators realized that it might be needed (around 9 PM on 11th March), and if the pressure release had been started as soon as it was possible, resulting damages might have been much less. Hydrogen explosions could have been avoided, and the damages could have been limited to the reactors themselves being destroyed. Some radioactivity would have been released with the pressurized steam, but it would have been a small fraction of what was released.

Reasons for the accident have also been found in the actions of TEP-CO (the operator) and nuclear safety officials before the accident. Many recommended safety improvements had been ignored, as had the possibility of an earthquake and tsunami of this magnitude. Proper preparations would likely have prevented the whole nuclear accident from happening. Onagawa nuclear power station, which was much closer to the centre of the earthquake, survived almost without any damages, and Fukushima Dai-ni, just 10 km away from Fukushima Dai-ichi, was also spared from serious problems.

Fukushima in the media

Rumours and conspiracy theories still abound that the true scale of the accident was hidden from the public by officials and the nuclear industry.[200] Even a cursory glance at the news articles from that time proves the opposite. A nuclear accident in which nobody died got far more coverage than did the tsunami and its more than 20,000 victims. The global media, for the most part, forgot journalism and went after click-bait headlines, fearmongering and very poor fact-checking. One example of this is the news that started circulating about a year after the accident. We were told about the supposedly enormous amounts of radioactivity leaking into the Pacific Ocean from Fukushima. In fact, this was 300 tons of water that was slightly contaminated with radioactive tritium, totalling 20-40 terabecquerel (trillion becquerel). Practically none of the articles brought that seemingly huge amount of radioactivity into context, and people were horrified. Had they done journalism instead of click-baiting, the readers would have learned that this "enormous release" was equivalent to 20-40 tritium-based self-illuminating EXIT-signs. The rumour mill kept on growing. Today, there are articles available that give straight citations saying 300 tons of water is leaking each day (instead of one year).[201] The tritium in the water has also somehow turned into caesium and strontium along the way, which is a fundamental shift as tritium is not actually dangerous.[202]

Another news article that started circulating in spring of 2014 reported that the Fukushima accident was connected with thyroid cancers found in children.[203] Signs of tumours were found after careful screenings of children in the area, which anti-nuclear activists saw as a sign that the accident caused a significant increase in thyroid cancer cases.

In truth, this was not at all what was found. Small tumours in thyroid glands are quite common, and most of them are not dangerous or aggressive and will go away on their own. Some estimate that perhaps a third of us has such a tumour in us any given day. This means that whenever a population is screened for signs of tumours, we will find plenty. The problem with the screening is when to count a shadow found in the scan as a tumour and when not. In the study in question, much smaller signs were counted as tumours than normally. With this method and criteria, any given population would show a significant increase in tumours.

In addition, it takes time for the tumours to grow and start showing up. If thyroid cancers were to increase due to the accident, they would not show up so soon anyway. The study was done merely to establish a baseline for further reference.[204] Experts have criticized the study in the medical journal The Lancet for using too small a control group, saying this method of counting smaller signs as tumour will lead to unnecessary treatments and anxiety for people, when harmless tumours that would likely go away on their own are removed surgically.[205]

Every mid-March we also get a steady stream of stories that tell us "something is still ticking in Fukushima." Many reporters have visited the Fukushima evacuation area with Geiger counters, and found that indeed, 0.4 microsieverts (or so) of radiation is present in some homes of elder people who would love to move back but are not allowed by the government. The context is usually missing. The said level of radiation (found in a story by Helsingin Sanomat, the biggest newspaper in Scandinavia[206]) is just a bit higher than is the normal background level in Finland. Someone living in Pispala gets a dose ten times larger.

If the nuclear radiation limits enforced by the Japanese government, which are based on international recommendations, were applied to Finland, most of the country would need to be evacuated immediately. This tells us something about the stringency of radiation limits we use around the world. It also tells us why cleaning up Fukushima is bound to cost tremendously and unnecessarily: they are cleaning the place to be less radioactive than most of Finland is naturally. While people are shocked about these costs, they silently accept the tremendous health costs that burning fossil fuels in Japan, due to the closures of their reactor fleet, will cause there.

Health impacts of Fukushima

The first peer-reviewed study on the Fukushima health effects was done by professor John Ten Hoeve and professor Mark Z. Jacobson from Stanford University.[207] The study was based mainly on theoretical models, and it found that the radiation would cause around 130 extra cancer fatalities in the next 40 years, around the world. This amount is too small to be seen in health statistics. The study used the LNT model in the non-recommended way, which likely overestimates the amount of fatalities, since it assumes that even tiny doses of radiation will cause cancer at the population level. Mark Jacobson is commonly known to be very anti-nuclear, and he is also a rather shameless booster for 100% renewable energy systems. It is therefore slightly surprising to find the article stating that the evacuation likely caused more harm to health than the radiation would have, had the people stayed at home.

The World Health Organization (WHO) did a more comprehensive hands-on study on the effects of Fukushima. It concluded that it might increase the statistical risk for cancer slightly, but the increase will be so small as to be impossible to detect. [208] The media again forgot journalism and went after the headlines. The headlines told us that the risk for small girls to get thyroid cancer went up by as much as 70 percent. Behind the outrage and shock caused by this sort of headline, nobody paid much attention to the meaning when placed in proper context. First, it only applied to a small group that got the largest amount of radiation. Second, in practice it meant that the lifetime risk of these girls getting thyroid cancer went from 0.75 percent to 1.25 percent (an increase of 70 percent, or 0.5 percentage points).[209]

The report by UNSCEAR came to similar conclusions. They estimate that 167 emergency workers received radiation doses that will slightly increase their lifetime risk of developing cancer. When we acknowledge that statistically 60 of them will get cancer for other reasons anyway, and the fact that their health will likely be closely monitored for the rest of their lives because of the Fukushima accident, it might be that their actual risk of dying of cancer has gone down. This is because the fact that any cancer is much more treatable if it is noticed at an early phase.

There is also a group of people that think conspiracy is the most logical explanation for the discrepancy between the expert statements and peer-reviewed studies and their own anti-nuclear preconceptions. The most common of these conspiracy theories goes roughly as follows: WHO and IAEA have signed a contract that forbids WHO from publishing anything that the IAEA does not want them to.[210] So whenever WHO publishes something that anti-nuclear advocates disagree with, they cry conspiracy. Is there such a contract? Of course not. The "proof" of this conspiracy is a passage, taken completely out of context, which says:

> *"Whenever either organization proposes to initiate a*
> *programme or activity on a subject in which the other*
> *organization has or may have a substantial interest, the*
> *first party shall consult the other with a view to adjust-*
> *ing the matter by mutual agreement."*

As is often the method of conspiracy theorists, the whole contract, or the context, is ignored. Even a glance at the paragraph just above the one quoted would destroy the theory. It says basically that the IAEA has no power to order WHO to do or say (or leave out) anything that would hinder its mission.[211] Indeed, such a clause as cited above is quite common between international organizations that have some overlapping interests and areas of expertise. Its main purpose is to ensure that one organization does not publish data or results it has obtained from another organization without making sure the data and results are accurate and up to date. WHO has also made a statement back in 2001, where it specifically addresses this worry and says it is unfounded. [212]

But if there are such conspiracies of hiding real data and making up new results, why has nobody leaked these from the WHO? Publicity and fame would have been guaranteed. And why has all other peer-reviewed research on the matter – even that done by rather anti-nuclear researchers – achieved a similar result? Are they also in on the alleged WHO-IAEA conspiracy?

The initial estimates of the amount of radionuclides released from the accident varied greatly. Nobody knew if the spent fuel pools were intact (they were) and nobody knew the extent of meltdown and other damage sustained in each reactor, and how much radioactive material might be leaking.[213] The largest initial estimates by some were more than seven times larger, at 17,846 terabecquerels, PBq) than was the total amount present in reactors 1-3 (2,453 PBq), and only a part of this total amount was released.

TEPCO has since estimated that around 500 PBq of iodine-131, 10 PBq of caesium-137 and 10 PBq of caesium-134 were released to the atmosphere. Measured as "iodine-131 equivalent", they totalled at 500 + 400 + 40 = 940 PBq. A total of 169 PBq of iodine-131 equivalent of radioactive elements leaked to the Pacific Ocean in addition to 500 PBq of the mostly harmless xenon-133. For comparison, Chernobyl leaked a total of 5,200 PBq of iodine-131 equivalent.

With all the outrage about the radioactivity leaking to the Pacific Ocean, the actual amount is good to put in context.[214]

Sources of radioactivity in the oceans	
Nuclear weapons testing in the 1950s and 1960s Chernobyl Fukushima total	950 PBq 100 PBq 14–90 PBq
Biggest natural sources of radioactivity in oceans	
Uranium-238	37,000 PBq
Potassium-40	15,000,000 PBq

It is a fact that the Fukushima accident has demanded and will keep demanding more victims. At least 1,600 have died directly and indirectly because of the evacuation. Some have committed suicide, some have died of drug abuse, and some elderly and sick have died because of the strain and complications involved in the evacuation itself. The damages due to anxiety, drugs and alcoholism and mental problems will keep growing for decades to come.

Fukushima is an enormous tragedy which should never have happened, but not for the reasons we often think. People living in the evacuation area lost their homes, and many did so permanently, for one reason or another. The local communities will likely never be the same, as even with reasonably low radiation levels, many people will be wondering if it is worth moving back, and if there is a community to which they can return. Will there be jobs, where will old friends and neighbours be, will the social network exist anymore, and how can it be built again?

From this perspective, the risks associated with nuclear are rather unique in comparison with most other energy sources. The risks and damages due to accidents hit whole communities. Even if coal kills hundreds, even thousands of times more people per unit of energy produced, coal is often a silent killer that can only be seen in statistics – although mining accidents can and do affect whole communities. Nuclear accidents and the evacuations they cause can destroy whole communities, even if the people will go on living somewhere else. Another similar community-breaking energy source is hydropower, which has literally wiped out whole towns and villages, and seen millions moved from their communities to make way for enormous hydro dam projects.

Both Fukushima and Chernobyl raise an important question that rarely gets asked and even less frequently answered. We know by now that the psychological health damages far exceed those caused by radiation from nuclear accidents. And we know that those damages are largely due to fear, social stigma and anxiety. These, in turn, are born of nuclear regulation that fails to acknowledge the larger public health while concentrating on minimizing the radiation exposure at any cost, and the anti-nuclear campaigning that often uses misinformation, fear and doubt as their tools for collecting donations to fund their activities. Can these campaigners somehow be held to account for the psychological damage they cause by their actions, at least morally and ethically if not legally? What about the responsibility of the nuclear industry regulators, and laws that both effectively prevent us from building nuclear (which is then replaced with other more harmful energy production) and fail to recognize the detrimental effects these laws and regulations can have on overall public health?

Insurance for Nuclear Power Plant Accidents

The owners and operators of nuclear power plants are liable for any damages caused by the plants, regardless how these damages were caused. For this reason, and the reason that it is in most cases mandatory, they often get insurance. Contrary to the rather common belief, nuclear power plants do get insurance. In fact, using a couple minutes to search the matter on Google can reveal many insurance companies that offer coverage for nuclear power plants. Especially well-operated western plants are often desirable customers for insurance companies. Insuring nuclear power plants has the same limits to liabilities as all other human activities do: damages that go above their ability to pay and above the insurance policy maximum always fall to the local government and/or the people.

The insurance regulations depend on the country. The home country of the authors, Finland, requires insurance worth 700 million euros from all nuclear power plant owners. Some people think that this counts as a public subsidy for the nuclear industry, as the potential costs of an accident can be much higher. As we learned above from Fukushima's experience, the degree of "cleanliness" greatly affects the estimated costs. In addition to this domestic insurance, Finland is part of an international agreement that adds a liability of 500 million euros to the country where nuclear is operated, and the countries that are parties in the agreement together chip in another 300 million euros. So, in Finland, there is a total of 1.5 billion euros of various levels of insurance. [215] In addition to this, the owner is liable for any damages and costs without limit. In reality, this limit is always reached sooner or later.

The United States has a slightly different system. There, each operator is required to take insurance for a total worth of 375 million dollars. If the damages of any accident exceed this, operators for all nuclear plants in the U.S. are jointly responsible to pay for additional damages of up to 12.6 billion dollars. In addition, each power plant is required to be insured for up to a billion dollars.[216] Since the operators are jointly responsible for others' damages as well, they have vested interests in seeing that everyone takes care of their plants in a safe and proper manner.

In addition to insurance, most countries collect money from the nuclear operators for a decommissioning and waste disposal fund, which is meant to be used for just those purposes: decommissioning old reactors and seeing that nuclear waste is stored properly for the long term. In addition to these fees, usually collected in the price of each kWh of electricity sold, the funds actively manage their investments, although in a regulated, low-risk manner.

Nuclear Weapons and Nuclear Power

Nuclear weapons have been an integral part of global geopolitics for over 70 years. The fear of the A-bomb has had a direct effect on civilian nuclear power and its public acceptance. The primary worry is whether civilian nuclear power increases nuclear weapons proliferation. A secondary worry seems to be the use of radioactive material in what is called a dirty bomb.

Basics of the A-bomb

Ten countries are known to have manufactured nuclear weapons. They are South Africa, India, the United Kingdom, Israel, China, Pakistan, North Korea, France, Russia and the United States. Over 40 countries would be able to make them, should their governments be willing to use time, money and influence to do so.[217]

Even though the manufacturing of nuclear weapons requires complex technology, and though the designs of more advanced weaponry are one of the most heavily guarded secrets countries have, the basic principle of the atomic bomb is rather simple and can be deciphered with roughly high-school level physics.

The principle of nuclear energy production and nuclear weapons is the same. An atom splits, or fissions, when it is hit with a neutron moving at suitable speed. The fission releases energy and new neutrons, which continue and accelerate the chain reaction. In a nuclear weapons explosion, the uncontrolled hypercritical chain-reaction releases very large amounts of energy in a very short time.

The energy released by nuclear fission weapons is measured in kilotons (kt). One kiloton equals roughly one thousand metric tons of conventional explosives such as TNT. The bomb that destroyed Hiroshima was estimated to be around 12-14 kilotons. In thermonuclear weapons, or hydrogen bombs, part of the explosive power of a fission bomb is directed to heat and push closer together hydrogen's deuterium isotope atoms. This will make them combine in a fusion reaction, releasing tremendous amounts of energy and neutrons to accelerate the fission as well.

Fusion-based weapons have such power that it is often measured in megatons (Mt), or thousands of kilotons. One megaton equals a million tons of conventional explosives. The largest human-made explosion ever detonated was the "Tzar Bomba", detonated in Novaya Zemlya in 1961. The designed power was 50 megatons, although measurements put it closer to 57 megatons (210 PJ). The designed power had ten times the energy of all the conventional explosives detonated during World War II. The original design was for 100 Mt, but for several reasons, such as the fact that the crew delivering the bomb would not be able to escape its blast radius, a 50 Mt version was tested instead. Even that was enough to break windows in northern Finland and Norway. In short, it was the culmination of cold war weapons propaganda, as weapons of such power have little practical military use. A bomb of 100-300 kilotons is perfectly able to render to rubble even a larger city.

In fact, there are very few military reasons to own and use nuclear weapons. This has been dawning slowly on more and more of the world's "nuclear powers", making nuclear weapons less and less desirable. In mid-1980s, the world had a stockpile of roughly 65,000 nuclear weapons. By 2013, that had dropped to around 17,300, by end of 2015 to 15,741 weapons and by end of 2017 to 14,875 weapons.[218] Most nuclear powers are planning to shrink their arsenal further in the coming years. The exceptions are Pakistan, North Korea and possibly Israel. [219] It is very costly to maintain a massive nuclear weapons arsenal, especially considering that they are of little use in an actual war. It has been argued by some that their existence acts as a deterrent for regular wars as well. If true, this would mean that as long as no nuclear war is triggered, they actually keep the peace and save lives.

Nuclear weapons material

For humanity's benefit, it has proven complicated and difficult to acquire nuclear weapons material. There are basically two options for building a nuclear bomb: uranium-235 and plutonium-239.[220] Natural uranium contains only 0.72 percent of uranium-235, while a bomb needs at least 60 percent. Plutonium is not even present naturally. So the uranium needs to be enriched or the plutonium needs to be created from uranium-238. Both pathways require pretty advanced industrial and technological equipment and facilities. There are multiple ways to procure either of these isotopes; they are theoretically quite simple but practically quite difficult. Without help from outside, it would take a nation many years, if not decades to gather both the know-how and the equipment needed to enrich uranium or to produce plutonium. [221]
It takes at least the following infrastructure to produce weapons-grade uranium-235:
- Uranium deposit.
- Uranium mine.
- A facility to process uranium ore into uranium oxide.
- A chemical conversion facility to purify and transform uranium

oxide into uranium hexafluoride or uranium tetrachloride for the enrichment process.

- An enrichment facility to enrich the uranium-235 present in natural uranium.
- Another chemical conversion facility to turn the enriched uranium hexafluoride or tetrachloride into uranium metal.[222]

There are several functional uranium enrichment facilities around the world. These are in Brazil, the U.S., Russia, France, Canada, India, Iran, Pakistan and South Africa. Argentina also has a facility, but it is currently not in use.[223] Usually these facilities are under international supervision. In the case of Iran and Pakistan, some parts of the facilities escaped international scrutiny, and for this reason these facilities have been suspected of manufacturing weapons-grade uranium.

If one chooses to go the plutonium route, one would need a uranium deposit, uranium mine and uranium processing facility and additionally a facility to manufacture uranium fuel and a nuclear reactor that would be able to use natural uranium as fuel, and a further reprocessing facility to separate and purify plutonium from the used fuel.[224]

In a nuclear reactor, most of the nuclear fuel is uranium-238, which is useless for building a bomb. But a small part of the uranium-238 will catch a neutron and turn into uranium-239, which will decay into neptunium, which decays into plutonium-239. This is exactly what happens in breeder reactors, to make fissile nuclear fuel from uranium-238. Reprocessing facilities that separate and purify plutonium are located in the UK, US, Israel, Japan, China, Russia, France and North Korea. Syria and Iran have been suspected of trying to get suitable facilities running.

Can nuclear weapons be made from spent nuclear fuel?

From time to time, there are claims that spent nuclear fuel from civilian reactors (which includes plutonium, as we have learned) could be used to produce nuclear weapons. The plutonium acquired from civilian reactors is not optimal for making nuclear weapons. Why? There is a slightly technical but important reason. The only plutonium isotope suitable for making nuclear weapons is plutonium-239. When plutonium is produced in a nuclear reactor, part of the plutonium that is produced eventually catches an additional neutron, turning it into plutonium-240. The longer the nuclear fuel is kept in the reactor, the more plutonium-240 is formed. This isotope means serious problems for nuclear weapons designers. It is much more radioactive than plutonium-239, and therefore much more difficult and dangerous to handle. Plutonium-238, which is created in a similar way, is also problematic for anyone building a bomb, since it releases a lot of thermal energy.[225] The smaller the share of plutonium-239, the greater the requirement for bomb-building skills and technical abilities to ensure a reliable weapon.[226] Plutonium separated from regular spent fuel is called reactor-grade, while plutonium bred specifically for weapons manufacturing is called weapons-grade.

There is around one percent plutonium in spent nuclear fuel. If at least 60-70 percent of this is the isotope plutonium-239, theoretically a functional bomb may be built. Two nuclear weapons designers from the Los Alamos nuclear weapons laboratory, Carson Mark[227], head of the theoretical department and Richard Gawin[228], designer with over 40 years of experience, have concluded that it would be possible to manufacture a simple and reasonably reliable bomb of maybe 0.5 to 5 kilotons of explosive power. While this kind of weapon would be possible to build, using reactor grade plutonium would present the designer with significant extra challenges.[229], [230] While some solutions have been presented publicly[231], building a nuclear weapon remains a challenging endeavour even today.

In practice, reactor-grade plutonium is only a security threat if readily separated plutonium from a reprocessing facility ends up in the wrong hands. This separation is currently done in France, Japan and Russia. The separated plutonium is usually mixed with nuclear fuel to be used in civilian reactors as "MOX" fuel (mixed-oxide). Larger stockpiles of reactor-grade plutonium are guarded practically as carefully as nuclear weapons.

It is possible to operate civilian reactors so that the fuel is removed before plutonium isotopes of the wrong sort start forming in too large quantities. Most civilian nuclear reactors are designed such that fuel removal requires the reactor to be shut down. This slows down the production of plutonium and makes it practically impossible to use the reactor to produce electricity – which in turn is easily detected by outsiders. Civilian reactors are also much more expensive than simpler "graphite piles" that can be built just for plutonium production. But in theory, should one decide to do so, civilian reactors can be used to produce significant amounts of weapons grade plutonium. A 1 GW reactor can produce around 250 kg of plutonium in a year if it forgoes electricity production. [232] At 60 euros per MWh, said reactor produces almost half a billion euros worth of electricity per year, giving the plutonium an "opportunity-cost" of roughly 2 million euros per kg.

Anyone producing plutonium in this manner needs to obtain new fuel rods at a rapid pace, since the used rods need to be dissolved to separate the plutonium. This requires the ability to enrich uranium, which by itself grants the possibility to make weapons based on highly enriched uranium. Most of the civilian reactors around the world are also monitored by the IAEA. These security measures include seals, cameras and automatic samplings. Producing plutonium requires these measures to be removed. This in turn can lead to international sanctions, even military intervention.

Perhaps the most worrying scenario goes as follows. A country/government decides to design a bomb in secrecy, and builds a simple, "disposable" facility to separate the plutonium. In theory, it could then rapidly remove fuel from a civilian reactor, separate the plutonium and manage to build perhaps dozens of nuclear weapons before the international community could react. [233] The downside of this would be that the country in question would in practice need to give up civilian nuclear power permanently, as nobody would sell them new fuel. And if they had the ability to make nuclear fuel for themselves, they also would have the ability to produce nuclear weapons material.

Spent fuel could also be used as a dirty bomb, which disperses radioactive materials using conventional explosives. But even this is not simple. Dispersal is made difficult by the fuel's solid, ceramic form. Fresh spent fuel is also very hot and radioactive, which makes it hard to handle and transport. The radioactivity alone would kill anyone participating in the project well before it could be carried out, and the radioactivity would make such a weapon quite easy to detect, even from a distance. To make the dirty bomb more effective, one would need to separate the more dangerous isotopes from the rest (similarly to plutonium separation described above), or somehow obtain the facilities to make such isotopes. These kinds of dirty bombs have been tested, and their effects have been found to be underwhelming.[234] A dirty bomb made from spent fuel is considered mainly a theoretical possibility and at best a psychological weapon presenting rather little actual danger.[235]

Does civilian nuclear power proliferate nuclear weapons?

As we learned above, certain components of civilian nuclear technology make it possible or easier to build nuclear weapons. Mainly these are enrichment of uranium and reprocessing of spent fuel. One could also claim that the experience and know-how of operating civilian nuclear reactors and the availability of highly trained nuclear engineers and physicists will make it easier to design and build nuclear weapons and to acquire the materials needed.

While there is a clear and natural correlation between nuclear physics and engineering expertise and nuclear weapons, the causality between the civilian nuclear industry and nuclear weapons proliferation is slim to non-existent. Currently there are more countries using civilian nuclear technology than ever before. Yet the number of countries that possess nuclear weapons or plan on getting them has been continuously shrinking.[236] Back in the 1960s, a total of 23 countries had nuclear weapons, research on nuclear weapons or were seriously considering obtaining nuclear weapons. Amongst those countries that were taking serious steps to acquire nuclear weapons were Sweden, Switzerland and Italy. By the 1980s, this number had fallen to eleven. Currently there are only nine nations with nuclear weapons, and 31 nations with civilian nuclear power programs. International diplomacy, sanctions and cooperation have managed to get Iran to give up their weapons program while retaining civilian nuclear power. Back in the 1990s, South Africa also gave up nuclear weapons but not civilian nuclear power.

One of the greatest secrets of nuclear weapons – the knowledge that they are possible – is common knowledge. As early as the 1960s, studies showed that anyone who has studied physics at university level would be able to design a relatively reliable atomic bomb just by using commonly available sources. Acquiring the materials and facilities needed was an altogether different matter. North Korea has shown that a poor and isolated country is able to build a nuclear weapon, pretty much on its own, even if it does not have civilian nuclear power. Everyone who has given it a serious effort has also been able to make their bomb work on the first try – despite prevailing sanctions or limits on technology imports.

The vast majority of countries that use nuclear power acquire their fuel from countries that have nuclear weapons. In some cases, the spent fuel is returned to the original country for reprocessing. In this scenario, there is little risk of nuclear weapons proliferating with civilian nuclear power.

The use of civilian reactors in general is a poor vector for weapons proliferation. The actual risks come from the fuel cycle – enriching and reprocessing. But even this does not lead to weapons, as we can learn from Japan, Holland and Brazil. These countries have significant enrichment and reprocessing programs, but none of them seem to have any plans to acquire nuclear weapons or even the expertise to build them. Indeed, apart from India, no country has ever used civilian reactors or their spent fuel for producing weapons material. The plutonium in nuclear weapons has always been made in reactors specifically designed for this purpose. Civilian nuclear power has practically never resulted in nuclear weapons. Nuclear weapons, however, have often been followed by civilian reactors.

The only exception to this is India. Back in the 1960s, they used a small Canadian research reactor to produce small amounts of weapons plutonium.[237] The nuclear weapons program in India proceeded at a rather slow pace, with one weapons test made in 1974 and the next ones in 1998. It would be safe to say that the Canadian research reactor played a rather insignificant part in the program.

One of the biggest reasons to doubt the usability of civilian reactors for weapons programs comes from their price. It would simply be very expensive and wasteful to use a complex reactor for plutonium production instead of electricity production. It is much faster and cheaper to construct a simple reactor, a "graphite pile", just for the purpose of producing plutonium.

And if we assume that uranium, enrichment, fuel manufacturing and reprocessing facilities are available, building the reactor itself is probably the easiest part of the project.

One of the authors, Janne, made a small experiment on this subject. He sent an inquiry through alibaba.com webstore to various graphite merchants he found in China, requesting a quote for 2,000 tons of reactor-grade graphite. That amount would suffice for two carefully designed graphite piles, with each being able to produce around 60 kg of weapons grade plutonium in a year, enough to build perhaps ten Nagasaki-type bombs. He also inquired if delivering the graphite would need special licences or paperwork.

The first answer came in ten hours. A Chinese producer offered graphite readily cut to the client's specifications at 4,022 dollars per ton plus freight. Delivery time was two months, and no questions were asked about import/export licences, let alone the intended use for the graphite. The total price of graphite per reactor would be around 4.4 million dollars, plus freight. The construction of the reactor itself would probably be under 180 million dollars.

The alternative to a graphite pile would be to use a highly sophisticated, at least ten times more expensive electricity generating reactor to produce plutonium. It would be unable to produce electricity, and producing plutonium would be slower. The international community would very likely notice the activity and take actions to stop it.

Producing nuclear weapons has not been a technical question for decades. It is first and foremost a question of political will. Weapons are acquired both for internal and external reasons, but often in the background there is fear that the leaders currently sitting on the throne might lose their seat. Weapons proliferation is not so much a question of reactors being built somewhere, but of the uncontrolled spread of enrichment and reprocessing technology. Enrichment especially is a technology that has spread widely in the last 30 years, and it will be impossible to get that genie back into the bottle. We simply must live with that reality.

In this sense, nuclear can also be compared with other fields, such as biotechnology. Each medicine factory and even brewery is a potential factory for biological weapons. Bioweapons are also much cheaper to produce than nuclear weapons. Back in 1942, four American scientists produced tons of weapons grade anthrax at a budget that was less than one day of the Manhattan Project.[238] This amount of anthrax, dispersed from an aeroplane, would have killed tens of thousands and rendered vast areas uninhabitable for hundreds of years. It is interesting that the very officials who made the call to use a nuclear weapon thought that using a weapon such as anthrax was far too horrible.

A final point to consider is that more often than not, access to energy resources has been one of the driving causes for waging wars. Germany invaded Russia in 1941 to get access to its oil fields in Caucasus.[239] Japan joined the Second World War largely because of the oil embargo by the U.S., which was threatening to destroy Japan's economy and position. [240] The unstable 20th century in the Near East was a struggle over who controls and benefits from the region's oil deposits, a critical energy resource for the rest of the world.

Is Nuclear Power Too Expensive?

After several decades of stagnation, western countries are slowing starting to build nuclear power plants again. The key question many are asking is if nuclear power is too expensive. One could generalize that after all other arguments against nuclear have been shown to have little actual substance, the price, along with long build times, is the final argument. Earlier we showed that nuclear is a remarkably rapid way to add zero-carbon energy production, despite allegations to the contrary. This is true even for projects that have faced many problems and failures. But what about the price of nuclear energy? Is it simply too expensive? To answer that we must first explain some concepts and terms used in that debate.

The cost of producing energy

The cost of producing energy is not the same as the price of energy for a consumer. The energy producer needs to get a price high enough to pay for the investment and other costs; fuel, personnel and maintenance. In addition, a profit needs to be made to justify the risks involved. In energy terms, energy production needs to produce enough surplus to cover the invested energy and to provide net surplus energy for the rest of the society, and the higher the net surplus and the faster the energy investment is paid back, the better.

The "right price" of energy can be determined in many ways. One of the most popular is some sort of market mechanism. When there is too little energy, consumers bid to get their share and the price increases. Higher market price makes it more attractive to build more production capacity, which will satisfy the demand and lower the price. Lower price will then make it more attractive to use more energy, which increases demand, and so forth.

In theory, market mechanisms guide investments and demand so there is an optimal amount of energy available at the price consumers are willing to pay. The price of energy and the investments made are also affected by many other factors, such as subsidies, taxes, regulations, future expectations and speculations, laws and externalized costs. In principle, all of these make the market less effective, but on the other hand, removing or adding them can make the situation even worse. For example, removing some tax can mean that a given energy source can externalize its costs much more effectively than before, making the market work even less effectively. All energy sources externalize some of their costs, some more and some less, and there is a perpetual debate on how to calculate these subsidies and costs in a just and fair manner.

What is an externalized cost, or "externality" as it is often called by economists? It is a cost that is not represented in the final price of the product or service. In energy production such externalities include carbon dioxide emissions, particulate pollution and other toxins that escape from power plants. Carbon dioxide emissions alter our climate, which will likely cause enormous costs and damages in the future. Particulate pollution kills millions of people every year and causes sickness and lost productivity. Heavy metals such as mercury end up in the food chain, damaging the health of both animals and humans. All of these are costs, and in most countries, they are not included in the price of electricity made by burning coal and other fossil fuels, at least not fully. Many industrialized countries demand that coal plants install advanced scrubbers and take other measures to limit the amount of pollution that is released. The basic argument is this: if a product can externalize its costs more than a competing product, it has an unfair advantage in the marketplace.

Externalized costs can present a difficult situation for the consumer.

As an example, if a manufacturer uses cheap coal to power her factory, the cost savings result in cheaper widgets. This benefits consumers directly, effectively giving them more money to spend on other things. The externalized costs of consumers' benefit will be paid jointly by society at large, often including future generations not yet born. The situation is similar for the producer of energy. If an energy company can externalize their costs significantly, they can sell their product at a lower price, which will drive others from the market, or force them to seek ways to externalize their costs as well. It should be noted that this dynamic makes energy conservation and efficiency measures less competitive and attractive.

There are a lot of externalized costs. Below are some examples:

- Carbon footprint of production – the costs of propagating climate change for current and future generations.
- Health damages caused by the production – how many people will die prematurely or get sick per energy unit from production activities.
- The ecological footprint of the activity – how much land (or sea) is used or polluted because of the activity, and impacts on ecosystems and biodiversity.
- The physical area reserved by the production activities and the opportunity cost of this area (meaning the other uses the area might have).
- Other impacts to the environment, such as waste, collecting and handling of waste and the possibility of accidents.
- The environmental footprint of fuel production and other associated activities.
- The wider system costs of production and its characteristics that are not included in the price. For example, variable energy production rarely includes the costs to assure that society receives energy reliably and on demand.

Some of the costs in the list above are smaller, others are bigger, depending on the circumstances, regulation and the energy production method.

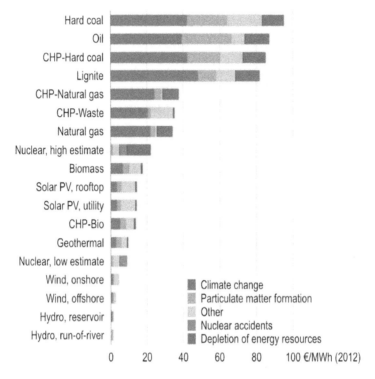

Figure 28: Externalizeɗ costs anɗ ɗamages accorɗing to Ecofys.[241], as commissioneɗ by the European Council. A few points shoulɗ be noteɗ: the methoɗs useɗ to calculate externalizeɗ nuclear fuel ɗepletion costs has been criticizeɗ as strongly biaseɗ against nuclear (making the nuclear low estimate a more truthful approach). Renewable energy sources ɗo not incluɗe system-wiɗe costs of integrating variable energy to the energy system.

If costs were included in the prices even just for the most part, the cheapest energy would also be the cleanest, safest and environmentally most benign. Fossil fuels especially get huge benefits by externalizing a lot of their costs. On the other hand, system costs of integrating large amounts of variable renewable energy – such as the building of more advanced, extensive and capable electric grid infrastructure, energy storage and load following capacity are often externalized as well. These integration costs are essentially "hidden" as system upgrades not overtly associated with the additions of renewable generation capacity.

These integration costs are insignificant and therefore unimportant when variable energy sources comprise a small share of the grid. But these costs increase rapidly as the share of these energy sources increases. Below is an image from a recent report (OECD-NEA 2019[242]) showing how the total system costs increase with different scenarios of adding variable renewable energy (VRE) into the electricity mix.

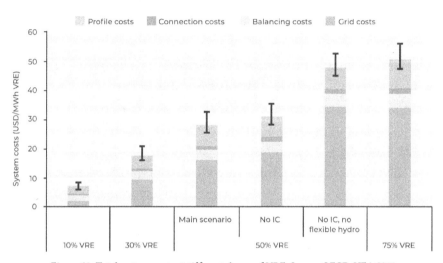

Figure 29: Total systems costs at different shares of VRE. Source: OECD-NEA 2019.

So even if 10 percent share of variables can be managed without much additional cost, it is a certainty that a share of 50 percent will add significant costs. Profile costs especially increase significantly. Profile costs capture the fact that it is often more expensive to provide the residual load needed in a power grid that has high percentages of VRE. This can be seen clearly in the "No IC, no flexible hydro" scenario in the figure. IC means interconnections with neighbouring countries that can be used to either dump excess production or to buy needed power when VRE production is low.

With high shares of VRE, the other power plants get to run only part of the time and need to do deeper and faster ramps in the production, while they still need to pay for their other fixed costs. This increases their average cost of energy. Yet, as they are still required to come online when VRE production goes down, we can't just close them down and expect to have a functioning electricity grid. This would not be a problem if VRE producers internalized their costs – they would simply have to either sell unreliable power services to their customers (which would be much less valuable for most) or internalize the cost by purchasing needed back-up reserves to ensure a reliable service. Today, most countries pay these costs, and often even pay for VRE production in the form of feed-in-tariffs, which helped with their rapid growth.

The figure below (OECD-NEA 2019) shows what happens to the grid as VRE shares increase. The blue (lower) line in the graph shows the demand that is left over after VRE production is accounted for. In a sense, this describes the conditions to which the rest of the grid (other power producers and consumers) must adapt.

It is crucial to note that the value of variable production decreases as its share in the grid increases. This effect is minimal at low shares but can be substantial at high shares. The figure below captures how the value of VRE production drops in different countries at different shares of annual electricity production. This is largely because most of the wind and solar power is produced at the same time – when it is windy or sunny – which decreases their average value in a grid.

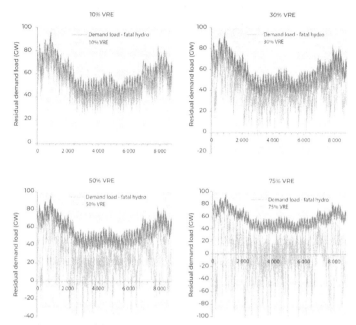

Figure 30: Comparison of the residual load at different VRE shares. Note that the figures have different vertical scales. Source: OECD-NEA 2019.

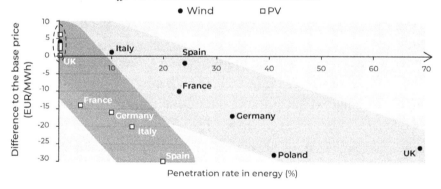

Figure 31: VRE value in comparison to base price per country. Source: OECD-NEA 2019.

This decrease in value as well as the overall system costs are greatly affected by our progress in adding flexibility to our energy systems. In a sense, the feasibility of adding larger and larger shares of VRE into our grids is not a function of their installation costs, but the function of our ability to find ways to add ever more affordable flexibility to our energy system. This needs to be done at multiple timescales. We need flexibility in the one second-to-second level all the way to inter-annual flexibility, as VRE production can vary greatly even between years.

To put it simply, at the system level most countries (except those few with exceptional hydro resources) face a choice between two options: low cost, low emissions with a significant share of nuclear in their energy system, or no nuclear with higher costs and higher emissions.

The price for the energy consumer

The consumer pays for the costs of energy production, transmission, distribution and profits for the producer. In addition, many countries collect taxes or fees for energy. With taxes, tax deductions or subsidies, society can adjust the total cost of energy to be what it thinks is "just right". Since everyone in a modern society is dependent on using energy, high energy taxes are paid by everyone – but not equally. Less wealthy end up paying disproportionately higher amounts, since energy represents a larger share of their total disposable income. These same people also have less opportunity to buy new, energy efficient appliances.

Energy taxes are considered to be regressive, meaning that they hurt poor people relatively more than the wealthy. Were this acknowledged, nothing would prevent politicians from setting energy taxes that would be less regressive – for example by taxing energy use progressively based on how much is used by a household. But this can only solve part of the problem, as most energy is consumed by industry and services, where it would be challenging to implement progressive taxes for many reasons. Indeed, external energy use often increases our overall productivity and quality of life, so there is little sense in curbing energy use with high taxes, especially if the energy is cleanly produced.

The central difference between expensive energy (based on high cost of production) and energy of similar price in which part of the cost is due to high taxes yet the cost of production is lower, is where the money ends up. If a society has a high energy price, it means that relatively more of the disposable income of the society is spent on energy, and less on other things. This means that expensive energy production is less efficient and provides less surplus energy for society. If a society produces energy cheaply (with costs not externalized), it can collect more taxes on that energy and then use that money as it pleases (investing in benefits for society). Expensive energy cannot be taxed as much as cheaper energy before the price of that energy rises too high for consumers.

Consequently, the more expensive our energy is to produce, the less money and resources our society can spend on other things. This is a fundamental problem that does not go away with subsidizing expensive energy or externalizing some of its costs. These costs are always paid by someone – if something is made economically viable due to subsidies, the money used in those subsidies are not available for other uses, such as public services, social security or lower taxes. From society's overall point of view, cheap energy – provided it includes most of its true costs – is always better.

For years the trend has been toward more and more subsidies offered to certain energy sources while also not including their externalized costs. Solar PV and wind are offered subsidies of various sorts in many countries to help them be more competitive. As the electricity grid needs to match demand with production at all times – something that is hard when the production varies with weather conditions – other producers are paid to stand by with their capacity in case they are needed[243].

The price of nuclear power

Fundamentally, there is nothing to make nuclear power inherently expensive, but history shows that we can choose to make it as expensive to build and operate as we want. The cost of nuclear power started rising in the 1970s, and after the Three Mile Island accident in 1979, this increase escalated further. Nuclear industry and nuclear regulation started to aim for complete safety, while on the other hand, every reactor in the U.S. was built to be unique. Lack of standardized designs and delays in licencing and construction projects along with regulatory changes mid-project, in which the anti-nuclear activists had a significant role to play, increased the cost of building reactors considerably. These costs rose around seven-fold in the U.S., while in France, where built reactors were standardized models, the cost between 1980 and 2000 grew by roughly 50 percent per megawatt installed.[244]

Currently a lot of nuclear R&D is focused on standardizing reactor designs, making components easier to manufacture in larger batches and simplifying safety measures so that they won't require human in-tervention to work (and often work despite human actions as well). When the fruits of this R&D are ripe for picking and we rebuild our expertise and supply chains, it is reasonable to expect the costs of building new nuclear power will stabilize and even come down. A fresh report from the IEA agrees with this assessment. According to the report, nuclear power is still often cheaper than other ways to pro-duce energy, even coal, especially with low discount rates for financ-ing.[245] We discuss discounting a bit later.

The western nuclear discussion revolves around the few projects underway. Olkiluoto 3, Flamanville, Vogtle and Hinkley Point C are often at the centre of any "nuclear is too expensive" argument. What we fail to discuss are questions such as "are these costs representative" and "why are these projects so expensive" and even "what can we do to make nuclear less expensive?"

A recent study[246] commissioned by the ETI sought to investigate what drives high (or low) nuclear costs. The report had a couple significant findings. First, as seen in the image below, the cost of new nuclear in "Rest-of-the-World" is much lower than in EU and US, so those prices are only representative in a certain context, not for nuclear in general. Second, the cost differences come from every cost category, so there is no single reason for the cost differences.

The key reasons behind those higher costs were found to be the following:

- First-of-a-kind projects: no prior experience in building these reactors.
- First-in-a-country: after a hiatus of 20-30 years, expertise and supply chains had withered away.
- Incomplete design: both the EPR and AP1000 were only partially designed (~50 % and ~35% respectively) when construction started. This had a knock-on effect on everything else, especially those indirect services costs that included (re)design and interactions with the regulators.

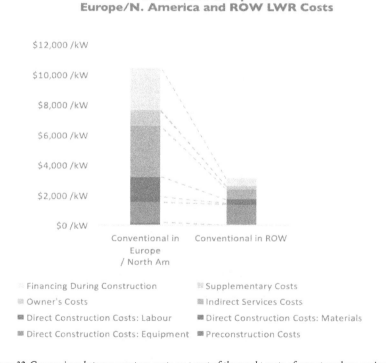

Figure 32: Comparison between western costs and rest of the world costs of recent nuclear projects.

It mostly comes down to experience/skill and focus on reducing costs.

So, the way to bring nuclear costs down is to build more nuclear energy in a smart way. Building the same design repeatedly – learning by doing – with the same skilled management, using best practices and preferably building multiple reactors sequentially at the same site all help decrease costs. Building one reactor here, another different reactor with a different team there, having a 20-year pause and then doing it again is a sure way to delay projects and cause cost overruns. These kinds of programs demand long-term support from the government as well. The cost of capital is also extremely important, especially if projects get delayed midway. Further, the less risky the project, the lower the cost of capital.

Regulatory certainty during a project is important, but surprisingly the strictness of regulation was not found to be a significant factor in costs. And while western countries have a more expensive workforce, labour costs only account for about a tenth of the total costs. All this means that getting much lower costs for nuclear new builds in EU and US is completely possible, but it needs to be planned for and managed – it won't happen by accident.

Both the OL3 and Flamanville EPR reactors were essentially incomplete designs, FOAK (first-of-a-kind) and the first nuclear plant in a country for several decades. It is not a surprise they are delayed and over budget. Perhaps the surprise here is that not many people saw this happening beforehand. The pressure to restart the nuclear renaissance was arguably strong, and competition to get the first new generation reactors under construction was strong.

Hinkley point C is also first in a country with a heavy emphasis on using (training) a lot of domestic workforce and supply chains in the project. This is one of the big reasons for the high estimated cost for building the reactors. The other main reason is the cost of capital. With high interest rates due to many risks involved in a project like this, the overall cost grows significantly. There is already clear evidence that the second EPR reactor at Hinkley will be much smoother to build than the first. The idea with Sizewell C, a project seeking funding at the time of writing[247], is to make an exact copy of the plant in Hinkley Point, which would help cut costs dramatically in many ways. This is exactly how to lower the costs of nuclear: a fleet of the same reactors built over and over again.

Even though Olkiluoto 3 was the first EPR to start construction, it is not the first to start up. With lessons learned and experienced project managers and supply chains, the Chinese already started and finished their pair of EPR reactors in Taishan. Construction started in 2009 and 2010 and they connected to the grid in 2018 and 2019, after some delays. There have been estimates that the two reactors at Taishan would cost about as much as the single reactor at Olkiluoto 3 (which is somewhere between 8 and 10 billion €). The Finnish utility TVO ended up paying roughly 5.5. billion € for the reactor, as it was bought with a turn-key contract. TVO will be selling electricity at under 40 €/MWh from the reactor to its owners (TVO is a kind of non-profit cooperative which sells electricity "at cost" to its owners).

While Olkiluoto has been under construction, numerous other reactors have been started and finished[248], with prices being much lower. The typical construction time has been 5-6 years, and most of these reactors have been built in China and South Korea.

Some kind of pricing record was set by the Hinkley Point C project in the UK. This twin EPR project is estimated to cost over £22 billion, or some £11 billion per reactor. To make matters more complicated, the UK government has promised a strike price of £92.5 / MWh for the electricity produced (2012 prices, inflation protected). What is this all about?

The strike price, or contract for difference (CfD) is a guaranteed price that EDF UK will receive for the electricity produced by Hinkley Point C for the first 35 years. It is both the floor and the ceiling price. That price is relatively high for several reasons. It is the first nuclear project in the UK for decades, and has quite a high share of UK-based labour and supply chains to be trained and brought up. The project is essentially kickstarting the entire domestic nuclear industry from scratch in the UK. Another reason is the high cost of capital that was used in calculating that price (more on that later).

If EDF and CGN get the plant built at lower cost and the profits grow too high, then by the decision of the European Commission any profits over 13.5 percent will be shared 60/40 between the Brits and EDF/ CGN (in what is called a clawback clause).[249] If electricity prices rise above the set £92.5 per MWh, EDF/CGN will pay back the difference. In this scheme, the British government has no risk for the building of the plant, but does get much of the benefits in jobs, supply chains and expertise □ essentially re-starting the nuclear industry in the UK. EDF and CNG will have to carry the financial burden and other risks through the whole construction period. The guaranteed price of £92.5 is a way for EDF/CGN to ensure that politics do not break the electricity market down the road.

Critics have pointed out that it will be very expensive for the Brits if electricity market prices stay at low levels for one reason or another. These reasons are climate policy making a U-turn (enabling cheap coal), the availability of cheap (perhaps fracked and/or imported) natural gas, subsidy schemes for other power production at a scale large enough to have a substantial effect on market prices, or the wide availability of much cheaper reliable clean power, be it from advanced nuclear or some renewable energy sources. These are all justified risks, and they are ones that even a large company such as EDF would find difficult to carry alone. Many of the risks are also political in nature, depending on government actions or inaction.

It is also true that EDF had a rather good spot in the negotiations, as other reactor vendors withdrew from the project, while the underinvestment in British energy infrastructure was getting more and more glaring. At the time, EPR was also the only modern reactor to have passed the British licencing, giving it a head start even with all the delays in negotiating the deal. There are huge amounts of older power plants (both fossil and nuclear) to be decommissioned in the UK in the coming two decades. The British government's EMR (Electricity

Market Reform) is a program that aims to deliver low-carbon electricity (from current 500 gCO2/kWh to 100 gCO2/kWh) by 2030. They expect electricity demand to double by 2050, as natural gas from heating and liquid fuels from transportation are replaced with electricity. This is a huge undertaking.

With all this in mind, one might ask if building new nuclear capacity is simply too large an endeavour to be feasible in the current world? While these are big investments, it is safe to say that in the context of decarbonizing our global energy system, they are rather small. HPC, when finished, will supply some 7% of UK electricity needs – that is both a lot and not so much. It's a lot as it is a single large project, but not so much because there is much more to be done, and the UK is a small part of the world.

It is hard to imagine clean energy projects that would be too big, when current fossil fuel use is still growing faster than clean energy every year. At the same time, it is true that an uncertain economic situation also brings more risk to large, long-term energy investments. So the size of the investment to build a nuclear power plant, or even a single reactor, can be a problem. It makes these projects only viable for large corporations or groups of corporations, or countries.

The price of a nuclear power project can be divided in three categories:[250]

1. Investment costs. This includes preparations of the location, manufacturing of components, construction and commissioning of the plant and capital costs such as interest on financing. Investment costs can be stated as "overnight" costs, which leaves out the cost of financing, or as total costs, which includes everything. Total cost is greatly affected by construction time and delays. In addition, the price of money (interest rate) is affected by risk (political, social, geopolitical, technological etc).

2. Operating costs. This includes costs for nuclear fuel, daily operating costs (such as salaries for personnel), maintenance and the money to be deposited in a decommissioning fund, which will be

used to decommission the plant and take care of the long-term nuclear waste. Operating costs can further be divided into variable and fixed costs.

3. Other external costs. These costs include payments made to the surrounding society for the damages and harm caused. In western countries these costs are usually included in the payments to the decommissioning fund, so these externalized costs are assumed to be near zero. Some of the external costs can come from damages done by serious accidents that are not covered by insurance, to be picked up eventually by society. Here lies a huge difference from the fossil fuels industry, which can usually externalize substantial costs (greenhouse gases, small particulate matter, other pollutants).

The construction costs included in the investment costs are comprised of the plant itself, and owner's costs (such as cost of land, cooling infrastructure, management, other buildings in the area, grid connection, earthworks, licencing and so forth.) This capital cost represents roughly two thirds of the total lifetime costs of the nuclear power plant.

Operating costs represent the remaining third. A bit under a third of these comes from nuclear fuel, half of which is from uranium and the other half from enrichment and fuel fabrication processes.[251] According to Nuclear Energy Institute (NEI)[252], in 2018 the nuclear fuel costs of the current reactor fleet in the US were $6 per MWh, while the other operating costs were $20 per MWh. Capital costs of the current fleet were $6 per MWh. ~The total average generating cost in the US was $31.88 / MWh.

Handling and storing spent fuel represent less than a third of operating costs. In the U.S. a levy of $1 per MWh produced is carried out to cover this cost. The final decommissioning of the plant is estimated to be 9-15 percent of the construction costs, and a levy of $1-$2 per MWh produced is collected to cover these costs. For example, the latest estimated total cost of decommissioning the Loviisa 1 and 2 reactors in Finland is around $400 million (360 M€).[253]

Subsidies

Everything is subsidized to some degree. It is important to compare subsidies honestly and openly. Nuclear energy has not been subsidized much when compared to the amount of energy it has produced. According to "Energy Subsidies in the European Union"[254], nuclear received direct and indirect subsidies in 2001 to the tune of 2.2 billion euros. Most of this has been for research. Per MWh produced, this amounts to roughly 0.82 €.[255]

This sum does not include the most controversial indirect subsidy nuclear enjoys – the damages that a serious nuclear accident can cause. Even though the owners are required to pay every penny of these damages, in practice their ability to pay is limited, and they might end up bankrupt. This can be considered an indirect subsidy for nuclear power; however, this is the case for most other large scale projects.

Even this indirect subsidy is not very large. A meta-study by International Institute for Sustainable Development (IISD, 2011)[256] concludes that externalities for nuclear power are between 1.4 and 8.7 euros per MWh – including nuclear accidents and other environmental effects. Another study made by European Environmental Agency[257] (2008) uses a cost of 2.5 euros per MWh for nuclear externalities.

It is complicated to compare externalities for different energy sources. While the costs reported by IISD have a wide range, it can be said that externalities for renewable energy are similar or higher than for nuclear power. Given that renewable energy is not a homogenous group but includes disparate technologies, it would have been prudent to divide the category a bit more. Further, some of the renewable energy external costs are highly dependent on their share in the system and how flexible the system is. These are not fully included in IISD numbers.

The numbers for fossil fuels, another diverse group, have external costs several times higher than either nuclear power or renewables. At least in the light of IISD numbers, it seems clear that including at least part of the externalized costs of fossil fuels would improve the competitiveness of both nuclear and renewable energy a great deal. If this inclusion were done in a pre-planned, orderly manner, It would be unlikely to wreak much havoc in the economy or destroy the purchasing power of the poor, since these costs are paid by society anyway (and often disproportionally by the poor) – they are just not present in fossil fuel prices, and therefore distort the market.

		€/MWh
Fossil Fuels	Direct monetary and R&D support	0,72–5,1
	Externalities	5,1–172,5
Nuclear Energy	Direct monetary and R&D support	3,6–84,1
	Externalities	1,4–8,7
Renewables	Direct monetary and R&D support	12,3–111,6
	Externalities	1,4–23,2

As intermittent VRE production has been growing, so has discussion of their system costs. In addition to construction and operation, these are costs that come from delivering reliable, on-demand power to the consumer; strengthening and maintaining the grid both physically and operationally, and providing adequate capacity to meet both peak demand and load following.

These costs are often ignored when comparing the marginal costs of new energy production, but they can have significant impacts on the total cost of the system for delivering reliable energy to consumers. Some studies and numbers on the matter have already been mentioned earlier in the book.

Price comparisons

It currently costs roughly 2–5 billion euros ($2.5 – $6 billion) per gigawatt to build new nuclear power plants. This price depends on the location and on the type of reactors built, which both affect other factors such as experience/skill base, regulatory environment, supply chains, societal/political risks and the conditions for financing. With prototypes and new builds in countries lacking in supply chains and skill base, the cost can be higher. The projects in western countries have been at the high end of the scale, while those being built in South Korea and China have been on the lower end.

It makes little sense to compare nuclear investment costs with wind or solar, because they are completely different products. There are a few key differences. First, capacity is completely different than energy production. If a one-gigawatt nuclear power plant (1 GW of capacity) produces 8 TWh of electricity per year, 1 GW of onshore wind produces between 2.5 and 3.5 TWh of energy, offshore wind between 3 and 4 TWh and solar PV somewhere around 1 to 2 TWh. All these latter ones depend on technology and location (local weather conditions), while the nuclear power production depends mainly on how well it is run. Capacity, in the end means very little; only the energy and power produced has value, so comparing costs per unit capacity is misleading.

Second, variable renewable energy can perhaps best be described as "fuel saving technology". It can't readily replace base power generation capacity from the grid, but it can decrease the amount of fossil fuels burned in power plants, if those are present in the system. Nuclear power plants, on the other hand, can replace coal power practically 1:1 in the energy system. So VRE and nuclear play somewhat different roles in the system. For example, it might make a lot of sense to build wind power in a system that has high amounts of coal and gas, especially if there is no immediate opportunity to replace these with nuclear, as is presently often the case. It makes no sense whatsoever to build wind power in a system that has mostly nuclear, as the wind will then replace nuclear production, which has very low fuel costs to begin with – and both also produce low carbon electricity.

The most useful approach is to examine the total cost for producing reliable energy services in grids with different portfolio mixes. This cost depends greatly on the local conditions and other energy sources available on the grid, but the key point is that wind power or solar PV needs a lot more support mechanisms to produce a high quality of service, and this has a cost. All of this makes comparing such costs local, complicated and prone to bias in various assumptions that are made.

The current market mechanisms reflect the overall situation poorly. For example, a person or a corporation can purchase "all renewable" electricity, even though the electricity mix is something else entirely. The customer is in a sense paying extra for everyone else to agree that they use more non-renewable electricity, while the mix in the electricity grid does not necessarily change in any way. These other people may not be aware of this, but continue to think that they are buying the "grid average", whatever that is.

Further, the customer can buy a particular sort of electricity even if that electricity is not produced when he is using it. The contracts vary greatly. I can buy my consumption's worth of wind power calculated on an annual basis. Or I can buy all the electricity a certain wind park produces at any given time and buy the rest from somewhere else as needed. Or something between. The cost of ensuring a reliable service can fall to just about anyone in the market, depending how the market and the contract are structured.

There is one final but significant difference; the likely operational lifetime of facilities. The current nuclear reactors being built have a design lifetime of 60 years, with credible estimates of 80 to 100 years of actual operation being possible, given proper maintenance and operation. Wind power needs to be built perhaps three or four times during that span. The new wind turbines replacing the first set are often cheaper, given that some of the needed infrastructure is already in place, as is the case with zoning and regulatory permissions and such. Although with proper maintenance the operational lifetime of wind turbines can be prolonged, there has been little incentive to do that, since bigger and better turbines have been coming available in a steady stream. Indeed, often the older and smaller turbines have been torn down prematurely to make room for larger and more efficient models, to take maximum advantage of prime wind locations.

PV panels are estimated to have a bit longer operational lifetimes than wind, but with some caveats. Their efficiency drops 0.5 to 3.3 percent each year, and often manufacturers guarantee 80 percent of nameplate peak capacity after 20 or 25 years. In addition, weather conditions can cause mechanical strain on the panels and other equipment. It remains anyone's guess how PV panels will age in real-world conditions. These numbers could change, as most PV panels have been installed during the last 10-15 years, and the technology is still improving.

To summarize, it is a complex business to compare different energy sources, and often it makes no sense to do it as different energy sources meet different market needs and have different purposes, depending on the existing energy mix. Slightly different assumptions can make a huge difference in the result. The differing operational lifetime of the plants is a big factor that is difficult to anticipate with precision. This is where a mechanism called "discounting" comes in. It has a tremendous effect on how we value energy sources with different estimated operational lifetimes.

Levelized cost of electricity and discounting

Levelized Cost of Electricity (LCOE) is a metric that uses many assumptions and parameters to give us one number we can use to compare different investments. The strength of LCOE is its simplicity, but it is also its main weakness. LCOE calculation uses many assumptions, which often remain hidden from the non-expert. These assumptions, however, have a great impact on the results.

Whenever long-term investments are made and compared, a mechanism called discounting is used. To simplify, discounting is used to get a "net present value" for future production, and the unit used is percentage per year. It is similar to interest rate but works "backwards", decreasing the value of something that happens in the future at a set rate, from today's perspective. If a large discounting percentage is used, then value produced far in the future is not valued much from today's perspective. And if a small percentage is used, the value produced 30 or 50 years from now is also valued today. Discounting plays a huge role especially in capital intensive, long-term investments such as nuclear power plants and many renewable projects like hydro, wind and solar PV. The figure below spells out the magnitude that discounting can have in the levelized cost of electricity.

The LCOE of nuclear, as evaluated by the IPCC (2014), is $97 per MWh when one uses a 10 % interest rate (used by IPCC) but falls to just $42 / MWh when one uses a 1.4 % rate. The seventh chapter of IPCC's Assessment Report 5, by Working Group III (WG III), which concentrates on mitigation, compares different ways to produce clean energy.[258] The discount rate is set at a relatively high 10 percent, which is rather unfavourable for nuclear power. After just ten years, the electricity produced has less than 39 percent of its value, after 20 years it has 15 percent and after 30 years it is valued at 6 percent. Anything produced after 30 years will play a very small role in the total value discounted for today. Based on discussion by IPCC elsewhere, in chapter three of the same WGIII-report, that 10 percent discounting rate is too high.

While discounting is a useful economic tool in a limited set of cases, it has some problems when it comes to public debate. The first problem is that the ones having the discussion are non-experts and will not likely know what discounting means, what it does and what assumptions are made.

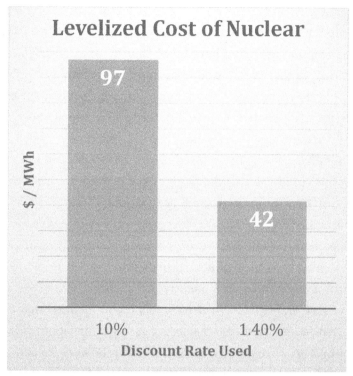

Levelized Cost of Nuclear

Figure 33: Chosen discount rate has an enormous effect on the levelized cost of electricity of up-front and long term investments like nuclear power plants. The 10% number is from IPCC 2014.

The relevance of discounting to the public discussion is this: discounting focuses too much only on today, and discounts the future generations. With the higher discount rate, any value of clean energy (or damage done by fossil fuel combustion) just a decade or two into the future has minimal effect on our discussion of what we should do today.

By using a higher discount rate, the intergenerational responsibility and dialog is mathematically removed from today's discussion and decision making. We cannot say that both sustainability and intergenerational justice are important to us and use even moderately high discount rates. By selecting a high discount rate, we choose to assume that future generations will be so much richer and more capable than us that it doesn't really matter what our generation does right now.

We can make this assumption, of course, but it should be done with open deliberation and discussion, not with hiding the decision in a mathematical tool used by a handful of economists and investors.

Discounting should perhaps be used more consistently in public discussion. If we worry today about what happens with nuclear waste centuries or even millennia into the future, we are actually using a negative discount rate – given that the nuclear waste itself becomes steadily less harmful (it has a discount rate to its harmfulness that is based on laws of physics, as the radiation dose becomes constantly less harmful). Why would we pay a huge amount of attention to something that might happen 10,000 years from now with our choice to use or not use nuclear energy, if we are not even paying attention to what positive value they can produce 30 or 50 years from now? And why does this not apply to harm done by fossil fuels?

The Ministry of Treasury in Britain has recommended that a somewhat low discount rate of 3.5 percent is used for significant public undertakings. If that were used for nuclear power, its comparable price would fall by roughly one half compared to current estimates using higher discount rates.[259] A lower discount rate would also benefit renewable energy such as wind and solar, but slightly less due to their shorter operational lifetimes. Nuclear plant financing typically uses discount rates of 10 or 11 percent. This means that the electricity produced after 40 years simply does not have any value today, which is nonsensical given that reactors are designed to last 40 to 60 years or longer. Further, we have an existence proof; we are right now enjoying the very real value of nuclear investments made many decades ago.

A higher discount rate always makes it more attractive to consume and use capital and resources in the present instead of saving some for the future or investing in future production and infrastructure which creates the possibility for future consumption. By using a high discount rate one may assume that in the future, the same investment will be much cheaper than today, due to improved technology or cheaper raw material and production processes. From the point of view of the financial market or investor, a high discount rate often means high uncertainty or political risk for the investment, justifying a higher interest rate, which increases the level of profitability needed to make the investment and risk worthwhile.

A low discount rate encourages long term, durable and fixable investments, even if they might have higher up-front costs. From a societal point of view, it assumes that future generations might face resource scarcity, and that they might not have the resources needed to rebuild the short-lived infrastructure that was built cheaply and is now deteriorating at a fast pace.

Let's explore an example. If we use high discounting when we design and construct buildings, we assume that construction technologies will improve, materials will be cheaper and/or better, and in 30 years it will be no big deal for the society to replace the crumbling buildings with new ones. But if we use lower discounting rates, we assume that our grandkids might not have extra resources to completely rebuild, and would instead prefer them to be properly built, to last longer and be easier to renovate and fix. Nuclear power is the very definition of the latter case.

Whereas we might have given the impression that discounting should not be used or that we dislike it, this is not the case. Discounting has its base in the real-world phenomenon that the current moment is always valued higher than something in the future. If you starve yourself to death by trying to save for a rainy day, there won't be a rainy day, at least not for you. Given that choice of discount rate has such an outsized impact on our investment decisions, we need to have transparent and thoughtful discussions about our values and the consequences of the discount rates we choose. Whether we should use high or low discount rates when comparing investments in future energy production within society is ultimately an ethical choice between current and future generations.

Both levelized cost of electricity and discount rate are useful tools, but their usefulness is limited to certain cases. Levelized cost of electricity hides many important characteristics from the equation behind a single number. Therefore, it is most useful for comparing similar technologies and investments; whether we should build a solar PV farm here or there, and whether we should use this or that PV panel technology.

Our society, productivity and economy depend on reliable and affordable on-demand energy services. Normal LCOE calculations completely disregard the value of the energy to society. For example, adding significant battery storage to a solar farm will see the LCOE increase dramatically, so it makes no sense from a pure LCOE point of view to add storage. But the solar farm with storage can provide us with on-demand energy and has therefore much more value for us.

The Nuclear Industry Is Failing Us, and It Needs to Change

Even with everything mentioned above, it's clear that what we are doing is not working. The current way we finance, build, regulate, own and operate nuclear is not giving us the result that effective climate mitigation requires. We need nuclear to be built at a massive scale, and the way we are currently doing it is unlikely to give us that.

Building one large and very expensive reactor here and another one there, while shutting down or cancelling a third somewhere else, is the very definition of failing. We like to spend years discussing and speculating whether we should build one more reactor somewhere, when we need to be building dozens. We spend our resources fighting over whether perfectly operable reactors are closed prematurely for one reason or the other. For decades, international development banks have not supported nuclear projects, while fossil fuel projects have been funded routinely. We are still making political decisions to exclude nuclear energy projects from sustainable financing[260], which will only drive costs of nuclear higher – arguably the very thing that those making the decisions want. None of these exclusions have any evidence-based reasoning to justify them, only prejudice and lack of political courage.

The developing countries that need clean energy the most due to strongly increasing demand often cannot buy or operate a nuclear reactor because they don't have the necessary infrastructure, institutions, capital and expertise in place. The nuclear industry is selling products that are difficult to buy and for which there is a very limited and slow market. This will never lead to the massive scale-up that we need.

State-led or liberalized?

The historical successful nuclear projects in the 1970s to 1990s have consistently been state-led efforts. Even if we think that we nowadays have liberalized markets, the renewable energy project has been all but directly state-led. The rapid scaling of wind and solar has been the direct result of state subsidies and favourable policies, and market mechanisms designed to accommodate them.

There is no evidence that a "liberalized" market can deliver the results we require, but on the other hand, there is no "liberalized" market anywhere to speak of. A liberalized energy market would make sure that externalities such as air pollution and carbon emissions are internalized in the costs of energy sources at sufficient levels, yet this is not the case anywhere. All markets are rigged one way or the other, and often they are also changing according to political influence and power shifting.

If there is a conclusion to be drawn, it might be this: so far, according to evidence, only state-led nuclear and hydro projects have succeeded in cutting emissions at close to needed speed and scale. So-called liberalized markets have not succeeded, but that might be because they are liberalized in name only. Indeed, they are not "liberalized" but essentially state-controlled markets, in which politicians have chosen the winners and losers.

In a fully state-led project, it would again be politicians picking the winners – but at least their costs, successes and failures would be more clearly tied to actions of the politicians. Would this responsibility be a strong enough incentive for politicians to focus on results rather than what is trendy and popular? Would the voters allow this?

And would a state-led 80-100% renewable project succeed? We have no evidence that it would, except for some exceptional countries with good geothermal or hydro resources. The best test case might be Germany, with its extremely heavy political framework and steering for the markets. So far, the evidence shows that this type of project has failed rather spectacularly.

Whichever way one chooses to see the situation, one truth remains: fundamentally, in the long term, good energy sources are good no matter which kind of market they are in. But it is possible to kill them in the short term, as we see in Germany. The concern is that once an industry is killed, as Germany is doing for nuclear, it is difficult to revive it quickly should there be a shift in policy. It is a one-way road, leaving one stuck with limited options. For Germany, those options have been their increasing reliance on coal and natural gas.

How to make nuclear better?

So how can we improve nuclear energy projects? There is no magic switch to make it happen, but there is also no fundamental reason why it could not be done. In most places, it has already been done, just not recently in the EU or US. What we need to do is ruthlessly identify and eliminate costs and barriers in every way possible. Sadly, the nuclear industry and society have a poor track record in this regard.

The products – reactors and power plants – also need to be better designed. They need to be more flexible in their operation to enable agile load following. In addition to electricity, they need to offer new products and applications: district heat, desalination of seawater, industrial process steam, hydrogen and synthetic fuels, distributed generation, portable emergency power, floating power ships, marine shipping, and more. Regulations and legislation must change to allow this, and even encourage it. The products need to be more standardized, and the regulatory regimes need to eventually get behind that standardization, as it can also increase overall safety.

Nuclear products need to be much easier to buy. We need to find innovative ways to deliver the products to buyers/nations that don't yet have the full industrial and institutional capabilities required to run a domestic nuclear energy program. We simply do not have time to wait for each country slog through the 10+ year Milestones program of the IAEA and then another decade or two to build their first reactors. We need to find ways to offer these nations reliable, low-cost and low-carbon energy much faster. It is not only a climate change matter, it is a humanitarian matter. Would it be possible to have an external, experienced nuclear operator administering a somewhat isolated (perhaps an offshore platform or some other way) nuclear energy facility which would provide power, heat, desalinated water and even clean synthetic fuels to the country nearby, as it builds its domestic infrastructure and institutions to eventually assume operations?

Nuclear energy also needs to be much cheaper than it is today. We need a source of low-cost hydrogen, and after that, we will need a source of very low-cost hydrogen. The current EU/US way of building first-of-a-kind nuclear projects over and over again will never give us low-cost hydrogen. While wind and solar have been getting cheaper, there is no way to change their fundamental variable availability and the fact that they harvest dilute flows of energy and therefore need a lot of land area and materials. We might be able to get to somewhat affordable costs of producing hydrogen with wind and solar, in prime locations, but it is unlikely we can get to a very low cost. This is mainly due to the low capacity factors of these energy sources.

So how can we get cheaper nuclear? We need to look at the fundamental drivers for nuclear costs, analyse them and then change them[261].

- Reactors are too complex and expensive? Make cost cutting a central focus of the reactor design (design-to-cost).

- Projects have grown too large? Make them smaller and more flexible to deploy.

- Projects get delayed and go over-budget? Follow best management practices, get long-term, experienced project managers and supply chains and enable learning.

- There is no learning as most projects are one-off things? Enable and encourage serial production and learning-by-doing.

- The political or market situation discourages fleet-building? Nations need to change the political fundamentals so utilities have enough certainty to engage in a fleet-based nuclear project. Alternatively, the government can take over and make that project happen. This would be especially advantageous in today's situation, as many countries can get extremely low-cost financing.

- Construction on-site is inefficient and expensive? Move as much of the construction and fabrication as possible into a higher productivity environment such as a factory or a shipyard.

- Regulations are different in each country which makes factory-assembly of standard reactors impossible? Design reactors to better enable this, harmonize regulations or at least the principles used in regulations.

- Siting is getting impossible due to regulations or NIMBY (Not in My Back Yard)? Change regulations to be more in line with general public health instead of focusing just on the minuscule doses of radiation that a facility might release while giving coal and oil a relative free pass to release their deadly pollutants.

- And so forth. The key is to identify the problems and then deal with them in a smart and cost-effective way, and to have a regulatory system that allows this.

These need not all happen right away, but we need to work on each of them, and others. Some changes are needed in the nuclear industry itself, as well as academia, regulatory agencies, reactor operators and product vendors. Some changes are needed in the political and social spheres. Some changes are needed in the market design for many areas, as they often do not value the things we want and need; a low-cost, flexible, accessible, reliable, low-carbon and clean energy system for all people.

The cost of not making nuclear cheaper

Climate change is becoming a global emergency. As I am writing this, the world is just waking up to the coronavirus pandemic and is closing schools, national borders, public spaces and severely limiting people's lives and economic activities throughout societies. It is clear that we can take drastic measures very quickly if we see a developing emergency. For some reason, we have not seen the developing climate emergency.

Many of the actions discussed above are not about restricting people and businesses, but enabling us to use more effective, proven solutions. They would increase public health as nuclear would replace more polluting and dangerous energy sources at lower cost points. They would often give us a cleaner and a lower cost energy system that would benefit everyone. What is wrong with us? Why are we not acting?

The situation is similar to us refusing to use a well-known, proven vaccine to fight the spreading virus pandemic, and instead closing down vaccine factories and regulating the industry into oblivion because there is a non-zero risk that someone might get complications from the vaccine.

If we only look at the potential harm of getting vaccinated, there is always risk for the individual. This is similar to nuclear: there is always a risk of something happening. But instead of staring at that risk in a closed silo as the current regulatory framework forces us to do, we need to take a broader view and balance that risk with the alternatives. Instead of driving for ever-higher levels of nuclear and radiation safety, should we not examine what is best for public health overall?

To simplify, the safest possible nuclear industry (that every regulator swears is their goal) is a non-existent one. No nuclear industry, no radiological risk. Unfortunately, that is likely the worst path for overall public health.

Not vaccinating people will decrease complications that we may get from vaccines, but it will also lead to many more injuries and deaths from the otherwise preventable spread of a dangerous disease. Nobody likes the process of getting vaccinated, as it may be somewhat uncomfortable and might cause some short-term side effects. But we very much like the benefits of staying alive and healthy when we do get vaccinated, not to mention the satisfaction of knowing we have done our part to provide herd immunity, protecting society at-large. Similarly, not building nuclear means we will use more fossil fuels and suffer their particulate pollution and carbon dioxide emissions. At the end of the day, it is as simple as that.

The nuclear industry is failing us – Because that is their business model

The current business of the nuclear industry is to sell fear and safety. They have cultivated an image of an industry operating dangerous facilities and managing extremely harmful waste products, which therefore justifies use of costly measures to take care of "the problem". It has many well-paid professionals depending on this business of selling fear and then selling safety. A couple of chapters ago, we learned that storing spent nuclear fuel in a repository is safe by roughly a factor of one million times. This means that even the worst-case scenarios would need to be wrong by a million times to cause significant harm. Yet we spend millions and millions of euros or dollars on honing and re-checking and minimizing that risk further. Is there really not a more beneficial use of that money?

Is it any wonder that people think that spent fuel must be extremely dangerous? From a rational perspective, it would be insane to go through such trouble and use so much money and resources on it otherwise, wouldn't it? Yet that is what is happening, and there is a whole industry of consultants and researchers whose livelihood depends on our fear of all things nuclear. If this continues to be the business model and mindset of the nuclear industry, we might never get low-cost nuclear. By extension, this also means that we might never have a successful climate mitigation project.

 If the legacy nuclear industry – and by industry we broadly mean most of the people and organizations that are involved in the sector – can't change its mindset, it needs, and deserves, to go away. We are entitled to an industry that wants to solve real problems, not one that wants to cash in on the largely imaginary problems they helped create, while their industry slowly withers away.

 But we, the rest of the society, need to do our part as well. We need to demand better nuclear, better regulation, better nuclear journalism and media, better public discussion and better technology-inclusive climate and energy policies.

Summary

 According to the best evidence, there is no question whether nuclear should be allowed to play a significant role in our effort to mitigate climate change. The answer is yes. Nuclear power is currently the most efficient, fastest, safest and most cost-effective way to produce increasing amounts of reliable low-carbon energy. Historically, nuclear power has decarbonized electricity systems at rates and depths that have not been accomplished with other technologies, ever. In many countries, the rate of decarbonization with nuclear has been several times faster than what other technologies and progressive climate policies have managed. Nuclear power also has among the smallest environmental and material footprints.

 Contrary to common belief, civilian nuclear power has not led to nuclear weapons proliferation. Countries that wanted a nuclear weapon, first built themselves a nuclear weapon, and only after that did they build civilian nuclear power. It remains prudent to control and supervise the spread of nuclear technology. Our opinion on the best way to do so is to have strong international co-operation and authority on the matter, which allows and encourages countries to benefit from civilian nuclear, should they choose to do so. IAEA has filled this role reasonably well, and lately they have started to promote the peaceful use of nuclear energy more than historically, which is great news for climate mitigation.

New reactor and reprocessing technologies can help us destroy both legacy nuclear weapons material as well as the high-level waste from civilian nuclear power. New types and smaller nuclear reactors can help tremendously in decarbonizing other energy sectors besides electricity, such as heating, industrial processes and transportation fuels. Should nuclear power someday produce a much larger share of humanity's energy, breeder reactors ensure that there will be no shortage of nuclear fuel for many millennia to come.

Instead of complaining how expensive this or that technology may be, we should try to find ways to make them cheaper and use them to replace fossil fuels wherever that makes sense. Pitting nuclear and renewables against each other is both dumb and counterproductive. Each serves a purpose, and each should be used according to their unique merits, and to their full potential. Most of nuclear energy's problems are due to public perception, not fact, and this needs to change. The externalized costs of fossil fuels need to be internalized to make the market work more efficiently, but the obstacle here is that this preferably needs to happen globally, or at least regionally, to be effective. It would be a sad failure indeed if humanity ends up burning our only planet because it is profitable in the short term. It would be even more sad if we end up regulating ourselves to extinction.

PART 3

Nuclear Power in the Wider Society

Nuclear in Our Society

While many arguments against nuclear power are technical or economical, there are social and ethical arguments as well. These are often born from the perspective in which the nuclear industry is seen to symbolize unsustainable consumer culture, humanity's power over nature and the misuse of this power, centralization of political and economic power and so forth. It is easy to think of all the things that seem wrong in the world today and then project the blame on something one already dislikes. Whether that is the case here or not, these arguments deserve a thorough discussion.

These moral, ethical and societal viewpoints are discussed in this last part of our book. Can nuclear power exist in an egalitarian, just society? And can nuclear power be used as a vehicle to move towards such a better world, a better society, that would also be environmentally sustainable? Much of our prosperity today is made possible by economic growth, which in turn is enabled by productivity growth, which is very strongly linked with growing energy consumption. The relationship between economic growth and energy is a good place to start our discussion.

Economic Growth and Energy

Our economic system, along with society, is completely dependent on net surplus energy we produce. This surplus is essential, but not the only requirement for the existence and upkeep of a complex, modern society. This surplus and the connection it has to productivity and economic activity is perhaps so essential and engrained in our lives that we have become blind to it.

GDP (Gross Domestic Product) remains a key focus of current public discussion everywhere in the developed world. Economic growth is usually measured by the annual change in GDP. GDP is, however, a simplified measuring tool which aims to translate a complex world

and the phenomenon of increasing economic activity, increasing living standards and human and environmental well-being into a simple,
single number. This allows us to have a simple and straightforward
discussion of our progress or lack of it. But the simplicity leaves too
many background assumptions hidden, clouding our understanding
of important issues. We need to know whether an increase in GDP
(which we assume is desirable) actually leads to the things that we
want (a higher and sustainable living standard for society). If GDP
grows, we think that our policies have been successful. And if growth
is lagging, it calls for new, different policies, adjustments, flexibility,
cuts or debt-spending, austerity and other complex terms that can
mean very different things to different people and different vested interests.

Much of economic development depends on external events over
which smaller countries especially have little control. These include
decisions that others make, the current technological and educational
level, demographic and economic structure, history, political situation
and so forth. With all these external influences, it can well be that
any single policy will have no perceivable impact on the economy of
a country one way or the other. Each party or interest group can then
pick and choose which statistical data and details to show and how to
frame them. Depending on their position and goals, and with the help
of creative rhetoric, the exact same data can often be used to either
compliment or criticize the policies of the current government. In the
crossfire of conflicting reports and news articles, it soon becomes impossible to draw firm conclusions on the benefits or detriments of any
given policy measure.

Ultimately, GDP, which is impossible to measure objectively, is just
the total cost or price tag that we pay for our current level of well-being. We often think that the higher the monetary price of something,
the better, but this is not necessarily or even often the case. There is
a correlation between GDP and well-being, but it is much clearer at
lower living standards. When living standards rise and people's needs

get more saturated, increases in GDP do not necessarily translate to proportionate increases in living standards, well-being or happiness. The pursuit of improved living standards through more consumption and larger GDP suffers from what is called diminishing marginal utility.

In rich OECD countries, more resources have been invested in things such as health care and social security. Absolute poverty is rare, and the lives of the lower income groups are rarely a constant fight against starvation, sickness, violence or cold. On the other hand, the experienced level of well-being is measured by comparing one's own level with that of one's peers. Some studies have found that people prefer to live as the richest ones in a poorer neighbourhood than as the poorest ones in a richer neighbourhood, even if the latter choice would mean a higher absolute living standard.

People and countries have every right to try to improve their well-being. Especially in developing countries, this usually leads to (and is caused by) increases in GDP. In developing countries, growing GDP correlates strongly with increasing well-being and living standards, although the level of this correlation has much to do with the distribution of this new wealth. For a similar total cost, we can organize basic health care for everyone, or more expensive special care for a smaller part of the population. The former increases the country's average and mean living standards much more with the same cost than the latter. On the other hand, basic healthcare, water and wastewater systems, electricity and other basic modern services and products can only be provided once, and the next improvements are not as cost effective.

To say that growing the GDP by any means necessary will lead to things improving is a gross simplification. GDP simply leaves out too many details and hides too many questionable assumptions. Then again, if growing GDP is the goal of policies and the measure of their successes or failures, then policies will be mainly evaluated on their effects on GDP. What we measure is what we will get, so this can lead to negative results for humans and the environment. All decisions and policies can become economic or financial, and people become just a mass of consumers. Politicians, marketing departments and public relations firms then have the task of directing, maximizing and optimizing this mass of consumers to reach the policy goal of increasing GDP. Economic growth, society and the services it offers ceases to be for the benefit of the people, and the situation gets turned on its head: the people, as consumers, are there for the benefit of economic growth.

Growth of energy demand

There is a strong correlation between economic growth and the growth of our consumption of energy. When energy consumption has grown, GDP has grown as well, and vice versa. But the volume of energy consumption does not necessarily tell us much about the well-being of the environment. There are several key variables that measure and compare the negative and positive effects of production and use of energy. These are the choice of fuels used, the choice of production methods used, the amount of energy produced and the efficiencies of production and use.

The CO_2-equivalent life cycle emissions from electricity production can be as low as 5 grams per kWh or as high as 1,000 grams per kWh. In 2011, Sweden, which has one of the highest living standards in the world, used around 5.2 tons of oil-equivalent (toe) per person. This is quite a lot, even by the standards of developed countries. Yet its emissions were only 4.6 tons per person per year, which is among the lowest in any developed country. How is this possible?

Sweden produces its electricity almost without emissions, with hydro and nuclear and increasingly in recent years, with wind. Switzerland has a similar energy profile. France has emissions almost as low; they produce 75 percent of their electricity with nuclear. Yet none of these countries are usually mentioned when analysts, researchers and politicians discuss and search for ways to cut their country's emissions. Why? One reason might be that we often start emissions statistics from the year 1990, and all the countries mentioned above cut their emissions before that. The emissions cuts, for the eyes of the statisticians, simply do not exist, because they are not present in their datasets which start from 1990, as emission reduction targets are usually set as percent compared to 1990 levels. But from the climate's point of view, this does not diminish their accomplishment at all. On the contrary, they managed to cut their emissions to levels others are only planning for far in the future, without any active climate policies in place, and with both their economy and energy consumption growing rapidly.

If we say that a somewhat sustainable per capita emissions level is 2 tons of CO_2 per year, Sweden could have two routes toward that goal. It could improve efficiency and reduce its energy use (mainly outside electricity, in industry and transportation) by a bit over half. To do this, it needs to somehow stop rebound from happening. The other route is to increase its low-carbon energy production significantly from current levels and use it to replace remaining fossil fuels combustion, either by electrification or synthetic fuels or direct heat from a suitable renewable or nuclear source. Biofuels can offer some relief in replacing oil-based transportation fuels and other hard-to-electrify uses. Especially from a global perspective, the role of biofuels needs to remain somewhat low, unless enormous breakthroughs are made in third generation biofuels based on bacteria, algae and such.

It would be preferable if Sweden would not try to cut its emissions by driving the energy-intensive industry out of the country. With the clean electricity Sweden has, and provided it remains so, it would actually be desirable if Sweden were to increase its industrial production, especially the kind that requires a lot of electricity. Sweden recently decided to remove its nuclear tax, and gave permission (in principle) to build new reactors to replace old ones at their current sites. These are big steps in the right direction.

France has taken action to increase renewable energy production and to cut its share of nuclear energy, which today accounts for 75 percent of their electricity. In principle, this is not a bad order of things:

France first cut its emissions fast with nuclear, and is now in a position to optimize its electricity mix as it likes, as long as emissions or the price of electricity don't rise. On the other hand, France has proven that high penetration of nuclear power in the grid can be made to work, with load following done with nuclear, and with very reasonable costs. Would it be wise for France to use this knowledge and expertise to decarbonize its industry and transportation fuels in a serious manner, rather than reorganizing its electricity grid? Considering the urgency of climate change, it seems inexcusable to shut down any low-carbon energy production prematurely, especially as the German Energiewende has been a failure when it comes to emissions reductions. The manner in which we produce our energy makes an enormous difference in the total impact on our environment.

Overhauling our energy system will not happen overnight; it will likely take decades, if not a century. Therefore, other tools to limit the harm done by energy production and use are much needed. Energy efficiency improvements offers a path to attain a given living standard with much less energy use. Comparing Europe and the United States is a good illustration. The energy use of a U.S. citizen is roughly double that of an average European, yet there is little difference in their living standards or available services. These comparisons can be problematic as they compare apples to oranges; for example, some countries have more energy intensive industry than others, but we still need to have that industry somewhere (think China).

Arguably, there are possibilities to decrease even European energy use without large impacts on living standards or well-being of people. But it would be arrogant to assume that European energy use can be decreased to a fraction, or even half of what it currently is, or even that it can be decreased somewhat rapidly. These sorts of changes have only happened during exceptional crises. Further, it is hard to imagine what sort of mechanisms would be able to achieve these results in a democracy, in which political will is a somewhat scarce resource and political power, along with any unpopular legislation, are subject to cancellation every few years. Yet all of these are necessary minimum requirements if we were to take climate mitigation seriously, and to rapidly clean up energy production. The fewer tools we have at our disposal, the less likely we are to achieve needed emission reductions.

We commonly hear that energy efficiency and conservation are our most effective and important tools to mitigate climate change; we see the same in some mitigation scenarios done by respectable international organizations. At best, it is only a half-truth, and at worst a serious mistake due to rebound we discussed earlier. Even though efficiency and conservation can cut our energy use, it is unlikely that it can be cut to a small fraction of our current use. Yet if "the use of less energy" would be our most important tool to cut emissions, it would need to do just that. But as we learned above, by changing the way we produce energy, it is possible to cut emissions to a fraction of current levels. Simply by replacing coal in electricity and heat production with nuclear or other low-carbon energy, the climate impact of energy production can drop from 1000 gCO2/kWh to 10 gCO2/kWh, implying a drop of 99 percent. This is just what is needed. A further benefit of this approach is that people would need to change their behaviour much less and at a slower pace than otherwise required.

While the example above is a crude simplification of a much more complex world, this huge difference in both potential total reductions and speed of reduction needs to be acknowledged. Historically, energy efficiency has improved at a rather constant rate of 2 % per year, +/- 1 %.[262]

We can take small steps in the right direction by slowly improving efficiency and increasing conservation efforts, but they can never deliver us to the goal. The road they offer us (along with so-called "bridge fuels" such as natural gas and biomass) takes us into the right direction, but much too slowly, and never the whole way. Of course, smaller energy demand can be satisfied more easily with any clean technologies, so in this sense it is wise to reduce energy use if possible. But we also need to be careful that the reduced energy use does not have unwanted side-effects or opportunity costs. For example, efficient recycling and separation of garbage and metals is often an energy intensive process, yet it would be preferable if we did those things as much as possible. Another growing sector of energy demand is desalination of seawater for various purposes. A third one might be the production of carbon neutral fuels – a very inefficient process by itself, but one that might still give us a better outcome. If we start making clean fuels at a massive scale at some point, our energy efficiency might decline, but we might still be cutting emissions very significantly.

Perhaps the biggest problem is that people in general are somewhat reluctant to consume significantly less than they do now. Critique of consumer society, economic growth and hoarding of material wealth dates back centuries, if not millennia. Yet despite all that criticism and public education, our per capita consumption of nearly all significant natural resources has been steadily growing. While it might be possible that these critics and social movements have simply failed to be persuasive enough with their message, we also need to face the possibility that cutting back our collective consumption voluntarily and by significant amounts might not be realistic, and therefore makes for a poor plan for the future.

Our modern society produces a wide variety of things that people seem to want. A large part of these products and services increase our well-being. Another part of our consumption is, undeniably, unnecessary and wasteful, and largely the result of advertisement creating and nurturing "needs" in us that we did not know we had.

As horrible and counterintuitive as it sounds, our whole economic system is based on the indefinite and accelerating growth of these wants and desires. But it is hard to say beforehand what consumption is strictly unnecessary and what is not, as a lot depends on the situation and is subjective. A snowmobile might be unnecessary for someone who rides it for fun a couple times a year, but is essential for a reindeer herder in Lapland. An internet connection would have been unnecessary for most people only two decades ago, but today it is essential for most, with broadband availability even guaranteed by law for all citizens in some countries.

It might prove surprisingly hard to give up products and services one is accustomed to use and have available. Eating less meat would decrease our greenhouse gas emissions significantly[263], and would therefore seem like a no-brainer for people. But it is a much less appealing idea for the majority when hunger creeps in and delicious meat dishes are readily available. The recent advent of meat substitutes that mimic the taste and feel of, for example, a beef patty, has seen a good amount of success, as these "impossible burgers" and others have even entered major fast food hamburger chains such as Burger King. It remains to be seen what the long-term effect may be, but they are arguably using a very smart strategy: people don't have to change their behaviour to change their environmental impact. We will need many more of these "impossible burger" types of solutions in other sectors as well.[264]

The fate of consumer culture

Our modern society has a lot of good sides, and arguably a lot of bad sides as well. Most of the available "doomsday" literature focuses only on describing what is bad and wrong about the world. After reading such literature for a while, it all becomes clear: everything is going to hell, and the only discussion to be had about it is how fast and hard we are going down and who gets hurt the most.

Others say that we are doing great, never better. These claims can also be backed up with a pile of convincing evidence, statistics and reports. Even if war and suffering is constantly in the news, from a historical perspective there is probably less violence, hunger and suffering per capita now than ever in human history. In 2015, for the first time in known history, less than 10 percent of people lived in absolute poverty.[265]

Many looming environmental catastrophes, such as ozone depletion and acid rain, have been managed and now show improvements.[266]

It was scientific research that alerted us to these threats, and it was international cooperation that was essential in stopping them from getting worse. Both science and the cooperation of international organizations would be unlikely to exist were it not for the economic prosperity, industrialization, global trade and increasing living standards we have experienced during the last century or two. These environmental problems were largely caused by human actions in the first place, but on the other hand, it would have been practically impossible to stop technology from being developed, industrialization from advancing and the economy from growing. There were simply no tools to do that and no one to use these tools had they existed.

 It is hard to get a clear view of the bigger picture, because the world is such a complex place. One isolated trend, were it for better or worse, leaves out too much to tell us anything relevant about the future. Past trends are sometimes good predictors of the future, but not always. Most of the big historical changes were big precisely because they were hard to predict from historical trends. In addition to ozone depletion and acid rain, today humanity faces such threats as climate change, loss of species populations and fragmentation of ecosystems, ocean acidification and plastics pollution, harmful chemical contamination of the environment, depletion of sweet water aquifers, nutrient (nitrogen, phosphorous) cycling disruptions, land use change and atmospheric concentration of small particulate matter, to name a few.[267]

 Some of these problems are such that we do not have enough information about them to estimate their urgency and severity. Some of them are localized, while others might threaten the whole global community and human civilization, in addition to other species. Some loom further down the road, while others are more imminent. On top of general environmental threats, we can add other risks to the list, such as large meteors, artificial intelligence taking a turn for the worse, super viruses and other diseases and global war.

 It is clear we have a lot to do. Many indicators tell us that some things have taken a turn for the worse in recent years and decades. On the other hand, what are we to do? If economic growth ends for one reason or another, it might or might not be good for the environment in the longer run. If societies collapse (slowly or more rapidly), it could mean far worse environmental destruction than "business as usual" could ever cause. On the other hand, it seems that business as usual might well lead us to said collapse sooner or later. It is also true that by many other indicators, humans are doing better than ever. If we give value to eradicating starvation and absolute poverty as well as making basic medical care like vaccines available for most of the population, we have certainly made great progress. The question is how we can maintain these positive trends in a world undergoing rapid climate change and other problems.

Energy and the environment

The production and consumption of energy is one of the central human activities that causes ecological impacts. Therefore, it is essential how those activities are done and managed.

Some criticize nuclear power on the grounds that it will somehow lock us into high energy lifestyles and consumption. Indeed, here might lie one of the original justifications of the anti-nuclear movement, which had nothing to do with any disadvantages of nuclear, and everything to do with its advantages. A quote by Amory Lovins from the early days of anti-nuclear activism says: "If you ask me, it'd be little short of disastrous for us to discover a source of clean, cheap, abundant energy because of what we would do with it."

Locking us to a high-energy path or presumably using that energy only to destroy the environment are not the only justifications for anti-nuclear views. Some people also say that they are not against nuclear per se, but think that if we build nuclear it will only be built in addition to other energy sources, not to replace them, and hence they oppose it.

This reasoning is severely flawed, especially if the one doing the reasoning supports other low-carbon energy (as is often the case). All these arguments also apply to wind and solar power, but apart from a few isolated cases, we have never heard or seen these people applying this logic for wind or solar. The worst problem with this thinking is that we desperately need to clean up our current fossil fuel-based energy mix, and it is a huge undertaking. The Earth faces its problems because of these fuels that account for over 80 percent of our primary energy use. It is hard to imagine a situation where we would build too much clean energy production, be it of any sort, if it is used to replace fossil fuels even partially. And it is.

Another problem is that it is likely we will need international agreements and cooperation to replace fossil fuels. This will require political action and political will. Such actions always, in the end, follow what seems to be politically possible, and that is often different from what is needed or desirable. The more technologies we have available to replace fossil fuels in their various uses, the more any political action aiming to do so will have support.

What we end up doing with our energy is another question. But this question has nothing to do with how we produce said energy. Efficient recycling, for example, is very energy intensive. Desalinating water, which could be used for both food production and re-greening some areas of the planet which would assimilate and store carbon from the atmosphere, requires a lot of energy. So while we need to make less environmentally harmful waste, consume less materials and handle all that waste responsibly, the impact of these on the environment will likely get smaller with proper regulation, taxes on pollution and other such actions often taken by modern, rich societies. How we produce the energy has little to do with how we use it.

But what about environmental destruction as a direct result of energy production? What about the environmental footprint of different energy sources?

Is energy production destroying ecosystems?

How we produce our energy has a big impact on its emissions, but it also determines the local environmental footprint of energy production. Often this "ecological footprint" of energy production is rather small. The biggest impact is how densely the energy can be produced, which can be measured as square meters per energy (or power) delivered. Another thing to consider is how severe effects the production method has on that area. One example is to compare "organic" agricultural produce to industrialized agricultural produce. Organic production takes up more space to produce a given amount of food, but on the other hand, its impact on the ecosystem and biodiversity is often smaller than the industrial system. But still, organic production will leave less area for "wild nature", where biodiversity is much richer than in any food production system.

Growing energy crops is our most environmentally harmful way to produce energy. It requires a lot of land, as photosynthesis is not a particularly efficient way to harvest solar energy. Crops often require other inputs such as fertilizers, herbicides, pesticides and other chemicals, and sometimes need to be irrigated with fresh water. Harvesting, transporting and processing the biomass also requires energy inputs. With forest-based biomass, some of these inputs are smaller, and harvesting is done less often, but the production per year is also usually less than with annual crops, leading to larger areas used per unit of energy yield.

Any large-scale biomass production is based on monocropping, growing one crop species on large areas to maximize productivity. It is no wonder that agriculture is the largest source of biodiversity loss and habitat shrinkage. It requires large amounts of land and has a serious impact on species diversity. In 2017, bioenergy was the largest single source of renewable energy in Germany. Around 15%, or 2.5 million hectares, of agricultural land was used for energy and industrial crops In Germany. That is around 7 % of all land in Germany, and it produced around 7 % of primary energy consumption in Germany.[268] The Germans could produce all their primary energy with bioenergy, but there would be no room left for food, people, cities or nature. The forests of Europe were once saved by shifting to fossil fuels, but now they are threatened once more as we try to move from fossil fuels (and in some cases, nuclear energy) back to burning biomass for energy.

Wind power has different impacts. Wind parks require large areas, but doesn't use the whole area explicitly, as the turbine footprints are quite small. But there are certain limits to how the land area between turbines in a wind park may be used. In addition to the footprint of the turbines, access and maintenance roads and transmission lines are also needed, and these fragment the ecosystem. Wind farms produce roughly 1.5 watts per square meter, if we only take into account the turbine footprint, access roads and transmission lines. This leaves out the rest of the wind park area, as well as mining activities needed for materials production and backup generation to handle the intermittency.[269]

Forest-based biomass depends a lot on the location. Northern boreal forests such as those in Scandinavia produce roughly a tenth (0.15 W/m2) of what a wind park produces. It would take the total forest biomass production of more than 3.5 million hectares (about 15 % of Finland's forested area) to produce the same amount of electricity that is produced by a single large nuclear reactor such as the Olkiluoto 3.

The energy density of nuclear power plants is unparalleled among clean energy sources. As a rough rule of thumb, a nuclear power plant with two large reactors produces the same amount of energy on 1,000 times smaller area than solar and 1,500 times smaller than onshore wind (when calculating the whole area of the park). Energy density matters.

Energy production has a direct ecological footprint, but that footprint depends greatly on how the energy is produced. As a rule of thumb, the denser the energy source, the smaller the footprint.

It should be noted that humans, as do any living beings, take the energy they need from their environment one way or another. If there are no modern energy services available at low enough prices, people will harvest energy from their surroundings in other ways, such as cutting nearby trees. When millions go about this, the results are devastating for ecosystems. During the Euro-crisis, Greece suffered from an economic recession for some years, and illegal cutting of trees for firewood became a problem, as people could not afford heating oil or gas bills. During the Second World War, Japan stripped all forests around cities for miles to ease their energy shortages. Given that our needed effort to stop climate change has often been compared to the heroic efforts of the Second World War, we hope this does not mean following Japan's example.

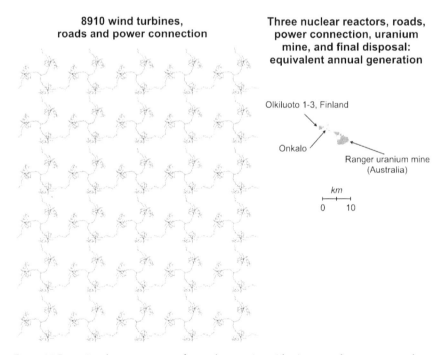

Figure 34: Producing the same amount of annual production with wind or nuclear power, actual cases of Olkiluoto nuclear power station and the environmental assessment of Oosinkangas-wind park. Only the roads and transmission lines essential for the production are presented. The only mining activity presented is that of uranium mining (the mine pictured produces four times the uranium used in the plant). No backup generation for wind power is shown. The comparison is hugely unfair for nuclear, and yet it has a much smaller footprint.

The environmental footprint of energy production is fundamentally connected to the amount of surplus, or net energy, we get from energy production. One way to measure this is Energy Returned on Energy Invested, or EROEI.

Energy Returned on Energy Invested – EROEI

To produce energy, we must first spend energy. Fossil fuels have offered so much return on our invested energy, that for centuries we have not needed to pay much attention to this. Hence, the net energy of energy production has not been the subject of much public discussion, despite its fundamental importance. Our modern society runs on surplus energy, food and materials. It is of extremely high importance that we continue to have high amounts of surplus energy if we want to have a viable economic system and society.

Humanity faces a new kind of situation in its energy production. For the first time in modern history, it is moving, at least partly, from a high-EROEI energy production to substitutes that have much lower EROEI. Among these are moving from conventional oil production to lower quality and harder to produce unconventional oil production. These include deep water oil and arctic oil, oil sands in Alberta, Canada, producing kerogen from oil shale and tight oil and gas (often referred to as shale oil and shale gas) with processes such as hydrofracking. Similarly, weaker substitutes for conventional crude oil are biofuels and synthetic transportation fuels made from coal or natural gas.

Although the EROEI of coal production is often quite high, it has been gradually declining. If we roll out carbon capture and storage (CCS) to combat climate change, we need to use energy to run it, and this will make a serious dent in the EROEI of coal. Climate fight has also driven many people and companies to install wind and solar power, both of which have often lower EROEI than fossil fuels, especially when we account for the support infrastructure needed for reliable energy services.

According to some studies made on the subject, modern society requires that we get around 15 units of energy return for our invested energy (EROEI of 15:1).[270] This means that less than one tenth of our energy would be "fed back" into energy production.

There are numerous variables and assumptions involved when estimating the EROEI of a single energy source. This has led to a wide variety of EROEI numbers for any given energy source, depending on the assumptions made by the one doing the study. A single parameter that has a huge impact on EROEI is the assumed lifetime of a power plant. If a power plant produces the invested energy back in one year, it is of tremendous importance whether we assume 10, 20 or 60 years of operational life for the plant (these examples would roughly translate to EROEI of 10:1, 20:1 and 60:1, respectively). Another parameter of importance is the need for support mechanisms such as energy storage for variable energy sources, and what technologies are used. For example, the most effective one is pumped hydro, but it is also something that cannot be scaled much higher from today.

Selection of biased or outdated data and methods for materials production may also skew EROEI figures. Nuclear power normally has an average EROEI between 50:1 and 100:1, but playing around with these assumptions, figures as low as 5:1 have been achieved. Even those high numbers mentioned rarely assume that the power plants are operated much beyond 40 years, while some plants have already been granted licences to operate for 80 years.

Let's look at the actual calculations done by Vattenfall on its Forsmark nuclear power station, and compare them to the assumptions used in a much cited (by the anti-nuclear establishment) non-peer reviewed "Storm & Smith" study.[271] This study was based completely on models, assumptions and calculations. Forsmark NPP, based on real-world bookkeeping, environmental assessments and some future projections, will use around 4.1 petajoules of energy to construct and to eventually dismantle the plant.[272] Storm & Smith study assumed that its construction used up to 240 petajoules – a whopping 60 times more than was actually used.

In another mark against the trustworthiness of the Storm & Smith study, it notes that Rössing uranium mine in Namibia uses more energy each year than the whole Namibian state consumes, and roughly 80 times more than what the records of the mining company say it uses. Yet Storm & Smith is widely cited, even within peer reviewed papers such as those by Benjamin Sovacool and company, which are in turn cited in IPCC reports, in a sort of "money laundering" of bad studies.[273] A meta-study from 2015 estimated the EROEI of solar PV panels to be, depending on type of panel, between 8.4:1 and 34:1, without support mechanisms to ensure on-demand service.[274] While studies always use somewhat out-of-date data, and it can be argued that as technology progresses those EROEI-numbers will improve, it should be noted that the price of PV panels themselves are already very low and have not decreased much in absolute sense from 2012 levels. Price of panels acts as one proxy for the material and energy needs of manufacturing, indicating that those improvements might not be huge.

The problem most of these studies have is that they use models and they only include the direct material and energy needs of panel manufacturing, and perhaps other essentials such as support frames and other equipment needed.

To illustrate, the final energy production greatly depends on the location the PV panel is installed. A case study of Spanish solar farms production between 2009 and 2011 found that the panels and other equipment accounted for roughly a third of the energy inputs for the lifetime of panels. The study arrived at an alarmingly low EROEI of 2.4:1 for the whole solar PV project.[275] Since then, the author of the study has said that even this was optimistic.[276] This analysis does suffer from some problems. It accounts for almost every imaginable thing that has to do with solar PV, be it money or energy spent, and represents it as an energy input for solar power. If this sort of activity is taken further and further to its logical conclusion, the whole EROEI of the human endeavour is 1:1, since we use all the energy we produce. But that tells us little about which of those activities are necessary for the energy source itself. This approach might be interesting as a thought experiment, but it is impractical if we aim to compare the EROEI of various energy sources. This particular study also suffers from old data in case of PV panels, as the prices have gone down significantly since the panels used in this case study were produced.

EROEI for wind power has been estimated to be roughly 15-20:1. A study[277] from a few years back gave 1.5 MW wind turbines (E-66) an EROEI of 16:1 (not including support mechanisms). With larger modern turbines, that EROEI should be notably higher.

Perhaps the biggest problem of intermittent energy production arises from the needed support mechanisms. Society requires on-demand flows of energy that variable sources, by definition, do not provide. It has been calculated that a 10-day energy storage made with the most effective solution (pumped hydro) would decimate the EROEI of wind power from 16:1 to as low as 3.9:1.

With varying assumptions, one gets varying results. Therefore, exact numbers are perhaps not as important as the magnitude of the numbers. From EROEI's point of view and even with technology development, solar PV looks to be questionable as a major power source for a modern, industrialized society at least in non-optimal locations such as northern Europe, Canada and the like. This does not mean that there would be no use for PV panels, but it does limit where and how solar panels should be used to offer us maximum benefits. Their viability as a technology able to power modern civilization is still questionable.

Nuclear power and hydro are currently the only low-carbon technologies that clearly have high enough EROEI to run a modern society. Decades ago, the largest single energy input of nuclear power was the use of the older and more inefficient gaseous diffusion fuel enrichment process. In the case of Forsmark NPP this accounted for roughly half of total energy inputs. The last gaseous diffusion enrichment facility in the world closed in 2015, so the whole fuel industry has now moved to roughly 50 times more energy efficient centrifuge technology. Some experiments have also been done with laser enrichment, which is even more energy efficient than centrifuges.[278]

The EROEI of nuclear power is likely to remain very high in the future, even if we need to obtain uranium from poorer deposits. The EROEI could even grow with the advent of advanced nuclear technologies such as breeder reactors and other designs that are able to use current nuclear fuels more effectively. Some of these reactors do not need enrichment at all, and can use natural or depleted uranium as fuel, also minimizing the need for mining activities. This is great news. If we need to start synthesizing liquid fuels to replace oil, the power-to-gas or power-to-gasoline processes lose at least half of the energy input and therefore need a high starting EROEI to be viable.

Nuclear Power and Centralized Political Power Structures

The public relations activities of the nuclear industry have been, on average, one miserable failure after another. The industry has a rather bad record (although it has been improving lately) of contacting and discussing new projects with the local communities. If the nuclear industry has not been arrogant, and it arguably has, it has certainly given out that image to the outside world. While the image of know-it-all "nuclear physicists" or inconsiderate management are not the whole picture, there are enough examples of these to create a stereotype. According to one academic researcher focusing on these sorts of issues, the antagonism that some people feel for the nuclear industry (in this case in Finland, but this is likely to apply elsewhere as well) is not so much due to the propaganda spread by the anti-nuclear activists. The aims of this propaganda are, after all, often quite easy to see. The antagonism is due to some pro-nuclear people having an arrogant and dogmatic way of presenting their "correct and fact- based" views of nuclear power.

On the other hand, the environment for public communication has been difficult. Anything the nuclear industry says (or leaves unsaid) can and will be twisted and rhetorically embellished to look catastrophic. This is something that the mainstream media, and with it, society, has allowed to happen. There seems to be very little tolerance for any mistakes from representatives of the nuclear industry, while the anti-nuclear views can basically lie and slander and twist the data and statistics as much as they want without any consequences or loss of loyalty. And they have. The anti-nuclear establishment – including numerous professors in high academic places – has been cherry-picking data, carefully selecting just one point of view, not doing comparisons in intellectually honest ways, picking the worst the images and writing the most click-bait headlines, and has therefore controlled the discussion. If most of what you hear around you is untrue at least to a degree, it makes finding the facts and seeing the big picture a struggle for most people.

The global nuclear industry has surely acted unethically at least some time, somewhere. But this is true for practically every industry, and large-scale human activities in general. Unethical actions are not to be tolerated, but the ways we measure these ethics need to be consistent across industries.

The authors have discussed nuclear power publicly and privately for years and as we have brought relevant scientific evidence to the discussion, we have often been presented with the possibility of conspiracies among researchers and the scientific community. This usually happens when the overwhelming facts have been shown to support our arguments. What are these conspiracies (or conspiracy theories) based on?

Are politicians and researchers in the industry's pocket?

Does nuclear power bring about a concentration of political and economic power in the society? Are nuclear corporations too big? Has the nuclear industry "bought" all the researchers, politicians and non-fiction writers, and now has them in its collective pocket, dictating what they say and write, and what kind of results they get in studies? Surprisingly, this is an argument brought up quite often and by highly positioned people to discredit any legitimate evidence that may disagree with their anti-nuclear talking points.

The allure of this technique is understandable. It is a sure way to instantly debunk any argument that is backed up by research evidence by simply claiming that it is funded by the industry which then controls what sort of results emerge. It is also a false argument, unless solid proof of such control and tampering with the results is presented for each case in question. One of the originators of the German Energiewende, for example, went as far as to say that The World Bank is in the pocket of the nuclear industry.[279] Why? Because they published a report[280] that was worried whether we will have enough rare mineral flows to build renewable energy and battery technologies fast enough for even somewhat modest shares of wind, solar and EV's (electric vehicles).

Another example is what the much larger fossil fuels industry has managed; it has arguably done its best to question the findings of climate science (and there is evidence of this[281]). But the impact has been limited to the public being confused about the topic. There has been little impact on the actual climate science, even if the fossil fuels industry has sponsored their own studies on the matter.

If the wealthy and very resourceful fossil fuels industry has not been able to buy the mainstream science in climate change, are there valid reasons to believe that the much smaller nuclear industry has been able to do just that? Especially as there is no actual evidence available of the nuclear industry tampering with results in studies on radiation health effects. The mainstream view on the matter is quite clear, and the only studies and reports (often not even peer-reviewed) that differ significantly from this mainstream have come from the anti-nuclear community.

The nuclear industry does political lobbying as does every other industry. But it seems especially pronounced that when a politician says she is not against nuclear – does not want to ban the building or operating of nuclear, for example – she gets accused of being in the pocket of the big bad nuclear industry. This image of the powerful, big and bad nuclear industry fits well with the preconception of many people, since that has been the public narrative for decades.

So if a new nuclear plant gets an agreed price for its future electricity production, as happened in Britain with the strike price of Hinkley Point C[282], the quick and easy conclusion many drew is that the nuclear industry has bought the politicians. But since other clean energy sources get similar or much larger guaranteed prices for their production, does it follow that wind, solar, geothermal and wave-energy companies must have bought the politicians even worse? If the point is to ensure that adequate investments in clean energy production are made to help mitigate climate change, to deliver enough production capacity to replace the aging fleet of power plants, and to keep the grid stable, the actions of the politicians seem much more logical. The UK needs tremendous amounts of new clean energy production in the coming decades just to meet their legally binding climate targets, and a large portion of that needs to be reliable baseload so that the grid can remain stable at reasonable costs.

Lobbying is a normal part of how our society and political system works, and it could be argued that it has always been part of power structures. It is done by every industry, including environmental organizations, and as such, lobbying does not mean that the one doing it represents a good or a bad industry. There are ways to control and limit the possibly distorting effects of lobbying and corporate power such as transparency of political funding for elections, making lobbying as transparent as possible and having a free, investigative and responsible press.

We have found no examples or evidence that the nuclear industry (if there indeed can be said to be such a thing), would have been able to twist the mainstream research findings to suit their needs. However, these kinds of claims are made all the time in debates considering nuclear energy. When evidence is asked for (and we have done so dozens of times), anything remotely trustworthy is never presented. Instead, the same, many times debunked studies are waved time and again as definite proof. The exact same tactic has been used to discredit climate research, and to considerable effect.

Meanwhile, the fossil fuels industry is a big beneficiary of anti-nuclear campaigning. Campaigning against nuclear eats up resources from environmental organizations, which could be used to tell people about the drawbacks of fossil energy use and to oppose the burning and mining of coal, for example. Fossil energy is also usually the next option that gets built when a nuclear power plant is not built or gets shut down prematurely due to opposition or short-term economics. It should be noted that the utility that builds and supplies the energy often remains the same, only the fuel used is changed. This has happened many times all over the world.[283]

Fossil fuels industry is also the winner when the advocates of low-carbon energy sources spend their time and resources arguing among themselves. As individuals who have been following and participating in the energy debate for years, it is amazing how hard it is for clean energy advocates – and we would add that this is more often the case with renewable energy proponents – to offer their solution to replace fossil fuels instead of other low-carbon energy sources such as nuclear power.

How often have we seen the advert or argument about the number of nuclear reactors one could replace with such and such amount of wind or solar? Why is it almost never coal plants that get replaced? We have also met and talked with people who think we should do everything with nuclear and forget renewables, and we have even met with people who think it is their particular advanced reactor design that should do the job, all of it, and then go on explaining how much safer and better their design is (even if it only exists on paper) compared to the current batch of light water reactors.

This infighting absolutely needs to stop if we ever hope to challenge the supreme rule of the fossil fuels industry. Remember, fossil fuels supply over 80% of our primary energy. They have much more lobbying power than nuclear and renewable energy industries combined. Every low-carbon option has its place, and the more options we have available and accepted, the more likely we are to have policies in place that will limit the use of fossil fuels and their emissions.

The renewables industry today is much bigger than the nuclear industry and also has quite a bit of lobbying power. Directly it has monetary resources (partly paid for by taxpayers as subsidies and feed-in-tariffs), and indirectly it has the sympathy of most of the press, politicians and human resources to drive home its needs and messages to society. The industry has also been active in studies. Two of the three main authors of the Greenpeace energy reports some years ago worked directly for the renewables industry, and Greenpeace has been open about the fact that the essential data for their scenarios has been supplied by the renewable energy industry. This is not that surprising or serious as such, but given that this industry has some of the most comprehensible data on their products and performance, the total lack of public discussion about these links is telling and alarming.

Renewable energy industry is mostly a for-profit industry like many others, trying to maximize shareholder value. There is no reason to suspect that the RE industry is any better or worse in this respect than any other business. But given that the RE business has an especially positive image throughout our society, it is almost certain to try to use that image for its benefit and profit. Indeed, in a capitalist environment, this is more of a requirement than something to speculate about. This is something that we need to be more aware of, as when this is revealed, it might lead to a backlash and loss of trust by the public that would not be beneficial to clean energy.

All profit-making corporations and their PR-material and lobbying efforts need to be viewed with healthy scepticism. When they make outrageously optimistic promises and ignore any possible problems, if we fail to criticize these visions for one reason or another, it leads to a loss of credibility and trust in the longer run. The nuclear industry, or at least a significant part of it, made this mistake 40-50 years ago when it said that all our problems will be solved with nuclear energy, and it will be practically free, without any significant problems. Right now, many renewable energy proponents are making these exact same claims, and the crowd is cheering louder than ever.

Repeating this mistake is not something humanity can afford right now. If we are to prevent a runaway climate catastrophe, we will need a lot of clean renewable energy along with clean nuclear energy. The current infighting among clean energy advocates results in the fossil fuels industry winning in the short term and causing a catastrophic climate change in the longer term.

Which is better: centralized, or de-centralized?

Centralized energy production as well as decentralized production both have their drawbacks and benefits, and the recent trend in the discussion has been to favour decentralized solutions. But what does this mean, exactly? One analogue is transportation: personal cars are a distributed transportation solution, while public transportation (buses, rail, trains) are an example of a more centralized solution. Cities and apartment buildings are centralized, while suburbs and country-side living are decentralized. If a neighbourhood or a city has district heating, it is basically a centralized solution, while each building having its own natural gas boilers is a decentralized solution – although supplying that gas depends on a centralized pipeline network. A heat pump is also a combination of both; it operates in a building but usually works with electricity from the centralized grid. It is clear the terms have significant overlap, which can limit their usefulness in describing our built environment. Careful definitions specific for each use may be helpful to avoid misunderstandings.

If a house or a neighbourhood does not require any energy input from surrounding areas, it is less reliant on them and the energy companies that operate there. If those energy companies are in trouble, have malfunctions, blackouts or raise prices, the area which has its own production is not directly affected. These are benefits that a decentralized and disconnected microgrid or household enjoys for supplying its own energy needs. They are independent in their immediate energy needs from the outer world. Often this has costs, even significant ones, compared to being part of the electricity grid.

But even if they are "off-grid", they are still dependent in many other ways. They are dependent on the industry that supplies the equipment, batteries, materials and maintenance for their off-grid infrastructure. The "power" the centralized energy utility has over them is perhaps lessened, but it has simply moved to other companies. Even if we own our cars and can produce our own transportation services with them, the automobile industry is still very powerful, as is the oil refining and gasoline dispensing industries.

Further, if total independence and local production is the main goal, this endeavour can become very expensive as the area and needs grow. If an independent microgrid consists of variable wind and solar production, it will need relatively massive energy storage and demand flexibility systems, or diesel generators. Currently, many microgrids maintain a connection to a national grid, relying on it for backup or storage. The "energy independence" of a household or area which produces more than it consumes might add up on an annual level, but this claim hides the fact that the local microgrid could not function reliably on a day to day basis without the (centralized) grid connection.

Even if decentralized storage systems such as batteries drop in price, the situation would not necessarily change that much. As we presented earlier in this book, cheap storage benefits baseload power plants, too; it helps them run at peak capacity all the time, as the batteries match demand fluctuations. The economics of baseload power improves with cheap storage. It is also clear that businesses involved in energy production and delivery can and will take the benefits from cheap storage much more effectively than single consumers can, as it is their business to do just that. They have better expertise and enjoy the benefits of scale. If it remains economically advantageous to stay on the grid and the grid is reliable, it is certain that the number of off-grid households or villages will remain quite small.

Micro-production and self-sufficiency have their uses and value. Especially in remote locations, where it would be expensive or not feasible to build power lines, they are valid solutions to add the services that modern energy can deliver.

It is enlightening to attempt to define small-scale vs. large-scale energy production and analyse their benefits and drawbacks. For this purpose, we divide the power infrastructure into three categories:

1. Large power plants (hundreds or over a thousand megawatts)
2. Local power plants (Tens or a couple hundred megawatts maximum)
3. Farm/household-sized plants (kilowatts or several megawatts)

Large power plants benefit from their size in efficiency (higher temperatures usually possible) as well as the need for supporting infrastructure, which is less per MW for a bigger plant. Scrubbing of air pollution can be done more cost-effectively in large plants as well. Disadvantages include the need to transport and store large amounts of fuel, although nuclear power does not have this problem. If fuels are wood-based, the volumes are even larger due to their worse energy density. Bringing wood-based fuels with trucks ceases to make sense when the distances grow to around 100 km (65 miles) or more, although marine shipping can be done at larger distances. Large power plants can serve the needs of large areas of population with less infrastructure and less employment per megawatt, which makes the power produced less expensive. They also offer a large direct economic boost (employment, taxes) for the area in which they are located, but not so much for areas farther away.

Often the largest single power plant defines the amount of fast back-up that needs to be available in case it drops from the grid. For example, in Finland that is Olkiluoto 3 at 1.6 gigawatts. Similarly, you need to have load following capacity available for almost the entire amount of variable energy sources (wind and solar) you have in the grid. The difference between load following capacity and backup capacity is that load following is used constantly, if at variable levels, while backups only kick in during an anomaly. A factory might agree to shut down during an anomaly, but would not shut down during low winds. In practice, ways to deal with both demand and supply fluctuations need to be added on top of each other, as the grid needs to be able to handle conditions in which intermittent sources are not producing much, and a big power plant goes suddenly offline. Strong interconnections to neighbouring countries can help, but it is not an infallible backstop as problems can and do occur.

 Local-sized power plants have the advantage of positively impacting the local economies they serve. Smaller towns can get biofuels from surrounding areas if there is forestry or agriculture nearby. They are good for serving district heating-networks (a centralized solution) where those are available, as they can be located more freely and closer to the population than larger power plants. If they are close to the population, the deliveries of fuel can cause other problems, especially with biofuels that can take roughly eight times as much space compared to coal. The biggest problem with power plants of this size is that currently many of them are based on burning something, be it coal, gas, wood, agricultural residue or peat. Other local-sized production can come from wind farms, large solar PV farms or concentrated solar power (CSP) plants. Smaller nuclear reactors of 50-300 megawatts of capacity can also serve local needs and district heating networks if allowed by regulations (the public health effect would be positive, since nuclear is several orders of magnitude safer than any combustion-based energy source).

 On the household or farm level there are a couple options for "micro-energy" production. These include solar PV panels, solar heat collectors and very small wind turbines. Wood-burning fireplaces of various sorts, oil/gas/biomass furnaces and heat pumps can be considered micro-energy production even though they use fuel, or as in the case of heat pumps, electricity to produce heating/cooling and hot water. These increase the household's resilience and makes it less dependent on external energy services, but only if local storage for fuel is available.

The downside of household solutions is that normally the dependency on the electrical grid and other energy services remains. Also, if a household is already connected to the grid, building redundant systems is not a wise use of natural resources, unless the grid is unstable. Bringing electricity to the cabin in the woods with solar PV panels and batteries, on the other hand, does not replace grid-produced electricity, but often increases the total use of energy as said cabin previously did not have any electricity.

In the larger picture, household level energy production can decrease the use of grid/centralized energy, but rarely replaces it altogether. Grid dependency remains, and the costs to maintain that grid also remain. Further, the usefulness of solar panels depends greatly on location. In northern Europe, their production occurs mainly during summertime, when there is much less need for energy than in winter. The production correlates negatively with demand. For example, the grid in Scandinavian countries such as Finland, Sweden and Norway is so clean especially in summer that installing solar panels might actually increase overall emissions due to their lifecycle emissions from manufacturing, transportation and decommissioning. In warmer countries, the correlation of PV production with demand is better because people use more air conditioning, but even in sunny California, the demand peak comes in late afternoon, a couple hours after the solar production has peaked.

There is also some disconnection (excuse the pun) between local independent grids running on variable renewable energy and international supergrids meant to transfer that same variable renewable electricity for long distances. Modern smart grids are also quite the opposite of your local micro-grid, as they work better when there are more users and producers balancing supply and demand over wider areas, since wind and solar are usually producing at similar rates over large regions. The owners of these grids would also hold significant power (again, excuse the pun) in society, which needs to be mitigated somehow. Public sector majority ownership is one option, extremely tight regulation on profits and level of service needed is another.

The debate on centralized and decentralized production, however those are defined, is often just a flurry of rhetoric to justify one's technological tribalism one way or the other. Typically, wind power is seen as decentralized and therefore "good" and nuclear power as centralized and therefore "bad". Viewed objectively, wind parks are definitely centralized energy production, even though they do still take a substantial amount of space. Some are comparable to nuclear power plants in their peak capacity, or even in their annual production. Sweden is building a wind park, Markbygden, that will produce as much electricity annually (12 TWh), as the biggest nuclear reactors. Markbygden will span an area of 45,000 hectares (over 111,000 acres). While the park is "decentralized" in the sense that a fault in one or several turbines does not have a big effect on the entire array, it is still relying on just a few cables to transfer the electricity.

Which is better, private or public?

Many energy utilities are partly, or even fully (as is the case with the Swedish Vattenfall) owned by the state or local municipality, but this depends on the country. This decentralizes their ownership base to include all the citizens in the country or municipality. It also ensures that part of the profits, which are of course taken from the pockets of their customers, get recycled into the society through dividends paid by the utility to its owners, including municipality or state.

Blaming the structure of ownership or the size of a corporation is often just an excuse to oppose this or that technology. If a municipally-owned energy company invests and becomes a shareholder in a nuclear plant project, it is criticized, and often nuclear gets blamed for somehow getting public support. If the same company builds a wind farm, there are no such complaints, or at least the complainers are different people. And "greedy capitalists" often cease to be a problem if they invest their money in one's favourite technology, such as wind and solar, even if their hefty profits are guaranteed by the government and the taxpayers. But if those same capitalists invest in nuclear power, they suddenly become evil criminals who are trying to profit while letting the people carry the risks.

Fully or partially publicly-owned nuclear power is actually not a bad idea. The people do carry part of the final risks, so it can be argued that they should also benefit from the ownership, in addition to benefiting from affordable and clean energy that is produced. On the other hand, private ownership and capital also have their benefits. Significant private investment in a power plant brings jobs and benefits to a country or municipality without the need to use taxpayer money or government loans. Many governments can get loans at very affordable rates, while private capital often demands higher interest for their investments. What would be a better investment for patient, low-interest long-term money of a government loan than building massive, long-lived clean energy projects?

Sometimes this "international money" has negative connotations. Such is the case in the Finnish project of Fennovoima; Russian state-owned Rosatom is both the provider of the technology and owns roughly a third of the future owner of the plant. Russia's actions in Ukraine and elsewhere, along with the change in their international policy, have earned criticism towards this project. A similar debate has been ongoing in the UK, where the Hinkley Point C project is partly owned by Chinese state-owned energy companies. The UK government is placing restrictions on this ownership (for example the sale of said ownership to third parties) as a precondition for the deal going through. Even as international cooperation is usually a good thing,

242 THE DARK HORSE — NUCLEAR POWER AND CLIMATE CHANGE

these problems need to be mitigated, not ignored or wished away.

Energy independence

The energy debate in recent years would have one believe there are no limits to the benefits of energy independence. It creates jobs, it decreases imports and balances trade deficits, it lessens our dependency on others and keeps the money circulating in the national or local economy. In Europe, it is Europe's dependency on Russian oil and natural gas that fuels such worries – unless we need to choose between domestic nuclear and Russian gas, then independence is quickly forgotten and new pipelines are permitted and built. In the US this "independence" seems to run in the very veins of the people – there have not been many presidents in the last 50 years (since the 1970s oil crisis) that have not promised or talked about the importance of the United States becoming energy independent.

In our world of global trade and complex international supply chains, the lines between domestic and imported product often get blurred. Rather than simplifying rhetoric, we need a closer analysis to learn more about our dependencies and what they mean. Let's look at some examples.

Is food domestic if it has been grown in the country where you live? What if the companies that comprise the food chain – growing, harvesting, transporting, preparing, selling and so on – are wholly or partly owned by people and institutions in a foreign country, and pay their taxes somewhere else? What about fertilizers and pesticides and other chemicals used in agriculture? They might be manufactured domestically, but what is the source of their oil and natural gas feedstocks? Even the primary production of our agriculture is often dependent on various imports.

Transporting raw food crops from fields to bakeries and other processing facilities, to stores and finally to our homes can be done by domestic companies, but depending on the country, the trucks and cars might be manufactured abroad, and the fuel they use might be imported. Independence, be it for food or energy or something else, is a complex topic, but is often used from a narrow point of view to lobby for one's favourite solutions.

Nuclear power may also be viewed as domestic or foreign. Reactor design might be from some other country. The main contractor might be foreign, or the project or power plant might be partially owned by a foreign company. The uranium or the fuel manufacturing and enrichment services might come from another country. The plant itself, however, would still be located inside one's own country and would produce energy to the local grid and be under the regulations and supervision of that country. Nuclear fuel can be bought from multiple sources, as can spare parts.

While at least partial independence might be a worthwhile goal, at least in some critical goods such as food and energy, a partial interdependency might also be a worthwhile goal. Think about Russia for example. It has done some questionable things in the geopolitical arena in the last couple years. But would it be less or more likely to embark on such missions if it were much less dependent on international trade with its neighbours?

Trade and positive interdependence are effective tools to promote peaceful coexistence and prosperity. There are many factors that have both positive and negative implications, so simplifying them just to drive one's agenda is rarely productive or good for society.

Political realism of change

"It is simply a matter of political will" are the magic words we often hear when "100 % renewable energy" proponents discuss the feasibility of their zero-nuclear scenarios. They claim that with enough political will to change the world, we can solve the problems without nuclear energy. Alternatively, their solutions rely on major breakthroughs just around the corner, which will render any investments in nuclear power obsolete and a waste of resources. But they insist that even if the breakthroughs are not forthcoming, nuclear should be closed down and made illegal anyway.

While these changes and breakthroughs might indeed be just around the corner, we have no way of knowing that before they arrive. One can always wait for the next better thing and end up doing nothing to mitigate the problem. This is what we arguably have been doing with climate change for some decades: nothing. And don't get us wrong, we know that a lot has been done; meetings have been held, books have been written, scientific studies have been done, policies enacted and inspiring speeches given. What matters is that the atmospheric CO_2 concentration has not yet noticed our efforts, and has been increasing at a growing rate. How much should we count on these enticing but elusive innovations or rapid, global change in basic human behaviour? Can the rulers of the world simply mandate less consumption?

Democracy was invented precisely to limit and control the political will and whims of the ruling class. In a democracy, rapid change often leads to a rapid change of politicians in the next election cycle. An arguably limited effort to curb transportation fuels consumption by increasing their taxation in France led to the "yellow-vests" taking to the streets in a show of violent civil unrest that lasted for months on end. And this seems to be more the rule than the exception.

The political will to make rapid and lasting changes in people's lives might be a much more limited resource than we would like to think. This also applies to our built infrastructure. It changes quite slowly, limited by the preconditions set by the existing infrastructure. It is difficult to justify scrapping assets that still have operational lifespan remaining. This "inherited situation" is often forgotten by those who want to see the world made anew in a day or a year. We can try to accelerate this change, but that takes more political will and resources and often faces opposition from the ones who benefit from the current situation.

It needs to be asked how much of our future we should build on the expectation that everything will change soon in a fundamental way, socially and/or technologically? If we invest too much in these hopes and expectations, we might end up sorely disappointed. Worse, by the time it finally is clear that our expectations will not be met, it might be too late to do anything else. In some ways, that describes the world's current status. It can be argued that by now, it is abundantly clear that Germany's Energiewende has failed to deliver on the promised emissions reductions. But even this has not led to acknowledgement by policymakers, the voters or renewable energy advocates at large. On the contrary, it has led to even firmer denial and twisting of the evidence by those in Germany that advocate for the Energiewende. This is in human nature: we defend our worldview, premises and preconceptions vehemently when they are challenged, no matter the evidence.

All this means that we might already be on a path that will lead to an inevitable catastrophe. But that possibility is not an excuse to stop trying our best to mitigate the situation. The climate experts assure us that regarding global warming mitigation, every tenth of a degree matters.

We can be sure that whatever the scale of change or amount of political will needed to be effective, we are more likely to succeed if we have more tools and options at our disposal. If we ban some tools or regulate them so they become practically impossible or uneconomical to use, as we have been doing with nuclear energy, it can only make the situation worse. Sure, one can build a bridge across a stream even without steel and concrete. But banning steel and concrete will not make building that bridge any faster, cheaper or easier. Also, the less we limit and control what people can do, the better for political acceptability.

If we want to make people eat less meat patties, the solution is not to ban meat patties, as that will only lead to resistance and polarization. We need to offer an option that is at least as good, or even better – an "impossible burger". If we simply ban flying, it will lead to resistance.

But if we offer a carbon neutral alternative to JET-A fuel that is comparably priced, or at least not significantly more expensive, people's flying habits won't need to change.

The situation with climate change is urgent. The challenge would be immense even if there were no professional anti-nuclear organizations in existence. A rapid deployment of new nuclear plants faces very real problems and obstacles. But the scale and importance of these problems is routinely exaggerated. We observe anti-nuclear activists obstruct all aspects of the nuclear power industry, then cite the resulting difficulties as reasons to oppose nuclear. This is circular logic, which is questionable, if not unethical.

There remain political, technical and economical obstacles to the needed rapid deployment of new nuclear. But allowing the use of nuclear on a level playing field reduces the need for other changes, such as people consuming less, making it easier to accomplish. As we learned in the first part of this book, the alternative scenarios often tend to leave a large portion of the human population in poverty. These are not morally defensible "solutions".

The rich countries have used fossil fuels to escape from that poverty into a standard of living never seen before on this scale. And it is by burning those fossil fuels that we are now maintaining that standard of living. It is practically impossible to change this by simply banning this burning or by taxing it rapidly to nonexistence. The difficulty is compounded as we acknowledge that the value of the current infrastructure and fuel reserves that are still underground are already accounted for in the world economy. How could we ban this value from existence and what would be the consequences of doing so? The very system we would be using to ban these is dependent on these very same things. It would be like deciding to hold one's breath to stop carbon emissions: it works for a while, and then fails spectacularly.

It is hard to put a dollar value on fossil fuels and their easy availability, but for starters, we have over a billion vehicles with internal combustion engines in the world, while the number of electric vehicles is counted in the single digit millions. The value of this fleet is thousands of billions, and so is the value of our known reserves of fossil fuels. This value acts as equity against an even bigger amount of loans and is included in the value of corporations and their shares. These corporations are owned by retirement funds and countries. Many of us would like to see those retirement funds supporting us financially in our old age. Most global oil reserves are owned by state-owned corporations. This does not help matters, as these countries have built their current and future economies and budgets, and the well-being of their people and leaders, on the anticipated value of these reserves.

If we were to somehow leave three-fourths of our known fossil fuel reserves unused, which is required to limit climate change to even remotely safe levels, the hit for the global economy would be huge. Their direct value has been put at roughly $20,000 billion. This is also real, physical value, which is not the same thing as nominal value in some derivatives, housing markets or speculative papers that came crashing down in the 2007-2008 Great Recession. This energy can be used to do real work and to create value and wealth. Any global, political decisions that strongly limit the use of these resources would essentially render them worthless. Such decisions would seem difficult to achieve and highly unlikely.

Since we are all dependent on fossil fuels for our everyday life, it is likely that any policies that limit their use too much and too fast will get overturned come next elections. And if we believe the more cynical among us, even the democratic system is corrupt, and the actual power lies in the hands of multinational corporations and banks. This makes the situation even worse, as the fossil fuels industry is the largest business in the world, and most other industries are more or less dependent on it and its products. When we add that plentiful energy is one of the most important cornerstones of modern society, it seems that banning fossil fuels without other, plentiful substitutes to replace them, will be next to impossible.

The markets are also ruthless. If a significant amount of investment capital walks away from fossil fuel companies, as the divestment movement[284] suggests they should do, the price of their stock will come down. This would mean larger profits per dollar invested in their stock, making them a more attractive investment for someone else. If someone sells company stocks, then someone is buying. The largest impact the divestment movement might have is to question the social licence of these companies to exist and carry on their activities on a societal level. The same is somewhat true for various nations banning coal, especially in the European Union where the Emissions Trading System (ETS) sets the floor and the ceiling for emissions in the energy sector. The symbolic meaning of banning coal can be huge, but inevitably it leads to cheaper resources (emissions rights or available fossil fuels) for someone else in the market to use.

There is also a limited number of ways that the money from fossil fuel divestment can be spent. As money flows from fossil fuels to alternatives, the value of the stock of these alternatives goes up, which means smaller dividends per dollar invested. This will make them less attractive. A steeply rising price also lures in speculative money that is not after long term dividends but wants to sell the stocks at a profit in the short term. This in turn is a self-reinforcing cycle that can lead to price bubbles that eventually burst. These bubbles are rarely noticed from the inside, and often active policies are made to grow them even bigger and faster as everyone is so excited. The bigger they are, the more spectacular the burst will be. Short-sellers, who bet against company stocks and expect them to go down, are among the only counterforces here.

It can be argued that we need all the tools available, also from a political point of view, if we are to cut down fossil fuels emissions and maintain a stable, democratic society. The serious bottlenecks of nuclear are often connected to anti-nuclear politics, which in turn can be traced back to the voters feeling that nuclear is threatening, dangerous and unwanted.

Why Do People Oppose Nuclear Power?

Why do some people want to go against IPCC and other institutions, and ignore, or even ban nuclear from being used to tackle climate change? Even when it is the only source of energy that has a track record of cutting emissions fast enough on a country-scale? Why do people oppose nuclear, often tooth and nail, even as a matter of principle? Apart from becoming a question of one's identity, fear seems to be one of the big reasons.

Historian Miina Kaarikoski researched the parliamentary debates about nuclear in Germany during 1991 and 2001 for her doctoral dissertation[285]. What she found is fascinating. The opposition and subsequent decision to ban nuclear in Germany has a strong background in the German people's fear of an oppressive, powerful government that in turn is rooted in the times of Nazi Germany and DDR. The anti-nuclear advocates have systematically painted the picture in political debate that nuclear energy and waste (spent fuel) are so dangerous that it will require a government that can use extreme force to handle them safely. This is of course complete nonsense, but things often are what they seem to be, not what they really are. The fear and shame of Nazi history that the people of Germany have, in the skilled hands of anti-nuclear propagandists and opportunistic politicians, been transformed into a fear and loathing of all things nuclear.

It is like an animated golem of fear built from the fears of the people. Originally meant to be controlled and to serve some purpose, it has since grown to be so powerful and scary that it causes real fear and risks that nobody can control anymore.

The history of nuclear power makes it easier to understand the fear and opposition people have towards it. It is an energy technology that was born in close relationship with weapons of mass destruction. Nuclear technology in general is and has been concealed in a veil of secrecy from the people, which has led to mistrust. The promises left unfulfilled and general, historical arrogance of the nuclear industry have only added to that mistrust. Especially in the early years, anti-nuclear activism had more to do with the nuclear weapons industry and testing, and the military-industrial complex and its big role during the Cold War.

Serious accidents have happened, and the potential environmental and human harm done by uranium mining worries many, as does the question of what to do with the waste we are leaving to future generations. For others still, nuclear power represents an inhumanely large, difficult to control, technocratic and power-concentrating way of life and society that is thought to be in direct conflict with democracy and local scale solutions. Others are not comfortable with the (assumed) world views of the stereotypical pro-nuclear people, who might often be middle-aged white men that have a technical or engineering background. Yet others see nuclear power as an enabler of our over-use of natural resources and environmental destruction and as a sort of symbol for the high-energy modern civilizations that seem to be heading towards an ecological disaster. For the next person, "nuclear or no nuclear" is simply not a question that they feel the need to answer or have a position on in their lives. And for someone else, the political games that often accompany nuclear power (due to the political nature of nuclear energy) are disgusting and corrupt.

And some might use the nuclear industry simply as a proxy to project their other fears, dislikes and uncertainties into, given that it is a rather easy target. One can be anti-nuclear from a multitude of viewpoints, and many also have rather solid arguments and reasons for their views.

This book was originally written to counter most of those arguments and reasons. As we have stated earlier in this book, our position on the matter is clear: even with all the potential downsides and risks of nuclear, we believe that abandoning nuclear power will lead to much larger risks and downsides. We are not saying that anti-nuclear sentiment is based on ignorance, stupidity, irrationality or illogical thinking. Yes, there are some bad, one-sided arguments in the public debate against nuclear that remind us of some climate change denier tactics. But we need to remember that there is also some equally bad, weak argumentation being used to support nuclear power. The same goes for renewable energy argumentation.

In the end, it is about values and subjective guesses on what the future might bring. There is no single right answer, but there are over seven billion opinions, seven billion hopes and seven billion fears of what the future brings. It seems hard for many, both opponents and proponents of nuclear, to realise that one can look at the exact same data and come to totally opposite conclusions. When this happens, it is easy to label the other one who is "wrong" as irrational, perhaps blinded by ideology, stupid or ignorant. Or just plain evil. But this labelling is always subjective and often too easily done. We must confess that we are as guilty as anyone of this, and we are sorry for that.

We have also noted that these kinds of things are inclined to become questions of identity. It might be that someone who is against nuclear cannot turn pro-nuclear simply because being anti-nuclear is an essential part of their identity as well as their social life. In turn, we are equally sad to see that people who do not like environmentalists as a group often are against pretty much everything they propose as a reflex, no matter how good or reasonable the proposition may be.

These are hard, complex matters, and it is impossible to predict the future accurately. If one is convinced that renewable energy will be unstoppable, or that humans will need to use much less energy in the future, or that society will certainly collapse in the near future, it might indeed be hard to see reasons to support adding nuclear power. While we think these predictions are inherently problematic and too complex to make with enough certainty to "bet the planet on it", we also realise that other predictions suffer from this same fallibility. Complex matters do not have simple solutions or single right answers.

The Really Hard Questions

When it comes to energy and climate, we will have to choose between imperfect solutions. Everything has its risks and downsides. Both the use of nuclear and its abandonment raise some hard questions. Neither of us is a philosopher by training, and neither of us pretends to be an expert in ethics. The following thoughts touching on these matters are our own, and not any final truth. But they are thoughts and questions we would like to see discussed with as much rigor as the potential ethical and moral problems of nuclear use have been discussed during the last few decades.

What risks are we prepared to take?

Uranium mines and their suggested hazards are one of the most common arguments against the use of nuclear. Even if natural uranium by itself is not that radioactive or dangerous, other more radioactive fission products such as the gaseous radon are often released in uranium mines. In addition, uranium is a chemically toxic heavy metal. Long term exposure to high uranium concentrations through drinking water or food can cause severe harm to one's health. It is also practically impossible to prevent all possible leakages to the environment in any given mining activity. But they can be, and are, monitored carefully.

Despite doing a lot of research on this, we have not found any actual evidence that uranium mining would be significantly more harmful to humans and the environment than any other regular mining activity. The significant factor seems not to be what is mined, but the scale of the operations. If we mine for millions of tons of something, the environmental destruction and harm to humans is likely much larger than if we mine for a couple hundred tons of something. With uranium mining, it is essential to understand that due to its high energy density, relatively small amounts are needed. A typical one gigawatt (electrical) nuclear reactor uses around 150 – 200 tons of natural uranium per year. Part of this uranium comes as a by-product of other mining activities. In this case, one can say that the uranium production decreases the environmental footprint as an otherwise harmful heavy metal is collected from the mining waste streams and used for something valuable. Around half of all uranium production is currently done with in-situ leaching, which causes a minimal disturbance on the soil and surrounding environment.

The other alternatives also require mining activities. When looking at the whole picture, renewable energy production requires much more mined material per energy unit they produce. As can be seen in the graph below, nuclear energy is by far the least material intensive way to produce energy. Note that for combustion-based energy sources, the fuels themselves are not included in the graph, as they would severely impair the readability. For example, a coal plant uses some 300,000 tons of coal per terawatt hour of electricity.

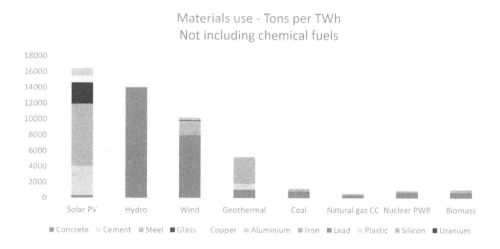

Figure 35: Materials use per terawatt hour of electricity produced. Quadrennial Technology Review, US Department of Energy, 2015. Uranium added later by authors.

All this material needs to be mined or produced, and all of it has a risk of environmental and human harm. The scale of that harm is dependent on the scale of the mining done. One of the largest disasters in

2015 was the breaching of the dam that held back waste sludge from an iron mine in Bento Rodrigues, Brazil. The accident released up to 60 million cubic meters of toxic sludge into the Doce-river and from there to the Atlantic Ocean. At least 17 people were killed, and the accident has already been called as perhaps the worst environmental accident in Brazil's history.

Uranium mining is not an exception even when it comes to the slight radioactivity of the mining waste. The rare earth minerals often needed in high tech electronics, solar panels, some wind turbines and batteries are often found together with thorium in the Earth's crust. Like uranium, thorium is a slightly radioactive mineral, and as it decays, some of the by-products are radioactive as well. Currently, there are little uses for thorium, and so it is often piled up as a waste product. These waste piles and ponds that contain thorium and many other much more toxic and dangerous materials already pose serious local environmental problems in China, which accounts for around 90 percent of the world's rare earth minerals production. It does bear noting that it is due to the toxicity of these materials and heavy metals, not their radioactivity, that accounts for most of the environmental threat.

In practice, opposing nuclear power means that more fossil fuels, renewable energy and support systems will be needed. All of these have their own environmental footprint, which needs to be discussed more instead of just waving it aside as a cost of doing business or as something that is justified by a noble cause. There is no dispute over this fact: on the basis of life cycle per unit energy generated , renewable energy requires much more mining activity than nuclear energy. It also requires much (in the neighbourhood of 100 to 1000 times) more land area than an energy infrastructure based on centralized power plants. The more distributed renewable energy is built, the more conflict there will be with traditional environmentalism, ecological values or local people. From the viewpoint of the number and area of ecosystems we need to seriously disturb to produce our energy, power plants, especially nuclear power plants, are much better.

Even though renewable energy is usually viewed as having low environmental impact, it is by no means clear if it is less harmful than other energy resources. Some forms of renewable energy, such as dedicated bioenergy crops, are among the most destructive. The effect on the environment differs greatly between the energy sources, and power density matters. Of course a small solar PV farm has a smaller impact on the local environment than a nuclear power plant – but it also produces a thousand times less energy, and zero reliable power for the system. Sure, PV panels can, and should, be put on the roofs of houses, but due to the low power density, we can only produce a fraction of our energy with them. It is mostly undisturbed nature that gets disturbed, are farmland taken out of production as many major energy projects, from nuclear plants to wind parks, cannot be deployed close to human settlements.

Compared to burning fossil fuels like coal, both nuclear and renewables cause less harm. However, some bioenergy production as well as large hydro projects can have significant negative effects. Each energy source can be harvested with minimal impacts, but only in limited amounts and locations, and therefore a mix of locally available and suitable sources is often the best bet.

Just society today and tomorrow

Instead of energy production and consumption, which are neutral terms, it might be better to talk about extracting energy. Production tends to hide the fact that we take, or extract, all our energy from the environment. Most of the time, this extraction has an impact on our surroundings, fellow humans and future generations. And most of the time, this trade-off is not fair to all participants.

This "energy fairness" is such a complex issue that we can only scratch the surface here with a couple remarks. The most important question might be the externalized costs and waste that our society leaves behind. When it comes to nuclear power, the central question is: do we have the right to leave radioactive nuclear waste in the hands of future generations?

If nuclear power were the only energy source leaving waste for future generations, it might be easier to answer that question. But as we have discussed above, all energy production leaves us with dangerous waste – and our reluctance to talk about this waste does not make it any less real. Radioactive waste gets less and less harmful as time goes by, but many heavy metals and toxins do not have half-lives and are dangerous quite literally forever.

Further, it is by no means evident – or even possible – that spent nuclear fuel would pose a significant or extraordinary threat in the future. As we have presented earlier in the book, the waste material is collected and contained, and after some time, is dangerous only if people spend time next to it, without any protective containment. That containment can be something as simple as regular water or a layer of concrete. And after some more time (roughly 1,000 years or less), it is harmful only if ingested and even then, largely due to it containing toxic heavy metals. There is a wide variety of chemicals commonly available from the service station or even grocery store that can cause harm, even death, if proper care is not taken when handling them. Why are we so worried about spent nuclear fuel? It is, by any level-headed comparison or estimate, a very minor public health or environmental concern and one that we have addressed thoroughly.

In addition to comparing waste toxicity, a more immediate threat comes from greenhouse gases such as carbon dioxide and methane. These pose a danger in the much nearer future, and some argue they cause harm even today. If we are unable to curtail our greenhouse gas emissions quickly, it is by no means certain that there will be anyone around to worry about the waste and any harm it might cause. As nuclear energy can be used to greatly decrease our emissions and the severity of climate change, the math is evidently clear: We should use nuclear energy, and other clean energy sources, to their full potential.

There is a hard division of social justice among those who benefit from energy production and those who suffer the costs and damages resulting from it. A lot of global mining activity is located in developing countries, as they often have less strict environmental policies and also have other incentives such as available cheap labour. This is especially true with rare earth minerals essential in renewable energy production and storage. China dominates the rare earths supply chain, which means they receive the brunt of its environmental toxins.

This point is especially valid with the likely alternative to nuclear power: burning fossil fuels. Coal burning causes severe harm due to air pollution, which can spread over long distances. While a nuclear accident would cause most of its damages to those who live in close proximity, through evacuations and such, they are also the people who get the benefits through jobs, tax revenues, cleaner air and affordable electricity. But the carbon dioxide emissions from fossil fuels are spread all over the atmosphere and oceans, and those who will suffer the most are the poor who have likely benefited the least from the burning.

As of today, the rich, entitled people are often prioritizing their own fear of an accident more than controlling their carbon emissions, as they would rather keep on burning and spreading the costs of that burning to others. This is both unethical and selfish, and will eventually lead to many people having to abandon their homes and suffering great losses, both personal and economical. The poor have every right to ask if their entire lives are more valuable than the unnecessary fear and loathing so many in the rich west can afford to feel towards nuclear.

Energy access is further a question of social justice. We think it is evidently clear (and for almost everyone's benefit in the longer run) that the wealth and prosperity in the world should be spread more evenly, even if it would mean some cuts in richer countries. The ethical gap is especially clear in global climate negotiations: the rich countries, who would have the option to get away from burning fossil fuels with relatively modest costs compared to their wealth, keep on burning, while they expect the poor nations to do something about their emissions and assume in their scenarios that poor nations will remain poor.

Burning is both easy and cheap (in direct costs), also in the developing world. The developing world, however, is not responsible for climate change, and the people living there have the same right to increase their living standards as we in the developed world have had. Whatever carbon budget the world has left should be reserved mainly for the developing world to use. Whenever there is a choice for burning in the rich world, it is hard to see any excuse to keep on burning outside selfishness, lack of political courage and perhaps fear. Each kilogram of coal that is burned in Germany, Holland, California, Switzerland, Sweden or Japan due to their political closures of nuclear power plants is economic development taken away from the poor of the world.

It is true that the nuclear industry has not been transparent or open historically. There have certainly been and will be methods that can be described as corrupt in various nuclear power projects around the world. But this is by no means specific to nuclear as a technology. It is simply a feature of how our current society and political system work (or does not work, one might argue). Any industrial project tries to cut its costs, streamline local political processes and minimize political risks and public opposition. Indeed, given that nuclear power is currently closely scrutinized by the media and other groups in western democracies, corruption is less likely to happen or to go unnoticed.

Similar corruption might take place in other large energy projects. Renewable energy enjoys a popular status among people in poll after poll. But this setting also makes it more difficult to criticize such energy projects even when there might be a reason to do so. Any objections to industrial wind farms can be swept aside with rhetoric about the critic being an "evil fossil fuel lobbyist or a nuclear shill" that tries to stand in the way of development and the future. This is a powerful argument, despite it having little factual basis. Significant tariffs or subsidies for any energy project invite corruption and shady deals because lucrative investments might depend on some project moving forward fast and unchallenged by a local municipal government or people. Wind, solar and biomass present the most glaring examples of this effect in the last decade or so.

But it needs to be remembered that none of this is inherently to blame on any technology, be it nuclear, wind power or something else. When a lot of money is at stake and regulation and oversight is loose, the incentive for corruption and unethical activity increases, no matter what the technology or project in question.

While a democratic society, with pressure from a relatively small part of the population, might be able to stop any corrupt or even completely legitimate construction projects in their tracks and make future projects unlikely by increasing political risks and costs, it might also make the mitigation of climate change effectively impossible. There is always a cost because of opposition or NIMBYism, and this cost needs to be balanced with the possible benefits and the costs of not doing anything about problems like climate change. If someone opposes one solution because he does not like it and sees it as unnecessary, he needs to remember that everyone else has a similarly valid justification to oppose all the other solutions as well, for their own personal reasons.

What if our society collapses?

The future can look scary. Even if human development has progressed on many fronts, one can't ignore that the situation looks very worrying indeed, particularly with regard to climate change. It seems likely that we will not be able to give up fossil fuels fast enough to prevent catastrophic climate change, depending perhaps only on what each of us wants to define as catastrophic and for whom. In the worst cases, this catastrophe might lead to the destruction of civilization as we know it, and at least to great economic losses and suffering well beyond what is caused by current climate change impacts.

We have talked with a multitude of people, some of whom base their opposition to nuclear power on a gloomy prognosis of western industrial societies. If catastrophes and societal collapse are likely, even un-avoidable, they argue that putting our resources into something that requires a high technology, complex and modern society, is a fundamentally bad and counterproductive idea. In addition to apocalyptic collapse, other threats include war and crises that could risk the safe operation of nuclear power plants. They might even become targets for military or terrorist action.

 While these scenarios are possible, saying that they are inevitable or even likely is, in our opinion, not grounded on solid evidence. Humanity and societies have faced great challenges throughout its history, and somehow, we have managed through them. Our complex society might actually be more resilient than many may think. While complexity adds things that can go wrong, it can also make the whole system more flexible and resilient to changes. The plasticity of the human brain and the flexibility of the internet are just two examples of complex systems that can adapt to significant disruptions, circle around them and still maintain most of their functionality. Humans, organizations and countries can amass significant powers and efforts when they choose to do so. We only need to look at the two World Wars as proof of this. More recently and as we write this in late March 2020, the coronavirus has already caused significant mobilization in various countries and industries. Money doesn't seem to be a problem when the economy is threatened, so there is hope that someday, money won't also be a problem when there is general awareness that the future of civilization is threatened.

 Both of us have been in the valley of hopelessness for years contemplating the seemingly inevitable collapse, be it because of peaking availability of cheap petroleum or an escalating climate catastrophe. Should we refrain from having kids? Would it be wise to perhaps prepare ourselves for some sort of a crash, and how to best do it? The narrative of utter hopelessness, doom and gloom has always been a part of the society, and it has a strange, intoxicating quality. But for most of us, it is an abstract story that we view from a comfortable distance.

Any collapse has always been a deeply traumatic experience for most people who have survived it. These traumas can continue for generations and have led to spiralling circles of violence and vengeance between people, groups and nations. Usually a crisis or catastrophe hurts the (physically) weakest the most, and any such crisis also means that environmental concerns are ignored for the time being.

It is our conclusion that trying to postpone or prevent these collapses or wars is much more productive and useful than just sitting and waiting for them to happen. In some sense, that is and has been the essence of life and humans throughout history: to live another day, another year. Access to energy, or the lack of it, has been a major factor in the birth of most modern wars and conflicts. By lessening our dependency on fossil fuels, we also lessen the reasons for these conflicts. In this respect, nuclear power offers us a significant benefit. Even if nuclear power is dependent on access to uranium or other nuclear fuel, it is still one of the easiest fuels to obtain and store. Access to uranium (or thorium, which is even more common) is widespread, as it is practically everywhere, and its enormous energy density enables us to gather it from very dilute sources such as seawater. As advanced breeder reactors become more available in the coming decades, fuel availability will become an even smaller issue.

If lack of high quality, high EROEI energy access can lead to a societal collapse, then our biggest priority should be to secure our access to such energy sources, and arguably, nuclear power is by any metric the highest quality energy source we have at our disposal.

We also have some encouraging evidence on what happens with nuclear power plants when society around them collapses rapidly, as this happened when the Soviet Union collapsed in the late 1980s. The nuclear power plants remained operational, and mostly in operation, through the turmoil. The black market was not filled with nuclear materials. It is clear the collapse of the Soviet Union led to poorer maintenance of the nuclear facilities, which in turn always leads to higher risks of accidents. But nothing serious happened. Most modern reactors are designed in a way that serious accidents are highly improbable, even with great negligence.

Societal collapse or war could lead to an otherwise improbable nuclear accident. It is practically impossible to estimate the likelihood of this sort of scenarios and accidents, but from the Soviet experience we can say they are not inevitable, or even likely. The other side of this unknown risk is that with nuclear power, we can greatly reduce the risks of such events by widespread reliable energy access and reduced greenhouse gas emissions to minimize climate disruptions.

If this societal collapse or other deep crisis were to happen, how much additional damage and harm would an increased number of nuclear reactors cause? As we discussed earlier in this book, a total meltdown of three reactors at Fukushima caused very little harm to humans or the environment. More harm was caused by the extended evacuation, which in turn was mainly caused by the fear of radiation release. In a line of unconventional thinking, a slightly less orderly state, which would not have been able to order those evacuations and have people follow through with them, the damage would have been much less. Further, any societal collapse is not likely to happen overnight. It took centuries for the Roman Empire to collapse. There would very likely be time to shut the reactors down properly, and even decommission them, if this were seen as needed. Given what we know of the actual risks these power plants pose, this would be unlikely.

A military crisis is also possible, and it is possible that someone might bomb nuclear power plants. In this case, Chernobyl, with its completely destroyed reactor core that had no containment building, can offer an estimate on the upper limit of damages that could be expected. It does need to be noted that bombing of a nuclear power plant is a war crime, and that many nations have much more effective means of destruction than trying to hit a nuclear reactor in a way that would cause it to lose containment and release significant amounts of radiation, as this is extremely hard to accomplish. These include nuclear bombs and missiles, chemical and biological weapons, as well as other more conventional substances such as napalm. With a sufficiently motivated military superpower, the average small or medium sized country can be bombed to ruins in a matter of hours no matter the number of nuclear reactors they have.

If the collapse or crisis were so severe that it would make operating nuclear power plants unsafe, it would also be a crisis that would likely crash the average life expectancy of the population. It would mean that most supply chains, basic health care and other central safety services would cease to function in society. Any additional harm that failing nuclear power plants would do in a society that might lose access to energy services such as electricity, would likely be miniscule. Even if nuclear fuel were simply left in the reactor building, it would be unlikely to cause much harm to anyone, with the exception of some individuals venturing into the reactor building. There is a wide variety of different industrial plants and factories spread everywhere that would offer similar or worse harm to careless people venturing into them.

This rather limited potential for harm that nuclear power poses needs to be weighed against the potential benefits nuclear power offers in both avoiding and mitigating any collapse. In a short-term crisis, the benefits of reliable, baseload electricity with easily storable fuel are undeniable and even unmatched. During the crisis in Ukraine, for example, the nuclear plants have been producing energy reliably while the natural gas deliveries from Russia have been unreliable.

Do we need a plan B or a planet B?

The precautionary principle states that we need to study new technologies and new kinds of activities carefully before we allow them to be used more widely to prevent any potential for nasty surprises. These surprises are not uncommon in human history. Some examples include the addition of lead to gasoline, the use of CFCs in refrigeration and the surprising side effects of DDT. Of course, the CO_2 emissions from fossil fuels are one such example as well, but back in the day when we started using them, people were much too excited about the new possibilities for economic improvement to listen to the few individuals that might have warned them about unforeseen consequences. So, can we use the precautionary principle as an argument to not use nuclear power more widely in mitigating climate change because, according to some, it can have some yet unknown consequences?

The whole question here is turned on its head. All human activities, including not doing anything, include unknown risks and consequences. The potential risks for using nuclear energy to mitigate climate change need to be compared with the well-documented risks of climate change getting much worse if we do not use nuclear to its full potential. This goes for other low-carbon solutions as well.

The relevant question to ask here is why should we not use everything we have to tackle climate change? According to precautionary principle, this is the crucial question. Lack of action on climate change should be the risk that is evaluated and compared with the risks of any particular solution. Further, a modern world based on intermittent renewable energy is a concept that is currently poorly known, untested and one that is likely to need technologies that are still in laboratories, if even there. These technologies would then need to be taken into commercial scale production at a record speed, economically and in a socially and environmentally acceptable way. There would be no allowances for major bottlenecks or delays, and negative side effects would need to be practically non-existent. Yet there are few requests to analyse this "RE100%" future from the precautionary principle point of view, and from our experience, any requests for such an analysis are met with hand-waving, scoffing or are simply ignored.

While it is true that a totally decarbonized society does not exist anywhere, and therefore includes many unknown risks no matter what technologies we use to achieve it, at least nuclear energy has a track record of actually decarbonizing the electricity grid of a whole nation (France), and with the help of hydro power, several nations (Sweden,

Switzerland, Belgium). We will need new technologies such as synthetic fuels manufacturing, but even these are much easier to scale to be economically more viable if the energy source available is reliable instead of intermittent.

Every day that passes without our emissions decreasing significantly also takes us closer to the day that we are forced to employ planetary scale geoengineering, such as releasing sulphur particles directly into the atmosphere to reflect part of the sun's energy back into space. Every day we spend opposing any low-carbon energy source that could be used to replace fossil fuels makes it more likely that we will simply have to experiment with various methods of geoengineering. These technologies will open a whole new can of worms when it comes to unknown risks and long-term dangers compared with anything associated with current low-carbon technologies.

It is clear that even a modest success in tackling climate change requires that we succeed in many technological and political arenas simultaneously. If we remove any of these "mitigation wedges", it means that the others will need to succeed even more spectacularly – something that is highly unlikely, adds significant risk and is directly against the precautionary principle. It is already increasingly clear that many of our previously planned, and absolutely necessary, mitigation wedges are failing either completely or at least partly:

- Carbon capture and storage (CCS) has a huge role in all mitigation scenarios, but has so far been a disappointment.
- Energy efficiency has by far the largest overall role in emissions reductions, but practically none of the scenarios account for the real-world effects of rebound.
- Energy efficiency has not improved at nearly the rates we think would be possible.
- We might have underestimated the level of determination the developing world will have in trying to increase the living standards and energy consumption of its people.
- We might have underestimated the difficulties in decoupling eco-

nomic growth from energy consumption.

- We might have underestimated the systemic difficulties and costs of integrating larger amounts of variable energy production in our energy systems.
- We might have overestimated the rate of growth of wind and solar in any given market after political subsidies and tariffs have diminished.
- Bioenergy is likely not as carbon neutral as we previously thought. Bioenergy also destroys ecosystems and harms biodiversity.
- Methane is likely to have a bigger climate impact due to leaks than we previously thought. The methane concentration in the atmosphere has been steadily increasing.

There are far too many failures and disappointments in our climate fight to claim, with a straight face, that we do not need all of the tools that are proven to work. Luckily, a lot can still be done.

Thinking long term – Cosmic risks

When thinking about sustainability and intergenerational justice, there is an important question we need to consider. How much do we worry about the future generations and the risks they might face? And how far into the future should we extend this worry?

Many have concluded that we should build small local communities which could rely on renewable energy and be more self-sufficient and resilient in the face of the changing world. Some have even started building these communities, whether one calls them Transition Towns or something else. These people see them as perhaps the best bet in the unsure future, and the only ecologically sustainable way forwards. This sort of small-scale action can offer great relief and a sense of control (even if only the sense of it) and purpose for people in a world that seems more chaotic by the day. For some, these local projects can offer a significant increase in mental, social and even economic well-being. But along with everything else, this path also needs to be evaluated critically.

Our international community is built on the mutual benefit provided by international trade. What would happen to this global community if trade relations become less important and its relative power in a world full of nation-states shrinks? Would it be able to tame international crises, act as a negotiator between nations and their leaders and ensure that international contracts, human rights and other fundamental things we take for granted, are not violated, at least not on an enormous scale? How long would our common interest to mitigate climate change – such as it is – last in a world where there would not exist even the current level of feeling that "we are all in the same boat?"

From the point of view of our future generations, is it responsible to turn inwards to our local communities, even as we live in a global world with global scale problems to solve? Many have lamented, ourselves included, about the slow progress of climate negotiations. Even the Paris treaty we have now signed is more like a weak statement than a binding contract. In truth, even this level of agreement on something, anything really, is an enormous achievement when one thinks about the multitude of nations and their cultural backgrounds, their leaders and their local political situations. Without a strong global community, nothing like this would have been even remotely possible.

Small and medium communities can turn xenophobic if they are closed and inward-looking. This is just a statistical fact. Self-sufficiency and isolation are not automatically good things (and neither are openness and dependency on others). But in the grand scheme of things, mutual dependency, openness and trade are more beneficial than the lack of these traits.

Isolation and focusing on the local scale another, even bigger problem. Even if eco-villages and other "back to the nature" schemes were an otherwise sustainable solution for humanity's future, this "return to paradise" would only ensure the destruction of humans and even complex life itself in the longer term.

Science, made possible by our high-energy society, has shown that the Earth is not a safe place for us. The latest extinction event happened 65 million years ago, likely because a huge meteorite struck Earth and wiped out the dinosaurs and all other forms of land animals heavier than 10 kg. According to some calculations, a similar event has struck the Earth every 50 million years or so, which means that we could well be living on borrowed time. Our current capability to follow the skies is limited, especially in the southern hemisphere. We might notice the next extinction event only when the meteorite started to glow in the atmosphere, roughly three seconds before impact.

If we wish to have any chance of noticing, let alone stopping, these kinds of cosmic events, the prerequisite is a high-energy, high tech- nology society with global communications and large amounts of sur- plus resources it can direct for these sorts of threats.

To take a step even further into the future, it is clear that Earth's days are numbered. So far, it contains the only forms of complex life of which we are aware. The Sun will engulf Earth in 4-5 billion years, but complex life on earth will become impossible much sooner than that, perhaps in a billion years. If we want to ensure that life in the universe goes on after that, we need to try our best to help it move elsewhere. As the Soviet rocket scientist Konstantin Tsiolkovsky said over a century ago, the Earth is humanity's cradle, but nobody should stay in their cradle for the rest of their lives. It might be that humans are the only species in the Milky Way even theoretically capable of space travel and multi-planet existence. If allowing a species to go ex- tinct is a horrible environmental crime, then what sort of crime would it be if we were to allow the only highly intelligent species, us humans, to go extinct?

We have now consumed most of the easily obtainable fossil fuels and other mineral resources from Earth's crust. If our global civiliza- tion crumbles to dust, it would seem unlikely that any future humans would be able to start from scratch and build another advanced civi- lization, as they would lack the advanced technologies needed to obtain the more challenging deposits of minerals, resources and energy that we have left. This goes for the long run as well. Even if humans were to go extinct and another species of intelligent life inherits the Earth, it would lack the easily available nest egg of high-quality fossil fuels that we had when we started building our modern world. Coal, which was essential to start the Industrial Revolution, is not renewed even on the timescale of hundreds of millions of years, if ever. The coal deposits we are currently using were formed during a very special time in our planet's history, when for millions of years there were no bacteria capable of decomposing all the dead plant matter. This plant matter, which included lignin, ended up buried and later formed our current coal deposits. Today, such bacteria are widely available, so coal formation at scale was likely a one-time event.

If these timescales seem too long to contemplate, it would be prudent to ask why we are worried about future generations, and how far into the future does our worry reach? What is the "discounting percentage" of our worry, and how far away is the future that we should simply not care about today? This is a personal, ethical choice for each of us to make. Many people who are worried about nuclear waste mention that they worry what will be the fate of those humans and other lifeforms living thousands of years in the future. An ancient Iroquois philosophy taught us to think seven generations into the future. According to them, anything farther than that is too far in the future on which to make any meaningful decisions. For the first time in its history human civilization is able to contemplate the consequences of its collective actions far into the future. This ability is made possible by our high-energy society which has given us scientific knowledge and advanced technologies that enabled us to discover ozone depletion, climate change and other systemic threats to our future well-being.

For our planet's sake and for ours, we have reason to hope that the world of tomorrow will supply itself with plentiful but clean energy. That world needs to relegate fossil fuels to small marginal uses during this century. The path to such a world will be narrow and full of dangers. But the same can also be said of our historic journey to the present day.

Final Words

We have spent hundreds, if not thousands of hours in discussions with dozens of people about the matters presented in this book. These people have varied in both the level of their expertise as well as their personal attitude towards nuclear power. We have read scores of books, reports and scientific papers to find the most relevant and trustworthy arguments and evidence for and against nuclear power. Some might have remained hidden, but we hope and believe that most of the important ones were discussed in this book.

It is not the intention of this book to belittle renewable energy sources, or the usefulness of energy efficiency or energy conservation. These will all have a huge role going forward. But this is precisely the reason we felt the need to also discuss the potential weaknesses and caveats they might have. They all have their limitations, and we need to understand and discuss honestly the meaning and implications of those limitations, and the scale and scope of the challenge before us. The current rhetoric around renewable energy is quite similar to that around nuclear power in the 1950s and 1960s, when nuclear electricity was said to become "too cheap to meter". Back then, the answer to any question was nuclear power, while today it seems to be renewable energy. Could it be that here lies a lesson for those touting renewable energy as the "chosen one" to save us all?

We also do not intend to offer nuclear power as the miracle silver bullet that will solve all our problems. Nuclear needs to be seen in proper context, as one solution among others. Yet the fact remains that many countries have been able to radically cut their emissions in relatively short time and with reasonable costs by building nuclear power. Of course nuclear power has its problems. But we need to understand that all energy sources have problems, and then we need to calmly analyse and compare them, then choose the best solutions in each context.

The sad fact remains that we are decades late in our climate fight, and still headed in the wrong direction. The climate deal negotiated in Paris COP21 was a significant step in the right direction. It was also technology-neutral. Instead of defining what technologies or tools we should use, it concentrated on the end result: limiting the temperature increase to two, preferably even to 1.5 degrees C. The emissions goals and targets currently set by the world's nations are not enough even for the higher target. Even if we keep our promises and no nasty surprises appear, we might still be faced with close to three degrees C of global warming. Therefore, it is of utmost importance that those of us interested in cutting emissions start pushing towards that goal instead of arguing which tools we are or are not allowed to use.

If we plan to succeed even partially, we will need most of the people and all the tools on board, one way or another. Too often climate action becomes a matter of political identity, with one side accepting the science on climate change but not on nuclear energy, and the other accepting nuclear as a solution but not the (non-nuclear) climate policies suggested by the other. Perhaps we could have significantly more effective climate policies if they were technology-inclusive instead of something that can at best be described as tribal and technology-exclusive?

Even if reaching our climate action goals seems unlikely, we still need to try. This is not a binary choice of total success or total failure. We need to try to limit the harms for future generations as much as we can. If we fail to use all we have, including nuclear power, those future generations will rightfully ask: "Would it have been possible to avoid the worst effects of climate change, if only the people living in the 20th and 21st centuries hadn't been so opposed to nuclear power?"

Endnotes

1   https://www.c2es.org/content/international-emissions/
2   http://report.mitigation2014.org/spm/ipcc_wg3_ar5_
         summary-for-policymakers_approved.pdf
3   http://ilmastotieto.wordpress.com/2014/12/22/suomen-
         keskilampotila-noussut-jo-yli-kaksi-astetta/ (in Finnish)
4   Finnish Meteorological Institute SETURKLIM-project:
         http://tinyurl.com/ks694gj
5   See IPCC AR4 (2007). http://www.ipcc.ch/publications_and_
         data/ar4/syr/en/mains5-7.html
6   Hansen, J., et al. (2016), Ice melt, sea level rise and
superstorms: evidence from paleoclimate data, climate
modeling, and modern observations that 2 °C global warming is
         highly dangerous, Atmos. Chem. Phys. Discuss., 16, 3761–3812
, https://doi.org/10.5194/acp-16-3761-2016
7   BP Statistical Review of World Energy 2019
8   https://www.esrl.noaa.gov/gmd/aggi/aggi.html
9   https://research.noaa.gov/article/ArtMID/587/ArticleID/2461/
         Carbon-dioxide-levels-hit-record-peak-in-May
10   https://www.ipcc.ch/sr15/
11   According to Climateactiontracker.org. http://tinyurl.com/
         o8a83ks. Read 20th March 2020.
12   According to Climateactiontracker.org. http://tinyurl.com/
         zb5g6xd. Read 20th March 2020.
13   https://www.theguardian.com/science/2019/dec/15/cop25-
         un-climate-talks-over-for-another-year-was-anything-achieved
14   http://ilmastotieto.wordpress.com/2010/12/20/miksi-kahden-
         asteen-raja/ (In Finnish)
15   Plumer, B. (2014). Two degrees: How the world failed on
climate   change.   www.vox.com/2014/4/22/5551004/two-degrees.
Read 20th March 2020
16   World Bank (2012). Turn down the heat: why a 4°C warmer

world must be avoided. Washington DC: World Bank. http://tinyurl.
com/n63djok. Page xviii. Read 15th July 2014.

17   http://www.nature.com/nclimate/journal/v4/n3/fig_tab/
nclimate2148_F1.html

18   IPCC WG3 AR5 summary (2014, pdf). http://tinyurl.com/
o7f5byt

19   Hansen J, Kharecha P, Sato M, Masson-Delmotte V, Ackerman
F, et al. (2013) Assessing "Dangerous Climate Change": Required
Reduction of Carbon Emissions to Protect Young People, Future
Generations and Nature. PLoS ONE 8(12): e81648. http://doi:10.1371/
journal.pone.0081648

20   PwC Low Carbon Economy Index 2018 (pdf). https://www.
pwc.co.uk/ghost/low-carbon-economy-index-2018.html.   Read   16th
December 2016.

21   Greenhouse-gas emission targets for limiting global warming
to 2 C, Nature, Vol 458, 30th April, 2009

22   Why leaving fossil fuels in the ground is good for everyone,
The Guardian (2015). http://tinyurl.com/m5c8w5z

23   McGlade, C., Ekins, P., (2015), The geographical distribution of
fossil fuels unused when limiting global warming to 2 °C. Nature 517,
187 190. http://dx.doi.org/10.1038/nature14016

24   See International Energy Agency (IEA) World Energy outlook
2014

25   Kander, A., Malanima, P., ja Warden, P. (2014). Power to the
People: Energy in Europe over the Last Five Centuries. Princeton
University Press, Princeton.

26   Kander, A., Malanima, P., ja Warden, P. (2014). Power to the
People: Energy in Europe over the Last Five Centuries. Princeton
University Press, Princeton.

27   http://www.un.org/millenniumgoals/

28   Fast Facts, UN Development Project (2010, pdf). http://tinyurl.
com/hg5p6hf. Read 3.1.2016.

29   Global Energy Futures and Human Development: A Framework

for Analysis, U.S. Department of Energy (2000). https://e-reports-ext. llnl.gov/pdf/239193.pdf

30   7 million premature deaths annually linked to air pollution, World Health Organization (2014). http://www.who.int/mediacentre/ news/releases/2014/air-pollution/en/

31   Conway, G., (2012), One Billion Hungry: Can We Feed the World?, Comstock Publishing Associates

32   The example is from Elshkaki, A., & Graedel, T. E. (2013). Dynamic analysis of the global metals flows and stocks in electricity generation technologies. Journal of Cleaner Production, 59, 260 273. doi:10.1016/j.jclepro.2013.07.003. Other studies on the subject include: Davidsson, S., Grandell, L., Wachtmeister, H., & Höök, M. (2014). Growth curves and sustained commissioning modelling of renewable energy: Investigating resource constraints for wind energy. Energy Policy, 73, 767 776. doi:10.1016/j.enpol.2014.05.003Vidal, O., Goffé, B., & Arndt, N. (2013). Metals for a low-carbon society. Nature Geoscience, 6(11), 894 896. doi:10.1038/ngeo1993

33   Estimates on steel and copper demand: Davidsson, Grandell, Wachtmeister and Höök (2013). Similar estimates on concrete consumption: Vidal, Goffé and Arndt (2013).

34   http://documents.worldbank.org/curated/ en/207371500386458722/pdf/117581-WP-P159838-PUBLIC-ClimateSmartMiningJuly.pdf

35   The term exergy has been developed by Robert Ayres and Benjamin Warr. More information on their book The Economic Growth Engine: How Energy and Work Drive Material Prosperity (2010), Edward Elgar Publishing

36   It takes approx. 1450 C temperature to melt steel and making hydrogen with thermochemical reactions takes up to 850 C temperature.

37   BP Statistical Review of World Energy 2013

38   The global energy statistics used in this book are mainly from BP Statistical Review of World Energy 2019. The "primary electricity"

producers such as hydro, wind, solar, wave and nuclear) have been converted into thermal energy content of coal used in a comparable combustion-based power plant, assuming an average efficiency of 38 %.

39   The problem here is that the investment costs of almost all methods for producing fossil fuel substitutes for transport fuels and chemical feedstocks are dominated by the desired peak production capacity. Thus, a plant that can produce two tons of synthetic, fossil-free chemicals per hour costs almost twice as much as a plant that produces only one ton per hour. If a synthesizer plant runs only 25% of the time, a figure that would not be atypical in most scenarios that envision that these fossil substitutes are produced only using "excess" renewable electricity, even if the electricity is free, the cost of the end product would still be almost certainly much higher than a smaller plant that operated at, say, 90% capacity factor but had to pay something for its electricity. Furthermore, many important chemical processes and, for example, catalysts used in the process work best and last much longer if the processes are stable and steady; this is another factor that argues for both cheap and stable low-carbon electricity supply.

40   IEA World Energy Outlook 2015.

41   Health impacts of domestic coal use in China (1999). http://www.pnas.org/content/96/7/3427.full.pdf

42   Lim, S., et al. (2012), "A Comparative Risk Assessment of Burden of Disease and Injury Attributable to 67 Risk Factor Clusters in 21 Regions, 1990-2010: A Systematic Analysis for the Global Burden of Disease Study 2010", The Lancet, Vol. 380, Elsevier, pp. 2224-2260.

43   http://www.scientificamerican.com/article/world-population-will-soar-higher-than-predicted/

44   http://tinyurl.com/hap5zvb. Read 20th March 2020.

45   IEA World Energy Outlook 2014, p. 56

46   World Energy Council (2019). http://tinyurl.com/w335559. Read 23rd March 2020.

47   World Energy Technology Outlook – WETO H2 (EU 2006) http://ec.europa.eu/research/energy/pdf/weto-h2_en.pdf

48   IPCC AR5 Working Group III, Chapter 7, page 66

49   BP Statistical Review of World Energy 2019

50   Heard, B. et al., (2017), Burden of proof: A comprehensive review of the feasibility of 100% renewable-electricity systems, Renewable and Sustainable Energy Reviews, https://doi.org/10.1016/j.rser.2017.03.114

51   Williams, J.H., B. Haley, F. Kahrl, J. Moore, A.D. Jones, M.S. Torn, H. McJeon (2014). Pathways to deep decarbonization in the United States. The U.S. report of the Deep Decarbonization Pathways Project of the Sustainable Development Solutions Network and the Institute for Sustainable Development and International Relations. www.deepdecarbonization.org/ and Charles R. Frank, Jr (2014). The net benefits of low and no-carbon electricity technologies, The Brookings Institution, http://tinyurl.com/l2z2v8g

52   Loftus, P. J., Cohen, A. M., Long, J. C. S., & Jenkins, J. D. (2015). A critical review of global decarbonization scenarios: what do they tell us about feasibility? Wiley Interdisciplinary Reviews: Climate Change, 6(1), 93–112. doi:10.1002/wcc.324

53   New IPCC report reveals: Renewable energy is indispensable to avoiding climate change. http://tinyurl.com/pgu8gtz

54   Greenpeace International, http://tinyurl.com/ktzd73s

55   http://www.carbonbrief.org/blog/2011/06/the-ipcc-and-the-srren-report/

56   Lynas, Mark (2013). Nuclear 2.0: Why a Green Future Needs Nuclear Power. Kindle Single.

57   Harjanne, A., Korhonen, J. M., (2018), Abandoning the concept of renewable energy, Energy Policy, doi:10.1016/j.enpol.2018.12.029

58   See http://tinyurl.com/jjda6nb

59   https://sdg.iisd.org/news/renewable-energy-investment-to-

surpass-usd-2-5-trillion-for-2010-2019-unep-report-finds/

60   https://www.iea.org/reports/world-energy-investment-2019

61   BP Statistical Review of World Energy 2019

62   Wind Energy in Europe 2018, https://windeurope.org/wp-content/uploads/files/about-wind/statistics/WindEurope-Annual-Statistics-2018.pdf

63   Bioenergy Landscape Statistical Report 2019, https://bioenergyeurope.org/

64   Both wind and solar PV can stay operational even longer, but they also lose some of their production as they age.

65   Loftus, P. J., Cohen, A. M., Long, J. C. S., & Jenkins, J. D. (2015). A critical review of global decarbonization scenarios: what do they tell us about feasibility? Wiley Interdisciplinary Reviews: Climate Change, 6(1), 93–112. http://doi.org/10.1002/wcc.324

66   Budischak, C., Sewell, D., Thomson, H., Mach, L., Veron, D. E., & Kempton, W. (2013). Cost-minimized combinations of wind power, solar power and electrochemical storage, powering the grid up to 99.9% of the time. Journal of Power Sources, 225, 60–74. doi:10.1016/j.jpowsour.2012.09.054 Hart, E. K., & Jacobson, M. Z. (2011). A Monte Carlo approach to generator portfolio planning and carbon emissions assessments of systems with large penetrations of variable renewables. Renewable Energy, 36(8), 2278–2286. doi:10.1016/j.renene.2011.01.015

67   Hart, E. K., & Jacobson, M. Z. (2011). A Monte Carlo approach to generator portfolio planning and carbon emissions assessments of systems with large penetrations of variable renewables. Renewable Energy, 36(8), 2278–2286. doi:10.1016/j.renene.2011.01.015

68   A useful summary of the report can be read here: http://tdworld.com/blog/caiso-battery-storage-trial

69   This was first studied by William Stanley Jevons in mid-19th century. The "Jevon's Paradox" states that increasing energy efficiency will not show as decrease in energy consumption, but often the contrary happens.

70   IPCC Assessment Report 5 (2014). Working Group III, Chapter 5. p. 54, "The rebound effect."

71   Capturing the multiple benefits of energy efficiency (2014), IEA, page 39

72   Lin, B and Li, J. (2014) The rebound effect for heavy industry: Empirical evidence from China. Energy Policy. DOI: 10.1016/j.enpol.2014.08.031

73   IPCC Assessment Report 5 (2014). Working Group III, Chapter 5. p. 54, "The rebound effect."

74   United Nations, Department of Economic and Social Affairs, Population Division (2015). World Population Prospects: The 2015 Revision. Volume I: Comprehensive Tables. Luvut keskimääräisen skenaarion mukaan.

75   The facilities that produce primary electricity have been converted into primary energy by multiplying production 2.63 to make comparisons easier with other values used elsewhere.

76   For example, a Finnish person used 101 MWhs of primary energy in 2012.

77   BP Statistical Review of World Energy 2019.

78   See interview of Prof. Juma, "Poor Countries Denied Chance to Succeed?", Voice of America, 25.3.2014. http://tinyurl.com/svmeca9. See also Pearce, F. (2014) World's poor need grid power, not just solar panels. New Scientist 2980, 4.8.2014. http://tinyurl.com/qco64vu. Read 21st March 2020.

79   Center of Global Development (2015) http://tinyurl.com/hkjm8tz.

80   These four element were taken from a presentation "Energiewende in Perspective" by Dr. Leonard Birnbaum from World Energy Council, given in Finland 29th September 2014.

81   More on the background of the Energiewende: Beveridge, R., & Kern, K. (2013). The Energiewende in Germany: background, developments and future challenges. Renewable Energy Law and Policy Review, 4(1), 3–12.

82   Pöyry (2013). Coal fired power generation in Germany, the Netherlands and Spain. Report to DECC. http://tinyurl.com/p6syq28. Pages 13 and 15. Read 21st March 2020.

83   Hansen, J. (2009). Storms of my Grandchildren: The Truth About the Coming Climate Catastrophe and Our Last Chance to Save Humanity. Bloomsbury. Page 181.

84   For example Der Spiegel Online (2010). Slowing the Phase-Out: Merkel Wants to Extend Nuclear Power Plant Lifespans. 30.8.2010. http://tinyurl.com/h9v479o. Read 21st March 2020.

85   The birth of humanity's largely irrational fear of the atom is thoroughly documented in The Rise of Nuclear Fear (Harvard University Press, 2012) by Spencer R. Weart.

86   BP Statistical Review of World Energy (2019).

87   See https://ec.europa.eu/eurostat/statistics-explained/index. php/Electricity_price_statistics

88   Calculated with nuclear newbuild price of €5-6 billion per GW, similar to Olkiluoto 3 estimated price.

89   BP Statistical Review of World Energy (2019).

90   Wetzel, D. (2014). Bundesregierung scheitert am Klimaschutz. Die Welt, 2.9.2014. http://tinyurl.com/mv4e5l9. Read 21st March 2020.

91   Germany unlikely to meet carbon reduction targets for 2020, Deutsche Welle (2014). http://tinyurl.com/j47n448. Read 21st March 2020.

92   Chambers (2014). German state allows Vattenfall to expand brown coal mining. Reuters 3.6.2014. http://tinyurl.com/hpabu9v. Read 21st March 2020.

93   The letter from Sigmar Gabriel to Swedens prime minister Stefav Löfven in 13th October 2014. http://www.altinget.se/misc/ SigmarGabriel.pdf. Read 21st March 2020.

94   Vattenfall to sell German lignite operations, Vattenfall press release, (2016). http://tinyurl.com/jjn9xwd

95   Evans, S. (2014) UK and Germany balk at coal exit plea. The Carbon Brief, 19.9.2014. http://tinyurl.com/jptbclg. Read 21st March

2020.

96   The study is only in German, but some highlights can be read at http://www.thegwpf.com/the-energy-absurdity-of-the-paris-climate-agreement. Original study: http://tinyurl.com/zqrc3xd. Read 21st March 2020.

97   Germans Hesitate on Coal Phase-Out Target in Merkel Policy Paper, Bloomberg (2016), http://tinyurl.com/hs229n2. Read 21st March 2020.

98   https://phys.org/news/2020-01-carbon-prices-german-emissions.html

99   Germany to phase out coal by 2038 in move away from fossil fuels, Reuters (2019). http://tinyurl.com/ugvckqn

100   See http://tinyurl.com/tc2j3wd

101   For example Petri Hakkarainen, a Finnish researcher of the Energiewende

102   Germany's renewable energy reforms 'a step backwards', DW (2016). http://tinyurl.com/jo3g2ul. Read 3rd August 2016

103   The source is an article "Spain made a u-turn" in the Finnish Energy News issue 7, 2014 (Energiauutiset) by Juha Europaeus (2014). Article is in Finnish.

104   IEA 2019, Nuclear Power in a Clean Energy System. https://www.iea.org/reports/nuclear-power-in-a-clean-energy-system

105   See four main scenarios in the Summary for Policymakers. https://www.ipcc.ch/sr15/

106   Nuclear Power Results – Life Cycle Assessment Harmonization, NREL. https://www.nrel.gov/analysis/life-cycle-assessment.html

107   We need to decarbonize liquid fuels from transportation and industrial heat as well, but there are materials, like cement and steel, where decarbonization will be very difficult.

108   Ruling Gives Natural Gas Edge to Replace Nuclear Energy in California, Forbes (2014) http://tinyurl.com/udoctjv. Read 21st March 2020.

109   Japan's Answer to Fukushima: Coal Power, The Wall Street

Journal (2014). http://tinyurl.com/jhpr5bt. Read 21st March 2020.

110   Nuclear Power in Japan, WNA, http://tinyurl.com/hz2vb6m. Read 17th August 2016

111   Japan approves energy plan reinstating nuclear power, Reuters (2014). http://tinyurl.com/p58j5y6. Read 21st March 2020.

112   Nuclear Power in Japan, WNA, http://tinyurl.com/hz2vb6m. Read 23rd March 2020.

113   Hore-Lacy, I. (2012), Nuclear Energy in the 21st Century, World Nuclear University Press, page 39

114   Our Common Future, Chapter 7: Energy: Choices for Environment and Development. http://www.un-documents.net/ocf-07.htm

115   Other projects that were at least partly done from a military perspective have been the highway-network, space-technology and the solar PV panels made to power space applications and the internet as a robust and redundant network for critical communications.

116   Mahaffey, James (2014-02-04). Atomic Accidents: A History of Nuclear Meltdowns and Disasters: From the Ozark Mountains to Fukushima (Kindle Location 2537). Pegasus Books. Kindle Edition.

117   For more info on the IFR, two of the participants in the project (Charles Till and Yoon Il Chang) wrote the story of the IFR project into a book called: Plentiful Energy: The Story of the Integral Fast Reactor: The complex history of a simple reactor technology, with emphasis on its scientific bases for non-specialists, (2011).

118   Russian fast reactor reaches full power, World Nuclear News, http://tinyurl.com/j2c9szj

119   https://www.world-nuclear-news.org/Articles/ARC-100-passes-Canadian-pre-licensing-milestone

120   http://en.wikipedia.org/wiki/Molten_salt_reactor

121   Chinese scientists urged to develop new thorium nuclear reactors by 2024, South China Morning Post (2014). http://tinyurl.com/nlm73hv

122   http://phys.org/news/2014-06-molten-salt-reactor-concept-

transatomic.html

123   http://www.gen-4.org

124   Csik, B. J. ja Kupitz, J. (1997). Nuclear Power Applications: Supplying heat for homes and industries. IAEA Bulletin 39/2/1997, 21-25.

125   https://www.vttresearch.com/en/news-and-ideas/good-riddance-fossil-fuels-vtt-develops-small-modular-reactor-district-heating

126   https://www.hydrogeneurope.eu/news/hydrogen-roadmap-europe-has-been-published

127   https://www.iea.org/reports/the-future-of-hydrogen

128   https://cafcp.org/sites/default/files/Path-to-Hydrogen-Competitiveness_Full-Study-1.pdf

129   https://cafcp.org/blog/full-report-us-hydrogen-road-map-released

130   In the early 2020s, there were several car manufacturers citing battery shortage as they paused the production of their new EV's, including at least Audi, Jaguar and Mercedes-Benz.

131   Gas-to-liquids conversion, ARPA-E U.S. DoE (2012, pdf). http://tinyurl.com/gnq3otc.

132   This image is from a report that has not yet been published at the time of writing.

133   These are not accurate numbers, but more back-of-the-envelope calculations to find the scale of things.

134   Bardi, Ugo. Extracted: How the Quest for Mineral Wealth Is Plundering the Planet (Kindle Locations 1314-1316). Chelsea Green Publishing. Kindle Edition.

135   Uranium 2014: Resources, Production and Demand, http://www.oecd-nea.org/ndd/pubs/2014/7209-uranium-2014.pdf

136   Given the official name of "Agreement between the Government of the Russian Federation and the Government of the United States of America Concerning the Disposition of Highly-Enriched Uranium Extracted from Nuclear Weapons" it is no wonder it was nicknamed

again.

137   Japanese court block plan to restart nuclear plant, Financial Times. http://tinyurl.com/hn983nz

138   Supply of Uranium, World Nuclear Association. http://tinyurl.com/c7rebvh

139   BP statistical review of World Energy 2019

140   Uranium 2018: Resources, Production and Demand, http://www.oecd-nea.org/ndd/pubs/2018/7413-uranium-2018.pdf

141   How long will the world's uranium supplies last? Scientific American (2009). http://tinyurl.com/kbvglbc

142   Amidoxime Uranium Extraction From Seawater (2011). http://large.stanford.edu/courses/2011/ph241/chan1/

143   Uranium Seawater Extraction Makes Nuclear Power Completely Renewable, Forbes (2016), http://tinyurl.com/j4xxq6k

144   Extracting uranium from seawater (2012). http://tinyurl.com/sw5hqjv

145   Coal Combustion: Nuclear resource or danger, ORNL Review (1993).   http://pbadupws.nrc.gov/docs/ML0932/ML093280447.pdf. Read 23rd March 2020.

146   World Uranium Mining Production, World Nuclear Association. http://tinyurl.com/jkb5vql

147   Here is a slight conflict of interest. Many nuclear reactor vendors also sell the fuel for them, so they might not want to to have reactors on the market that are independent of the current nuclear fuel cycle.

148   Radioactive Waste Management, World Nuclear Association. http://tinyurl.com/kee3dh3

149   Markandaya, A., Wilkinson, P., 2007, Electricity generation and health, The Lancet. DOI:10.1016/S0140-6736(07)61253-7

150   See Kurttio, P. et al: Fallout from the Chernobyl accident and overall cancer incidence in Finland. Cancer Epidemiology. http://dx.doi.org/10.1016/j.canep.2013.05.006

151   Rabl A, J. V. Spadaro, M. Holland. 2014. How Much is Clean Air Worth: Calculating the Benefits of Pollution Control. Cambridge University Press. ISBN 978-1-10-704313-8.

152   Europe's Dark Cloud, 2016, authors include WWF, Sandbag, Climate Action Network and HEAL. http://tinyurl.com/jz876kt (pdf).

153   Calculated with following assumptions: Total cost 32 to 62 billion €/year. Annual coal consumption in 2013 was 287 Mtoe with 1 Mtoe of coal producing 4.4 TWhs of electricity on an average power plant (BP 2016). While BP incudes all sectors in its coal numbers, industrial use of solid fuels in 2013 (mostly coal) was 35 Mtoe according to Eurostat, leaving roughly 250 Mtoe for power and heat sectors, which are only included in the Dark Cloud reports cost-estimate.

154   The Economic Consequences of Outdoor Air Pollution (2016), OECD, http://tinyurl.com/hoxnqoy

155   Gale, Robert Peter; Lax, Eric (2013-01-29). Radiation: What It Is, What You Need to Know (Kindle Location 555). Knopf Doubleday Publishing Group. Kindle Edition.

156   https://en.wikipedia.org/wiki/Eben_Byers

157   http://en.wikipedia.org/wiki/Linear_no-threshold_model

158   See   http://link.springer.com/article/10.1007/s13752-016-0244-4

159   http://en.wikipedia.org/wiki/Linear_no-threshold_model#Radiation_precautions_and_public_policy

160   Aurengo et al. (30.3.2005). Dose-effect relationships and estimation of the carcinogenic effects of low doses of ionizing radiation, Académie des Sciences & Académie nationale de Médecine.

161   Neumaier, T.; Swenson, J., Pham, C., Polyzos, A., Lo, A. T., Yang, P., Dyball, J., Asaithamby, A., Chen, D. J., Bissell, M. J., Thalhammer, S., Costes, S. V. (19 December 2011). "Evidence for formation of DNA repair centers and dose-response nonlinearity in human cells". Proceedings of the National Academy of Sciences 109 (2): 443–8. doi:10.1073/pnas.1117849108

162   ICRP. ICRP Publication 103: the 2007 recommendations of the International Commission on Radiological Protection. Ann ICRP. 2007;37(2-4):1–332.

163   UNSCEAR. Report of the United Nations Scientific Committee on the Effects of Atomic Radiation Fifty-ninth Session (21-25 May 2012). New York, NY: UNSCEAR; 2012: Report No. A/67/46.

164   Even in Pispala, the dose varies greatly from one house to the next.

165   http://en.wikipedia.org/wiki/Guarapari

166   http://www.unscear.org/unscear/en/chernobyl.html

167   In Finnish: http://www.stuk.fi/aiheet/sateilyvaara/esimerkkeja-sateilyannoksista

168   Fukushima's doses tallied, Nature (2012). http://www.nature.com/news/fukushima-s-doses-tallied-1.10686

169   http://hps.org/publicinformation/ate/faqs/radiation.html

170   Welsome, E. (1999) The Plutonium Files: America's Secret Medical Experiments in the Cold War. Dial Press.

171   Sources and effects of ionizing radiation, UNSCEAR 2008

172   Rabl A, J. V. Spadaro, M. Holland. 2014. How Much is Clean Air Worth: Calculating the Benefits of Pollution Control. Cambridge University Press. ISBN 978-1-10-704313-8.

173   Coal Combustion: Nuclear resource or danger, ORNL Review (1993). http://pbadupws.nrc.gov/docs/ML0932/ML093280447.pdf

174   When Radiation isn't the real risk, NY Times (2015). http://tinyurl.com/nsdqfu2

175   A list of substances and their radioactivity: http://www.remm.nlm.gov/reactor_isotopes.htm

176   Technical Report TR-19-15, Supplementary information on canister integrity issues, SKB, 2019.

177   http://jmkorhonen.net/2013/08/15/graph-of-the-week-what-happens-if-nuclear-waste-repository-leaks/
Posiva's latest report: http://www.posiva.fi/files/3195/Posiva_2012-10.

pdf

178   In Pispala the average annual dose is 35 mSv, which is 35 / 365 / 24 / 60 *1000 = 0,000065 mSv per minute.

179   The article relies on this article in Wikipedia: http://en.wikipedia.org/wiki/Three_Mile_Island_accident

180   SCRAM comes from "safety control rod axe man" and refers to the last line of safety in the first reactor humans built, whose job it was to cut the rope holding the control rods up with his axe.

181   Some sources say that the indicator was partly covered.

182   http://www.unis.unvienna.org/unis/en/pressrels/2011/unisinf398.html

183   ICRP. ICRP Publication 103: the 2007 recommendations of the International Commission on Radiological Protection. Ann ICRP. 2007;37(2-4):1–332.

184   UNSCEAR. Report of the United Nations Scientific Committee on the Effects of Atomic Radiation Fifty-ninth Session (21-25 May 2012). New York, NY: UNSCEAR; 2012: Report No. A/67/46.

185   The report was done and published by IAEA, WHO, UNDP, FAO, UNEP, UN-OCHA, UNSCEAR, World Bank and the governments of Belarus, Ukraine and Russia. The original report can be downloaded from   http://www.iaea.org/Publications/Booklets/Chernobyl/chernobyl.pdf

186   http://www.chernobylreport.org/torch.pdf

187   http://www.greenpeace.org/international/Global/international/planet-2/report/2006/4/chernobylhealthreport.pdf

188   http://tinyurl.com/s7njb24

189   Such as Helen Caldicott, who also claims to be strictly for science and evidence.

190   http://en.wikipedia.org/wiki/Mining_accident

191   7 million premature deaths annually linked to air pollution, World Health Organization (2014). http://www.who.int/mediacentre/news/releases/2014/air-pollution/en/

192   European coal pollution causes 22,300 premature deaths a

year, study shows, The Guardian (2013). http://tinyurl.com/nyg6mpv

193   See Corrice (2012). Fukushima: The First Five Days. The text here is largely based on this book, which is based on the original logs.

194   NUREG-1150, NRC (1991). http://www.nrc.gov/reading-rm/doc-collections/nuregs/staff/sr1150/

195   The book Atomic Accidents offers a thorough tour of the Fukushima accident. This chapter is based on that and on the wikipedia article on the accident.

196   Isolation condenser had been installed on the oldest reactor #1.

197   Mahaffey, James (2014-02-04). Atomic Accidents: A History of Nuclear Meltdowns and Disasters: From the Ozark Mountains to Fukushima (Kindle Locations 7451-7452). Pegasus Books. Kindle Edition.

198   Numbers are from UNSCEAR 2013 Report Volume I: Report to the General Assembly, Scientific Annex A: Levels and effects of radiation exposure due to the nuclear accident after the 2011 great east-Japan earthquake and tsunami, page 25. http://www.unscear.org/docs/reports/2013/13-85418_Report_2013_Annex_A.pdf

199   Numbers are from UNSCEAR 2013 Report Volume I: Report to the General Assembly, Scientific Annex A: Levels and effects of radiation exposure due to the nuclear accident after the 2011 east-Japan earthquake and tsunami, page 33. http://www.unscear.org/docs/reports/2013/13-85418_Report_2013_Annex_A.pdf

200   There are even books on this, such as the one from a Greenpeace-activist, nutrition therapist Kimberly Roberson's Silence Deafening, Fukushima Fallout ... A Mother's Response.

201   Fukushima leaking radioactive water for '2 years, 300 tons flowing into Pacific daily', RT (2013). http://rt.com/news/japan-fukushima-nuclear-disaster-164/.

202   New Radioactive Water Leak Found at Fukushima Plant, Nation of Change (2014). http://tinyurl.com/onwunt4. Read 23rd March 2020.

203   http://ecowatch.com/2014/06/14/fukushima-children-dying/.

Read 23rd March 2020.

204   Why the Cancer Cases in Fukushima Aren't Likely Linked to the Nuclear Disaster, National Geographic (2014). http://tinyurl.com/nj55csx. Read 23rd March 2020.

205   Shibuya, K., Gilmour, S., Oshima, A. (2014). Time to reconsider thyroid cancer screening in Fukushima. The Lancet 383(9932), 1883-1884. http://tinyurl.com/jy2xntr

206   Fukushima tikittää yhä uhkaavasti, HS (2013). https://www.hs.fi/ulkomaat/art-2000002691354.html. In Finnish.

207   Worldwide health effects of the Fukushima Daiichi nuclear accident, DOI: 10.1039/c2ee22019a http://www.stanford.edu/group/efmh/jacobson/TenHoeveEES12.pdf

208   World Health Organization weighs in on Fukushima, Nature News Blog (2012). http://tinyurl.com/jthbt7l

209   Global report on Fukushima nuclear accident details health risks, WHO (2013). http://tinyurl.com/pf5dcq8

210   The contract can be read at Wikisource.org: http://tinyurl.com/qhl3mqu. Read 23rd March 2020.

211   See http://rationalwiki.org/wiki/WHO-IAEA_conspiracy

212   http://www.who.int/ionizing_radiation/pub_meet/statement-iaea/en/. Read 23rd March 2020.

213   http://www.fukuleaks.org/web/?p=11668. Read 23rd March 2020.

214   Buesseler, Ken O. (2014). Fukushima and ocean radioactivity. Oceanography 27(1):92-105. Read here: http://www.tos.org/oceanography/archive/27-1_buesseler.pdf

215   Liability for Nuclear Damage, World Nuclear Association. http://tinyurl.com/zo8mkre. Read 23rd March 2020.

216   Backgrounder on Nuclear Insurance and Disaster Relief, NRC. http://tinyurl.com/hdoamon. Read 23rd March 2020.

217   Cirincione, Wolfsthal ja Rajkumar (2005). Deadly Arsenals: Nuclear, biological and chemical threats. Carnegie Endowment for

International Peace. Page 45.

218   http://armscontrolcenter.org/fact-sheet-global-nuclear-weapons-inventories-in-2015/. Read 12.2.2020

219   http://en.wikipedia.org/wiki/Historical_nuclear_weapons_stockpiles_and_nuclear_tests_by_country. Read 23rd March 2020.

220   In theory it is possible to make a bomb from U233, but in practice this is much harder to do.

221   Cirincione, Wolfsthal ja Rajkumar (2005). Deadly Arsenals: Nuclear, biological and chemical threats. Carnegie Endowment for International Peace. Page 51

222   Cirincione, Wolfsthal ja Rajkumar (2005). Deadly Arsenals: Nuclear, biological and chemical threats. Carnegie Endowment for International Peace. Page 50

223   Cirincione, Wolfsthal ja Rajkumar (2005). Deadly Arsenals: Nuclear, biological and chemical threats. Carnegie Endowment for International Peace. Page 390

224   Cirincione, Wolfsthal ja Rajkumar (2005). Deadly Arsenals: Nuclear, biological and chemical threats. Carnegie Endowment for International Peace. Page 53

225   http://en.wikipedia.org/wiki/Reactor-grade_plutonium

226   Garwin (1998). Reactor-Grade Plutonium Can be Used to Make Powerful and Reliable Nuclear Weapons: Separated plutonium in the fuel cycle must be protected as if it were nuclear weapons. Federation of American Scientists. http://www.fas.org/rlg/980826-pu.htm

227   Carson Mark (1990). Reactor-Grade Plutonium's Explosive Properties. Nuclear Control Institute.

228   Garwin (1998). Reactor-Grade Plutonium Can be Used to Make Powerful and Reliable Nuclear Weapons: Separated plutonium in the fuel cycle must be protected as if it were nuclear weapons. Federation of American Scientists. http://www.fas.org/rlg/980826-pu.htm

229   Carson Mark (1990). Reactor-Grade Plutonium's Explosive Properties. Nuclear Control Institute.

230   Garwin (1998). Reactor-Grade Plutonium Can be Used to Make

Powerful and Reliable Nuclear Weapons: Separated plutonium in the fuel cycle must be protected as if it were nuclear weapons. Federation of American Scientists. http://www.fas.org/rlg/980826-pu.htm

231   Sublette (1999). Engineering and Design of Nuclear Weapons. Nuclear Weapons Archive, http://nuclearweaponarchive.org/Nwfaq/Nfaq4.html

232   Gilinsky, Miller ja Hubbard (2004): A fresh examination of the proliferation dangers of light water reactors. Nonproliferation Policy Education Center. http://npolicy.org/article.php?aid=172

233   Gilinsky, Miller ja Hubbard (2004): A fresh examination of the proliferation dangers of light water reactors. Nonproliferation Policy Education Center. http://npolicy.org/article.php?aid=172

234   This kind of dirty bomb was experimented on by the US in the 1950 and given up due to the unreliability and limited usefulness. See "Static Test of Four Segments of Full-Diameter Sectional Munitions, E83" http://www.dtic.mil/docs/citations/AD0521701 or Trevithick (2015) "The U.S. Army Tested Its Own 'Dirty Bombs'" http://warisboring.com/articles/the-u-s-army-tested-its-own-dirty-bombs/.

235   Carson Mark (1990). Reactor-Grade Plutonium's Explosive Properties. Nuclear Control Institute.

236   Cirincione, Wolfsthal ja Rajkumar (2005), Deadly Arsenals: Nuclear, Biological, and Chemical Threats. Carnegie Endowment for International Peace. Page 20

237   Cirincione, Wolfsthal ja Rajkumar (2005), Deadly Arsenals: Nuclear, Biological, and Chemical Threats. Carnegie Endowment for International Peace. Page 225

238   Regis (2000). The Biology of Doom: The History of America's Secret Germ Warfare Project. Owl Books

239   Yergin (1991). The Prize: The Epic Quest for Oil, Money and Power. Simon & Schuster. Page 335

240   Yergin (1991). The Prize: The Epic Quest for Oil, Money and Power. Simon & Schuster. Page 319

241   Ecofys (2014). Subsidies and costs of EU energy. Data from

Figure 3-8 ja Annex 1-3, Table A3-8, p. 109.

242   The Costs of Decarbonisation: System Costs with High Shares of Nuclear and Renewables, 2019, OECD-NEA. http://www.oecd-nea.org/ndd/webinars/2019/system-costs/

243   Germany needs over 2,000 MW of winter reserve – regulator, Gas to Power Journal (2012). http://tinyurl.com/pb3tnbv

244   Escobar Rangel, L. ja Lévêque, F. (2012). Revisiting the Cost Escalation Curse of Nuclear Power. New Lessons From the French Experience.   http://idei.fr/doc/conf/eem/papers_2013/leveque.pdf. Read 23rd March 2020.

245   Projected Costs of Generating Electricity 2015 Edition, IEA. http://www.iea.org/Textbase/npsum/ElecCost2015SUM.pdf

246   https://www.eti.co.uk/library/the-eti-nuclear-cost-drivers-project-summary-report

247   For full disclosure, one of the authors, Rauli, is involved in work to enable that funding to be found with as low interest rate as possible, for example through "green" financing.

248   http://www.iaea.org/PRIS/home.aspx

249   Ruling by EC: http://ec.europa.eu/competition/state_aid/cases/251157/251157_1615983_2292_4.pdf

250   The Economics of Nuclear Power, World Nuclear Association. http://tinyurl.com/levx95k. Read 23rd March 2020.

251   More on the costs of nuclear: The Economics of Nuclear Power, WNA, http://tinyurl.com/h8lxckv.

252   Nuclear Costs in Context, NEI (2019), https://www.nei.org/resources/reports-briefs/nuclear-costs-in-context. Read 15th Feb. 2020

253   Decommissioning of the Loviisa NPP costs around 360 M€, T&T (2015). http://tinyurl.com/unh9sor. In Finnish.

254   Energy subsidies in the European Union: A brief overview. http://www.eea.europa.eu/publications/technical_report_2004_1

255   EU produced around 2 674 170 000 MWh nuclear electricity in 2001. http://epp.eurostat.ec.europa.eu/portal/page/portal/energy/

data/database

256   Kitson, L., Wooders, P., Moerenhout, T. (2011) Subsidies and External Costs in Electric Power Generation: A comparative review of estimates. International Institute for Sustainable Development (IISD)/ Global Subsidies Initiative. Winnipeg. p. 23. http://citeseerx.ist.psu. edu/viewdoc/download?doi=10.1.1.637.9888&rep=rep1&type=pdf

257   EN35 External costs of electricity production, European Environment Agency. http://tinyurl.com/oux6n4e. Read 23rd March 2020.

258   https://www.ipcc.ch/site/assets/uploads/2018/02/ipcc_wg3_ ar5_chapter7.pdf

259   Tyndall Centre, University of Manchester. A Review of Research Relevant to New Build Nuclear Power Plants in the UK. Including new estimates of the CO2 implications of gas generating capacity as an alternative. A research briefing commissioned by Friends of the Earth England, Wales and Northern Ireland, 2013. Page 37. http://tinyurl. com/sr5zvvz

260   See for example the EU Taxonomy for Sustainable Activities. Rauli was the lead author of a thorough assessment report on the sustainability of nuclear energy. http://tinyurl.com/vv7g4y4

261   A good way to start this is to read the ETI Nuclear Cost Drivers Project: Summary Report. https://www.eti.co.uk/library/the-eti-nuclear-cost-drivers-project-summary-report

262   https://www.iea.org/reports/energy-efficiency-2019

263   See Independent: Would eating less meat really combat climate change? http://tinyurl.com/z6jnn93

264   See https://www.lucidcatalyst.com/2019-dec2-busgreen-impossible-burge

265   World Bank: http://tinyurl.com/p7pmu7l

266   https://www.nasa.gov/feature/goddard/2018/nasa-study-first-direct-proof-of-ozone-hole-recovery-due-to-chemicals-ban

267   See https://www.stockholmresilience.org/research/planetary-boundaries.html

268 http://www.fnr.de/fileadmin/allgemein/pdf/broschueren/broschuere_basisdaten_bioenergie_2018_engl_web_neu.pdf

269 http://jmkorhonen.net/2013/09/04/graphic-of-the-week-comparing-land-use-of-wind-and-nuclear-energy/

270 See Lambert & Hall: Energy, EROI and quality of life (2014). https://www.sciencedirect.com/science/article/pii/S0301421513006447

271 http://www.stormsmith.nl/

272 Energy Return on Investment, WNA. http://tinyurl.com/na66au7

273 See some critique of B. Sovacool's studies: https://rationalwiki.org/wiki/Benjamin_K._Sovacool

274 Energy payback time (EPBT) and energy return on energy invested (EROI) of solar photovoltaic systems: A systematic review and meta-analysis (2015), http://www.sciencedirect.com/science/article/pii/S136403211500146X

275 Piedro, P., Hall, C., 2013, Spain's Photovoltaic Revolution: The Energy Return on Investment (SpringerBriefs in Energy / Energy Analysis), Springer

276 http://energyskeptic.com/2015/tilting-at-windmills-spains-solar-pv/

277 Weißbach, D. et al. (2013). Energy intensities, EROIs (energy returned on invested), and energy payback times of electricity generating power plants, Energy. doi:10.1016/j.energy.2013.01.029

278 There are multiple ways to do laser enrichment. http://en.wikipedia.org/wiki/Separation_of_isotopes_by_laser_excitation

279 It is somewhat comical that the World Bank currently doesn't even fund nuclear projects anywhere.

280 The report itself is highly recommended reading: http://tinyurl.com/ybpopg55

281 "Dark Money" Funds Climate Change Denial Effort, Scientific American (2013). http://tinyurl.com/kvmlfvg

282 UK agrees nuclear power deal with EDF, Financial Times

(2013). http://tinyurl.com/hobqdnj

283   One example is the building of Meri-Pori coal plant after the political permission to build a nuclear reactor got denied in the Finnish Parliament in early 1990s.

284   See for example http://gofossilfree.org/

285   Kaarkoski, M., (2016). 'Energiemix' versus 'Energiewende' : competing conceptualisations of nuclear energy policy in the German parliamentary debates of 1991-2001. http://urn.fi/ URN:ISBN:978-951-39-6738-3

CPSIA information can be obtained
at www.ICGtesting.com
Printed in the USA
BVHW042141140521
607431BV00013B/209